Date Due

TUDOR GEOGRAPHY
1485–1583

THE SURVEYOR AT WORK

Vignettes from The Surveyor *of Aaron Rathborne,* 1616

TUDOR GEOGRAPHY
1485–1583

BY

E. G. R. TAYLOR, D.Sc., F.R.G.S.

WITH SIXTEEN PLATES

1968

OCTAGON BOOKS, INC.

New York

Originally published in 1930 by Methuen & Co. Ltd.

Reprinted 1968
by special arrangement with Methuen & Co. Ltd.

OCTAGON BOOKS, INC.
175 FIFTH AVENUE
NEW YORK, N. Y. 10010

Printed in U.S.A. by
NOBLE OFFSET PRINTERS, INC.
NEW YORK 3, N. Y.

PREFACE

THE History of Geographical Thought has yet to be written. The present volume deals only with that fateful century or so during which Englishmen of all ranks were forced gradually by circumstances to think geographically as they had never done before. The world location of England had been completely altered : from her slumbers on a remote margin of the Old World, she had awakened to find herself on the very threshold of the New.

Elizabeth's day saw the map and the globe as the necessary furniture of the closet of scholar, merchant, noble and adventurer alike, and dreams of Empire were formulated which found expression in Drake's achievement and Humfrey Gilbert's splendid failure. The date of the latter has been chosen for the term of this study, for it was marked also by the withdrawal of John Dee, the man behind the scenes of overseas enterprise : it saw, too, the firm establishment of the younger Richard Hakluyt as the foremost propagandist for expansion. His work as a geographer, and that of his emulator, Samuel Purchas, will form the theme of a later volume.

E.G.R.T.

August, 1930

v

CONTENTS

LIST OF PLATES

TUDOR GEOGRAPHY
1485 – 1583

TUDOR GEOGRAPHY, 1485–1583

CHAPTER I

A SURVEY OF ENGLISH GEOGRAPHICAL LITERATURE TO 1550

I

WHILE the part played by sixteenth-century Englishmen in the material expansion of geographical horizons has been very fully discussed, little attention has been paid to the development of English geographical thought during the same period ; yet the English enterprises, far from being shots in the dark, were undertaken only after a full consideration and review of all the expert knowledge available. That such a review often brought little enlightenment was the fault of the age, for the sudden supersession of the stereotyped pre-Columbian system of cosmography had brought bewilderment as well as revelation. In England, too, notwithstanding the work of the Cabots, and their associates, medieval conceptions remained but little disturbed for half a century after the date when the sum of £10 from the Privy Purse had rewarded ' him that found the New Isle '. Topics that were pressing questions in Seville, in Lisbon, in Rome— whether, for example, ' Antillia ' or ' Indies ' was the more correct designation of the new Isles, whether Isabella was indeed Ophir, by what law the magnetic needle was governed— found no echo in London for two generations. Individuals interested in the new geography were to be found, but they were exceptions, and made little impression on their contemporaries.

An analysis of the geographical writings produced in England during the first half of the century merely establishes the rule of neglect—the exception of interest : but this analysis must

1

be prefaced by an inquiry into the nature of the English geographical works, available in manuscript form or in print, that had preceded the sixteenth century, and were already available for English scholars. It must be recalled that geography, in so far as it is scientific—that is to say, all exact geography—has its roots in astronomy, in a knowledge of the shape and size of the earth, of the apparent motion relative to the earth of the heavenly bodies, knowledge which allows accurate fixing of position by astronomical means ; hence the debt of geography to astrology, based on just such astronomical knowledge, is great. The cosmographer, whether a Ptolemy or a Mercator, was in fact in the first instance a mathematician and an astronomer, so that geographical literature embraces, or rather is to be sought within, many astronomical and mathematical works. Another branch of study, namely history, alike classical, medieval and renaissance, included as part of its necessary furniture the study of topography, and of descriptive and human geography, so that geographical literature also includes relevant sections of chronicles and histories. Books of travel, surveyors' and navigators' manuals, and works on natural philosophy and physical phenomena, must all likewise be included in a survey of the beginnings of geographical thought, in addition to works specifically termed geographies and cosmographies.

Taking this comprehensive view, we find the founders of English geography in the Schoolmen of the thirteenth century, although even these had their twelfth-century forerunners in William of Malmesbury, Geoffrey of Monmouth, Gervase of Tilbury, William Fitz-Stephen, and the otherwise unknown author of a *Cosmographia*, Bernard Sylvester. All alike are outshone, however, by Giraldus Cambrensis, whose *Topographia Hibernica*, *Topographia Cambriae*, and *Itinerarium Walliae* (to give his works as Bale lists them) served as a model and a standard for nearly four centuries.[1]

Giraldus' descriptive geography was matched in brilliance by the mathematical geography of John Holywood, or Sacrobosco, author of a *Tractatus de sphera mundi*, written about

[1] A complete catalogue of English geographical and kindred **works** for the period under review will be found in Appendix I.

1233, and recommended by John Dee in 1570 as still the best work for elementary instruction in the subject.   Sacrobosco's contemporary, Robert Grosseteste, Bishop of Lincoln, also wrote treatises of the Sphere, and of the Astrolabe, besides various tracts on Natural Philosophy ; but greatest of all the Schoolmen was Roger Bacon, who embodied in the geographical section of his *Opus Majus* a careful summary of the recently completed Asiatic journeys of William of Rubruck and John of Planocarpini.   Geography owed a debt to Roger Bacon not merely for this treatise, and for such tracts as that *De fluxu et refluxu maris* ;   his general teaching as to the importance of applied mathematics and of the experimental approach to science profoundly influenced such men as Richard Eden and John Dee, that is to say, the pioneers of the English Geographical Renaissance.   Finally, to this same illustrious period, the mid-thirteenth century, belongs the oldest extant English map of Great Britain, that drawn by Matthew Paris, and greatly superior to his *Mappa Terrae Habitabilis*, which is presumably the *Descriptio Mundi* referred to by Bale.[1]

In the fourteenth century the outstanding figure is Nicholas of Lynn, who wrote of the use of the Astrolabe, and who is perhaps to be identified with the astronomer-friar of Oxford whose description of the far north beyond 54°, contained in a book called *Inventio Fortunatae*, is unfortunately lost since the sixteenth century, although it was then often cited.   The *Itinerarium* of Hugo de Hibernica, a minorite and Nicholas' contemporary, is also unknown to-day.   A fourteenth-century manuscript that has survived and is of great interest is the anonymous ' *Treatis of geometrie, whereby you may know the heghte, depnes and the brede of most what erthly things* ', the existence of which proves that the application of geometry to the practical measurement not only of buildings and walls, but of the land-surface, was not a lost art at this period. Chaucer's work *De Sphera*, and his *De Astrolabio*, written for his little son Lewis, must also be recorded on the mathematical side, besides the works of the Merton School of Astronomers, while the catalogue of Medieval Geographical Literature fitly

[1] See Appendix I, p. 164.

closes with the *Polychronicon* of Ranulf Higden, written in Latin, translated into English, and containing a *Mappa Mundi* (i.e. a verbal description, not a map, of the known world), compiled from a host of sources, running from Pliny, Isidore and Macrobius down to Giraldus Cambrensis, and thoroughly typical of its day.

A fifteenth-century (1408) copy of a *Rutter* [1] of the English coasts, and of the coast of Western Europe as far as Gibraltar, is almost certainly from an original of much earlier date, and so the first half of the fifteenth century is a blank, save for one notable and exceptional work, the well-known *Libel of English Policy*,[2] which is, in truth, the first English text-book of political and economic geography. The anonymous author's survey of trade and trade routes, and his just appreciation of the influence of geographical position, make his work as fit to open the Modern period as 'the *Polychronicon* was fit to close the Medieval.

Poggio Bracciolini, the Papal Secretary, visiting Oxford about this time, is reported to have said that English scholars preferred dialectic to the New Learning, but it is in harmony with the fact that the seamen and merchants of the Bristol Channel entry were already learning from the Portuguese of the Azores to suspect a wider world, that such hints as we have of intellectual interest in geography come from the West Country. John Frea, a Balliol man, but born at Bristol, translated excerpts from Pliny, including the famous Book II, while he prepared also an edition of Diodorus Siculus which (if Bale is to be believed) the same Poggio Bracciolini stole after Frea's death in Rome in 1465 and published as his own in 1472. This version was Englished by John Skelton, the poet laureate, but not printed. Another Bristol man was Thomas Norton, the alchemist, necessarily therefore a student of mines and metals, while a Welshman, David of Llandaff, or David Morgan, is catalogued by Bale as writing a work *Antiquitates Cambriae*, and a *Geographia*, although these cannot now be traced. About the same time Thomas Kent, an Oxford man, prepared, among other mathematical works, his

[1] Printed by the Hakluyt Society. Vol. 79, Series I.
[2] First printed by Hakluyt, 1589.

Tabulae Astronomiae.   All these works were of course in manuscript only, but it is to be remembered that manuscripts were
still being copied and circulated, in spite of the introduction of
printing.   Meanwhile the printing press in London was giving
fresh life to the medieval *Mappa Mundi.*   William Caxton
himself translated and printed an old French work under the
title *The Ymage or Mirrour of the Worlde,* while in 1480 he
printed the English version of *Polychronicon.*   From the latter
Wynkyn de Worde extracted the *Descrypcyon of Englande,*
etc., and printed it in 1497.[1]

From the same press came the delightful little *Informacōn
for pylgrymes to the Holy Londe,* of which a single copy alone
survives.   This is the first English guide-book, and differs re-
markably little in style from the guide-book of to-day, especially
in respect of the remarks chosen for translation in the Greek
and Turkish phrase-book with which it concludes.   It is itself
a translation from a Latin original, but it bears internal
evidence of embodying in part also the personal experience of
the anonymous English author, who has admirable advice to
give on choosing a comfortable cabin and making due preparation for being a poor sailor.   His succinct description of the
Mediterranean climate, too (quoted in Document 1), is a model
of its kind, and the first such description in English, although
it may be noted that the Venerable Bede, whose *Historia
Ecclesiastica* had been printed on the Continent in 1475, was
also observant of climatic characteristics.

Also printed abroad was an edition of *Proclus : De Sphera,*
by the noted humanist, Thomas Linacre, later the tutor of
Princess Mary, while there appeared in England from R.
Pynson's press, about 1500 or earlier, an edition of one of the
most famous and influential among travel books, that purport-
ing to be by *Sir John Mandeville.*   The value of this book has
been obscured by the incredible tales which it contains, but it
embodies also the real advances in geographical knowledge
and geographical thought that were made in the thirteenth
century, and great geographers like Mercator showed no lack
of judgement when they gave it due consideration.

[1] Caxton also prefixed this ' Descrypcyon ' to his Chronicles published
in 1480.

II

Although the first few years of the sixteenth century saw Bristol merchants following up John Cabot's discovery by a series of voyages culminating in that of the younger Cabot in 1509, their activities were barely recorded, and excited little interest. That there were islands beyond the seas to the west became generally known, but even though English fishermen continued for some time regularly to frequent the Newfoundland Banks, there is no evidence that the information they could supply was ever examined. A book of general reference, known as Arnold's Chronicle, and published by the Antwerp printer, John of Doesborowe, in 1503, contains a geographical section which must be accepted as fulfilling the needs of the English reading public. This section is entitled *The Copy of a Carete Cumposynge the Circuit of the World and the Cumpace of every Yland.* It is a verbal ' Mappa Mundi ' of the crudest character, professedly based on ' great books of all the parts, countries and provinces ' of the world made ' by Julius Caesar ', but actually compiled at second hand from Aristotle, Isidore and Ptolemy. The Ocean Sea is described as lying about the Four Quarters of the Earth, and the general description of these latter is followed by a scanty itinerary from Calais by Venice to Joppa, i.e. a direction for pilgrims, much inferior to the *Informacōn* already published by Wynkyn de Worde.

In this connexion some other pilgrim literature may be mentioned, although its geographical importance is slight. In 1506 an account of the Pilgrimage of Sir R. Guylforde was published by Pynson, while manuscript versions of the Pilgrimage of the Norfolk parson Sir R. Torkington to the Holy Land in 1517, and of that of R. Langton to Compostella in 1522, are also extant.

On the Continent, a résumé of the great discoveries up to date was to be found in a little volume the size and price of which made it freely accessible to the general reader. This was the *Paesi novamente retrovati*, which appeared in 1507. It contained, among other chapters, the narration of the third voyage of Vespucci, under the title of *Mundus Novus.* In the same year Waldseemüller published his *Cosmographiae*

Introductio, attaching to it a Latin translation of the four
voyages under the title *Quattuor Americi Vesputii Navigationes.* These books, and especially the ' Paesi ', were the
basis of many slighter compilations, and notably of (at least)
two tracts issued by John of Doesborowe in 1508, under the
titles : *Van der nieuwer welt oft landtscap nieuwelier ghenoden
vaden doorluch tighen conn. van Portugal door den alderbeste
pyloete ofte zeckenedr d'werelt,* and *Van de wonderlichede en
costelichen van Pape Jans landendes.*   These are the originals,
as Arber [1] points out, of two out of a group of three tracts
published by the same printer in England in 1511, under the
titles :

(*a*) *Of the newe landes and of ye people founde by the messengers
of the kynge of portyngale named Emanuel.*

(*b*) *Of the X dyvers nacyons crystened.*

(*c*) *Of pope John and his landes and of the costely keyes and
wonders molodyes that in that lande is.*

In the first tract, one paragraph deals with the voyage to
America, the remaining nine with the voyage to India.   The
name America (misspelt), which does not, of course, occur in the
original *Mundus Novus,* appears in the following passage :
' We at laste went a lande, but that lande is not nowe knowen,
for there have no mesters wryten thereof nor it knoweth, and
it is named Armenica.'   This first tract was the ' shiete of
printed paper (more worthy so to be called than a boke),
entytuled of the new founde landes ', which came into Richard
Eden's hands over forty years later, and was still, amazing
though it may seem, the only English work on the subject of the
revelation of a Fourth Continent.

It may be argued, of course, that since Latin was still the
universal language of learning, and Italian at this time the
language of culture, the absence of a vernacular literature had
no significance.   The point will presently be met by a contemporary pronouncement.   During the period under consideration—the first decade of the sixteenth century—the leading
intellectual circle in England was that grouped about the person
of Sir Thomas More.   This circle was linked through Erasmus
with a continental group of men who, while also preoccupied

---

[1] Ed. Arber, *The First Three English Books on America,* 1895.

with the changes foreshadowed in religious thought, were yet keener students of cosmography. Among these may be specially mentioned the Portuguese historian, Damian à Goes, the Swabian mathematician, Simon Grynaeus (both of whom personally visited More and his London friends and the University of Oxford), and the Swiss poet, Henricus Glareanus.

To Damian à Goes and to Erasmus, the expanding world was primarily an expanding field for evangelization ; to Sir Thomas More, Vespucci's furthest south, Cape Frio in Brazil, provided a realistic threshold from which Hythlodaye stepped off into Utopia. More's son-in-law, John Rastell, had, however, a more practical mind. After an abortive attempt (in 1517) to explore the New World in person, an attempt thwarted largely by stupidity and ignorance, he hit on a method of popular (and probably Royal) education through the medium of the stage. His *New Interlude of the Nature of the Four Elements* is in effect a versified cosmography, lightened by irrelevant scenes of rather coarse fun. Bale's reference to the author is as follows : ' Insignis hic cosmographus, de trium mundi partium, Asiae, Africae, Europae descriptione, ingeniosissimam ac longissimam comediam primum edidit, cum instrumentis et figuris, quem vocebat Naturam Naturatam.' Actually ' Natura Naturata ' was one of the characters in the Interlude, not its title, which was as quoted above.

The one surviving text is badly mutilated, but the ' argument ' is complete (Document 2), and the opening sections follow exactly the lines of contemporary text-books on the Sphaera Mundi. A diagram of the four elements (a modification of which was used by Rastell as his device or colophon in his rôle of printer-publisher) was brought on the stage, besides instruments for demonstrating the shape of the globe, and a large world map. The lines referring to the New World are well known, but a puzzling point that deserves attention is the ' figure ' on which Experience points out the leading countries in turn. This (if his gestures and words be followed) must have been either a polar projection of the northern hemisphere in plano, or a half-sphere, for it showed a complete circuit eastwards from England and back to it again without a break, and after his demonstration Experience adds :

> ' Lo all this parte of the yerthe which I
> Have here descrybed openly,
> The north parte doe it call
> But the south parte on the other syde
> Ys as large as this and full as wyde
> Which we know nothing at all
> Nor whether the most parte be lande or see. . . .'

It is in the Messenger's Prelude that reference is made to the need of a vernacular literature of ' works of cunning ', i.e. learning.

> ' For divers pregnant wits be in this land,
> As well of noble men as of mean estate,
> Which nothing but English can understand.
> Then if cunning Latin books were translate
> Into English, well correct and approbate
> All subtle science in English might be learned.'

Whatever date may be ascribed to the printing of the extant copy, the Interlude appears from internal evidence to belong to the year 1519, and may be accepted as the first work on modern geography of English authorship. As such, the views which it expresses on the relations of the New World to the Old are of importance, although they were probably derived from the continental World Map from which the ' figure ' already mentioned was drawn. In particular the distance between the ' New Lands ' and those of the Khan of Cathay, marked on the Waldseemüller ' inset map ' as 1,500 miles, is said by Rastell to be ' lytell paste a thousande myle '.

Now the Interlude finds its most obvious explanation as propaganda for English enterprise overseas, and the author has definitely in mind the planting of a permanent colony in America, but as he emphasizes the low stage of culture of the natives, and notes as local sources of gain only the timber, pitch, tar and wood-ashes that might be substituted for similar Baltic produce (apart from the fisheries), it can be legitimately inferred that he looks upon the New Land merely as a half-way house to the only valuable objectives then present in men's minds, Cathay and the Spice Islands.

The conservatism of English contemporary thought, however, outside the more advanced intellectual circles, is well expressed by the passive resistance offered by the London merchants, approached through the great Companies, to Wolsey's project for just such a venture by way of the north-west in 1521. The Bristol men, familiar with the Newfound-land trade, had readily promised two ships, but the London men demurred, partly on the ground that there was no Rutter for those parts, and partly because there were no English-born mariners to take charge.[1] Such pretexts would readily arise in the minds of men to whom the lands outside the stereotyped tripartite world were so vague as still to seem unreal.

The New Interlude does not quite complete the sum of the interest shown in the new discoveries by the More circle. John More, in 1533, made a translation of one of the works of his father's friend, Damian à Goes. This was *The legacy or embassate of prester John unto Emanuel Kynge of Portyngale*, published by W. Rastell, taken from a book in the form of a letter to Johannes Magnus, Archbishop of Upsala, dated Antwerp, 1531, which embodied the original *Legatio magni imperatoris Indorum Presbyteri Joannis*, published at Dordrecht, 1518. A few years later (1536) one of the younger generation of Rastells took part, with Thomas Butts, son of the Royal Physician, Armigel Wade, afterwards a government official, and Oliver Daubney, a merchant and later a friend of the elder Hakluyt, in the strange expedition of a group of intellectuals to the New World of which we have a glimpse long after through the pen of Richard Hakluyt the Preacher. This, however, is to anticipate, and it is necessary to return to a consideration of the geographical literature of the second quarter of the century.

III

Intercourse with Antwerp and the Low Countries must have had a wider influence on English geographical thought than we can find direct evidence for, and the same must be true of the influence of Spain. The latter influence came through the succession of English merchants resident in St. Lucar and Seville, of whose names those of Robert Thorne (with his

---

[1] Sir John Bridges, the Lord Mayor, who had business connexions with the Levant and Seville, was, however, a subscriber.

apprentice, Emanuel Lucar), Roger Barlow, Henry Latimer and Bridges are among the first that we know. The practical activities of these men will later be considered in detail, so that all that need be mentioned here is the light that they indirectly throw upon the geographical equipment of an educated Englishman of their day. Thorne himself laid but little claim to formal knowledge—it was his two friends, Barlow and Latimer, who were ' somewhat learned in cosmography '. He had, however, the advantage of having been born at Bristol, and of having there heard practical discussion of cosmographical problems in his own father's house. He himself had handled maps and could read them, although he was no cartographer. The point for emphasis, however, is the assumption he makes, no doubt with ample justification, that his ecclesiastical corres- pondent of 1527, the diplomatist, Dr. Lee, who was personally known to him, needed those instructions in the very rudiments of map-reading which Thorne's letter [1] contains. Cosmo- graphy was then no part of formal University teaching.

Thorne's map (as preserved by Hakluyt) is a copy of a very conventional current rendering of the Old World,[2] to which he had added a rough delineation of the New, for it must be remembered that the excellent contemporary Spanish charts were carefully guarded from unauthorized copying. Yet the influence of the charts can be seen in Thorne's assumption that Ocean ways lay all across the Polar regions. Academic writers all postulated a land bridge or bridges or an Arctic land that would interrupt northern navigation quite apart from ice, but the Spanish chart-makers only drew coast-lines where coast-lines had been located, and so upon their charts all the far north lay open.

As is well known, Thorne's letter bore no immediate fruit, for John Rut's voyage of 1527, although it was an attempt to find an English passage to the South Sea, was not intended to be a voyage across the Pole. There is, indeed, good reason to believe that it was based on information obtained from Verrazzano, who had made a chart on parchment for Henry VIII which Richard Hakluyt saw and handled more than half a

[1] First published by Hakluyt in the *Divers Voyages*, 1582.
[2] But see below, p. 48.

century later. Harrisse points out [1] that the time and occasion of its presentation must have been late in 1525, or early in 1526, when the Florentine pilot, having returned from the discovery of Nova Francia, found King Francis I a prisoner in Spain.

From Michael Lok's map of 1582,[2] professedly derived from Verrazzano's, and from the map of Vesconte de Malliolo, based on one similar to it, the main outlines of the original can be reconstructed. It showed two tempting possibilities : a broad north-west passage, between Labrador (Greenland) and Newfoundland, and an isthmus in 40° N., across which the South Sea could be seen from the Atlantic Ocean. Supposing John Rut to have carried a copy of this map, then the Piedmont pilot he had on board (whether Albert de Prato or another) would have been capable of interpreting the Florentine's instructions, and the doings of the two ships are explicable : they first attempted the route by the north-west (making a rendezvous at Cape Spera, which was marked on the map, in case of failure), and then they turned south to look for the isthmus. The southern exploration finally brought one of the ships to Santo Domingo, when the captain told the Spaniards that he had been sent out to seek a northern route to Tartary. The records of this voyage came into Hakluyt's hands some time between the publication of the *Principal Navigations* and 1613, for he showed them to Purchas during the latter year, as we learn from the second edition (completed March, 1614) of *Purchas his Pilgrimage*. Purchas quotes one or two facts and figures from Rut's ' discourse ', and incidentally makes it clear that after leaving St. John's, the *Mary Guilford* was making for Cape Ras (Race, 46° 40' N.), 25 leagues to the south, and not turning back to Cape Bas (52°), as a misprint in the letter as published in the ' Pilgrims ' would suggest. This is in harmony with a subsequent search along the coast of Norumbega for an isthmus, or strait, in 40° N. leading to ' those Islands that we are commanded '. John Rut, when he wrote from St. John's, had lost none of his crew, so that it must have been the *Sampson* which went furthest north, and

[1] Henry Harrisse, *The Discovery of North America*, 1892.
[2] R. Hakluyt, *Divers Voyages*, 1582.

after meeting with disaster sailed to the West Indies, professedly to obtain a fresh pilot.   The voyage of 1527 had no English chronicler, and the next geographical publication— *The Rutter of the Sea*, 1528—was borrowed from a French original,[1] while the translator, one Robert Copland, a London stationer, naïvely confesses his ignorance of sea-terms and ways.   The copy he made use of was bought in Bordeaux by a merchant, and covered the routes and ports connected with the wine trade between France and England.   The English version proved extremely popular, a new edition (perhaps the fifth) being called for as late as 1587.   The later editions included an additional English section, ' *The New Rutter of the Sea for the North Part*, 1541 A.D., Richard Proude ', which was based on the old English MS. rutter already mentioned.   The date 1541 is approximately that of an old Scots rutter to be noticed in its place.[2]

While the welcome given to the Rutter of 1528 speaks of a departure from a certain conservatism on the part of English mariners, the general level of geographical thought in England is probably better exemplified in the manuscript *Cosmographia* transcribed for the Royal Library in 1530, and by the *Mappa Mundi* entitled ' *Here beginneth the Cumpass and Cyrcuet of the Worlde* ' published by Wyer in 1535.   The latter may be dismissed first ; it is from the same crude original as the *Copy of a Carete* in Arnold's Chronicle, 1503, but with additional matter on the Earthly Paradise and Hell.

The *Cosmographia* is an altogether more noteworthy production.   Written, to judge from internal evidence, not much after 1510, by a monk resident in London, it follows the traditional medieval pattern, and is borrowed from the usual medley of classical and medieval writers.   The compiler, however, brings the historical references up to date, and makes use of such contemporary authors as Aeneas Silvius and Sabellicus.   Yet, so far as the new discoveries are concerned, they are merely given summary treatment in a short section on Islands, and are not related to the body of the book, which assumes the conventional tripartite world.   The source of information for

[1] Of 1483.   See Sir Travers Twiss, *Black Book of the Admiralty*, p. lxiv.   [2] Chapter IV.

the Discoveries appears to be a version of the *Paesi*. The three illustrative maps—of the Holy Land, the Habitable World, and the Cosmos, are alike in accordance with the medieval pattern. The two latter maps (Figs. 1 and 2), found here in conjunction, are of extreme interest, for they place beyond any doubt the conclusion, to be arrived at also on other grounds, that a medieval geographer using a map of the ' T in O ' type did not thereby indicate his belief in a flat earth. He was frankly diagrammatizing the Oecumene, which (in his view) occupied part of the upper surface of the earth globe. Nor was the anonymous author of this *Cosmographia* of 1530 consciously at fault when he retained these old maps in spite of his knowledge of new lands to the west and south beyond the old. These lay on the other, or rather the under, side of the globe, of which a diagram on a flat surface could show only one half. The wonder of Columbus' journey, and later of Magellan's, to their contemporaries, was that each sailed *beneath* the globe.

With all, however, that can be said in its defence, the *Cosmographia*, like Wyer's edition of the *Mappa Mundi*, indicated a lag in English geography far behind the standard reached on the Continent, where, for example, Gemma Phrysius' edition of Peter Apian's six-year-old Cosmography had just been published.

Here it will be convenient to mention and dismiss a group of works printed by Robert Wyer, belonging to the period 1527–42, namely : (1) Here beginneth a boke of knowledge of thynges apperteyninge to astronomye, (2) Here begynneth the Compost of Ptolomeus, (3) Here beginneth the difference of Astronomy. These are all little text-books of judicial astronomy, good and evil days, prognostications and so forth, and have no bearing on geographical science. To certain copies of the Compost of Ptolomeus, however, was added a tract, ' Hereafter followeth the Rutter of distances from one Port or Countrey to another ', which is, in fact, the inferior *Mappa Mundi* already mentioned.

IV

Although the poverty of English geographical literature in the second and third decades of the century has been em-

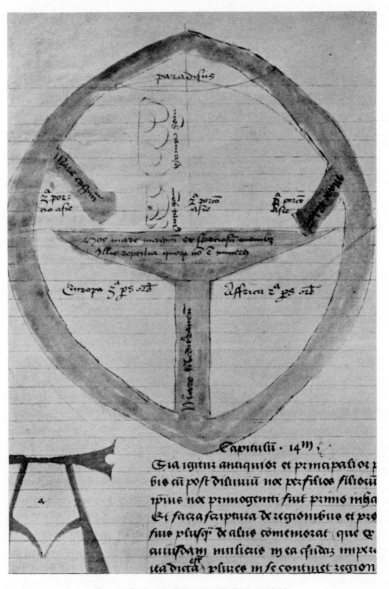

FIG. 1.—MAP OF THE HABITABLE WORLD
From the Anonymous Cosmography, MS. Brit. Mus.

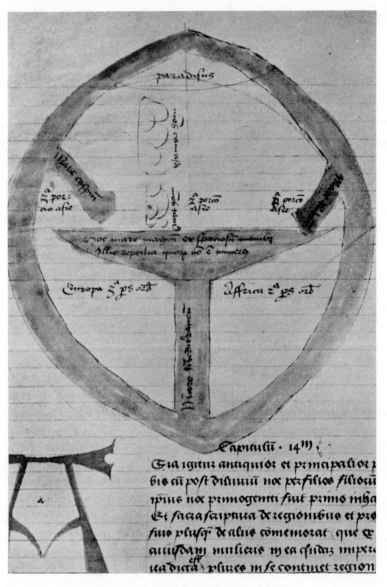

FIG. 1.—MAP OF THE HABITABLE WORLD
From the Anonymous Cosmography, MS. Brit. Mus.

phasized, there were two contributions from contemporary historians which must be noticed. Both the *Scotorum historiae a prima gentis origine* of Hector Boethius, Paris, 1526, and the *Anglorum Historia* of Polidore Vergil, Basle, 1534, contain important topographical and descriptive matter. Written, the former in Scotland by one of the founders of the University of Aberdeen, the latter in London by an Italian ecclesiastic long resident (and naturalized) in England,[1] it is significant that both were published abroad, the English history by Simon Grynaeus, whose personal relations with English men of letters have already been mentioned.

The Scottish history soon appeared in more popular form, being translated into the Scots tongue by John Bellenden, Archdeacon of Murray, as ' *The history and cronikles of Scotlande with the cosmography and description thairof* ', Edinburgh, 1536, while from this Scots version William Harrison prepared an English rendering for Holinshed's Chronicles in 1577.

Another pair of books are important as affording insight into the current practice in England as regards land-survey and measurement. *The boke of Surveying* of Master Fitzherbert, first published in 1523, and frequently reissued, deals merely with a steward's survey of a Manor, the dimensions of the parcels of which are well known. The *Book of Measuring of land* of Richard Benese, edited by Thos. Paynell, 1537, is the first to be written of a practical character. Benese and Paynell had alike been monks of Merton Priory, and the former became Surveyor of Works to Henry VIII. His instruments were merely a rod one perch in length, and a line four perches long, knotted at each perch ; his methods were in principle those of an ordinary chain-survey. Benese's book was accepted as a standard work for forty years or more, and its first publication was four years after the appearance of Gemma Phrysius' tract on Triangulation, the influence of which will be discussed later.

The years 1542– 7 are those in which many French Cosmographers and Navigators, with Huguenot sympathies, sought service in England under Henry VIII and Admiral Lord Lisle (John Dudley). This important period was marked by the circulation of Alexander Lindesay's *Rutter* of the Scottish coast,

[1] He was granted denization on 2 October 1510 (Rymer Foedera).

and of many French manuscripts, maps and charts which will be dealt with in a later chapter.[1] Mention must also be made of a publication of 1543 which was of prime importance for English science at large, namely, Robert Record's *Ground of Arts*. This, the first English Arithmetic, with its ingenious methods of simplifying difficult operations, opened up to the general reader all those subjects, including the mathematical branches of Geography, in which a knowledge of Arithmetic has to be assumed.

The year 1546 was noteworthy for the publication in Rome of George Lily's *Map of Britain*, and the same author supplied geographical material to two Italian writers, namely, Polidore Vergil, and Paulus Jovius, Bishop of Nocera, the latter of whom published Lily's *Nova et antiqua locorum nomina in Anglia et in Scotia*, with his own *Descriptio Britanniae, Scotiae, Hiberniae et Orchadum*, published at Venice in 1548. The addenda to the *Descriptio* due to Lily included also a tract *Elogia quorumdem Anglorum*, in which the great men honoured include Thomas Linacre and Sir Thomas More (whose portraits hung in the Bishop's gallery) : thus it emphasizes the relationships between this noted Italian geographical and historical writer and the English humanists.

In the same year that Lily's map appeared, Thomas Langley, formerly Chaplain to Archbishop Cranmer, published for the profit of ' artificers and other persons not expert in Latin ' a translation of part of an earlier work of Polidore Vergil, ' *De Inventoribus Rerum*', under the title of '*An abridgement of the notable woorke of P. Vergil*'. Simultaneously (i.e. in 1546), Peter Ashton dedicated to Sir Rafe Sadler, a Privy Councillor and gentleman of the Privy Chamber of Henry VIII, a translation of the ' Commentarj delle cose de Turchia ' of Paulus Jovius, under the title, *A shorte treatise upon the Turkes Chronicles*. While the interest of this work was mainly historical (and topical in view of the Turkish menace under Soleiman the Magnificent), it gives incidental topographical information concerning Eastern lands, and afforded an enlargement of his geographical horizon to the English reader.

Many other translations from the Italian were made about

[1] Chapter IV.

tc̄ Mediante̅ naturꝝ intencio q̄ gꝛaua ad centꝝ non ꝑueniunt ꝑ hoc fruſtr
uidetur. Nam tanta concauitas circa centꝝ non fit eo natura ſed eo diuine iuſt
oꝛdinacōe ubi et iginis eodē modo ad auciandū pꝛedictos metanū conſeruatus fo
ſunt cuit caſiditatis pꝛopter frigus terre ipm igni undiqꝫ circūplectens quo au
eut undiqꝫ conſtrictus. Et locus pꝛugatoꝛiꝰ hic nitia uiſcera terre ponatur tam
diuinaꝫ diſpenſacōem alibi diuerſa loca diuerſis aliquado deputatur aīabꝰ ut
uidetur gregꝰ ſentire li 4 dialoꝛa 39 Ut igitur de facili imaginari poſſu qua
ii terre moles in quatuoꝛ equales poꝛciones ambitu oceani et aꝑhꝛatis diuiſo
et ſola ſeptentrionalis inhabitatur co ſequenti figura cognoſcetur.

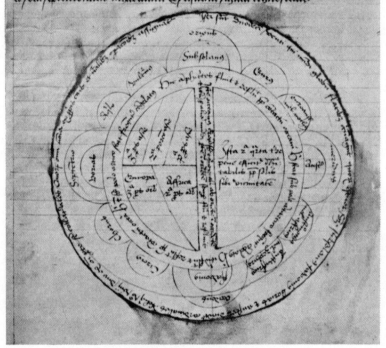

FIG. 2.—MAP OF THE COSMOS
From the Anonymous Cosmography, MS. Brit. Mus.

this time by William Thomas (afterwards Clerk to the Privy Council), who spent some years of exile (1544–7) in Padua and Bologna. These included the *Travels of Josafa Barbaro*, from the ' Viaggi Fatti da Vinetia alla Tana ', Venice, 1545, which contained both Barbaro's and Contarini's Eastern travels, and was the original afterwards used by Ramusio. Thomas's translation, made for the New Year 1551, was, however, never printed.

To this period must possibly be assigned a little manuscript book of maps and tide-tables, dedicated to the Earl of Arundel (who succeeded to the title early in 1544), which was preserved in his library (afterwards Lord Lumley's and now part of the King's Library), entitled, *A small Treatise contayning the times of full seas, low waters, openings and neapes for all times of ye yeare, of the havens about the coasts of France, Flanders, Britane, Wales, Ireland and Spain.* A companion manuscript of Marshall's *Rutter for the Sea about Scotlande, the Islands of Orkeney and Schetland*, i.e. an English version of Lindesay's Scots Rutter, has not survived.[1]

The Earl of Arundel was one of a group of patrons of learning and of antiquarian research to whom English geographical science was greatly indebted. A catalogue of the geographical volumes in his library (and those added by his son-in-law, Lord Lumley) will be found in an Appendix. Amongst those who may be termed the practical or working antiquarians, as opposed to such noble patrons, John Leland was the first, and his *Laborious Journey and searche for Englandes Antiquities* was edited and published by John Bale in 1549. Leland numbered among his many friends Humfrey Lhuyd, private physician to Lord Arundel, and himself a noted geographer and antiquary.

Before the date 1549, however, a very direct stimulus to English geographical thought had been given by the arrival of Sebastian Cabot in the country by official and royal appointment. Soon after his arrival, a young Cambridge scholar, Clement Adams, Fellow of King's, assisted at the preparation of a new edition of Cabot's world map of 1544, although doubt has rested on the interpretation of the phrase, ' cut by Clement

[1] But a copy is included in Add. MSS. 37,024.

Adams ', employed by Hakluyt.[1] The map, according to
Harrisse, was published in 1549, and simultaneously a
new chapter opened in English geographical thought and
practice.

[1] Adams was undoubtedly a professional cartographer, for on 29 December 1550 he was paid £5 ' for his charges and pains sustained about
the new making of a plott of Scotland ' (Acts of the Privy Council,
Ed. VI).

CHAPTER II

A SURVEY OF ENGLISH GEOGRAPHICAL
LITERATURE: 1550–1583

I

THE chapter which opens in 1549–50 is, on the practical side, the story of the new beginning of the English search for Cathay; on the theoretical side it is a story in which Richard Eden, Richard Willes, the elder Hakluyt and John Dee are among the leading figures. Among these men the last-named forms the subject of a later more detailed study, the conclusions from which will be assumed in this general survey.

With regard to the elder Hakluyt, the material available is scanty, but it has all been collected by Dr. Parks,[1] although without any attempt to estimate the lawyer's contribution to geography as such. Nearly all that can be brought together about Richard Eden's life and work, too, has been printed by Ed. Arber,[2] but again without critical examination of his equipment and accomplishment as a geographer—the aspects to be touched on here.

That the way was being prepared for a better geographical education of students is indicated by the publication of Wm. Salisbury's translation of *Proclus' Sphaera,* and the preparation of an English manuscript version of *Sacrobosco's* work on the same subject by the Italian scholar Wm. Thomas. Even more important was the appearance in 1551 of Dr. Record's *Pathway of Knowledge,* an introduction to geometry and to the use of the quadrant, which formed a companion volume to his English Arithmetic. The scepticism and unrest produced by the religious changes stimulated an interest in Judicial Astronomy,

---

[1] G. B. Parks, *Richard Hakluyt and the English Voyages.*
[2] Ed. Arber, *The First Three English Books on America.*

and the number of *Almanacks and Prognostications* published (these containing tables of Ephemerides valuable for geography) was very great. What seems to have been the first of a long series of such booklets by a man who did very much for geography in other ways—Leonard Digges—appeared in 1553 from the press of Thomas Gemini. This printer, a scholarly foreigner, was also an engraver, and in 1555 published in London an engraved *Map of Spain* (afterwards made use of by Ortelius), dedicating it to King Philip and Queen Mary. If it be recalled that John Dee was now writing one after another of his astronomico-geographical tracts,[1] the kind of work going on around Richard Eden when he took up his pen in the interests of discovery can be appreciated.

As is well known, Eden had close personal relations with Sebastian Cabot, Richard Chancellor and Stephen Borough, and his unusually deep knowledge of cosmography must have both paved the way for, and been enhanced by, these friendships. From his twice mentioning the fact in print, it is clear that his perusal of the *Decades* of Peter Martyr when a lad (*adolescens*) was of as great significance to him, in turning his attention to geography, as the visit to the cousin in the Middle Temple was to the younger Richard Hakluyt. The third edition of the *Decades*, from which Eden's translations were made, was published at Basle in 1533, when the young scholar was twelve or thirteen years old. His first translation, however, was not of the *Decades*, but of the section of Sebastian Munster's *Cosmography* dealing with the New Lands. In the Preface to the Reader (1553) he reveals his familiarity with Gemma Phrysius' globe, and with the writings of Peter Apian, whom he describes as ' the great astronomer of our time ', as well as with the standard geographical work of Aeneas Silvius (Pius II), and with the older classical writers. Moreover, he was a disciple of Roger Bacon, and hence affirmed the important principle that ' no man knoweth further . . . than is tryed and founde by experience '. He writes therefore critically and carefully.

Less than two months after Eden's dedication of this his first work to Northumberland as promoter of the first Cathay

[1] Appendix IA.

voyage, the Duke was beheaded, and there is little doubt from the tone of his address a year later (1554) to Philip and Mary, that Eden, in making his translations of the *Decades*, and of excerpts from Oviedo and Gomara, was anxious to prove his loyalty to the new régime by the glorification of Spain. At the same time he knew that all that he could learn and write was of value to his own countrymen, and he put together from every available source what was known or believed of Moscovia and Cathay. It is clear, however, that here he obtained considerable assistance from a compilation that had preceded his own by over twenty years, the *Novus Orbis*, edited by Simon Grynaeus (Basle, 1532, 1535, 1537 and 1555), which in its turn owed much to Madrignano's *Itinerarium Portugalensium*, a Latin version of the *Paesi Novamente Retrovati*, which was first published in 1508. Eden, when he wrote, had also the advantage of personal acquaintance with the Spaniard Zarate, later the historian of Peru (who visited London in King Philip's service), and of discussion with Richard Chancellor of the results of his first voyage, before the great pilot set off on that one from which he was not to return.

Eden was careful to lay no claim to originality in his work. In explaining why he undertook the translation of Biringuccio's Book of Metals, he adds :

'like ignorance has been among us as touching cosmography and navigation, until I attempted according to the portion of my talent and simple learning to open the first door to the entrance of this knowledge into our language, wherein I would wish that other of greater learning would take some pains to accomplish and bring to further perfection that I have rudely begun, not as an author, but as a translator, lest I be injurious to any man in ascribing to myself the travailes of other '.

Actually, however, his English equivalent of *Novus Orbis* included, besides translations, the original section on the English Guinea voyages of 1553-4, while in addition to introducing English readers to the great Spanish chroniclers, it made them aware of Vespucci, Maximilian Transylvanus, Pigafetta, Johannes Faber, Paulus Jovius, Herberstein and Ziegler, to name only the authors of the most important works that were included. That Eden was a close student of the great Flemish cosmographer Gemma Phrysius is revealed by many quotations, and the volume closes with the passage from Gemma's *De Principio* explaining the theory of determining longitude with a timepiece.   Other contemporary writers quoted include Damian à Goes, Erasmus, Gastaldi, Matthias à Michou and Vadianus, while there are frequent interpolations from the writings of the Italian mathematician and philosopher, Jerome Cardanus, whom Eden may have met at the house of their mutual friend, Sir John Cheke, during one of his visits to London.   The inclusion of a copy of the Papal Bull of 1493 in the *Decades*, both in the original and in translation, is a fact not without significance.   As parting the spheres of the Portuguese and Spanish discoveries, a meridian line is defined in the Bull, but the point is reiterated more than once that the Spanish sphere is to the west and *south* of the island commonly called the Azores or the Cape Verde Islands.   Thus the prosecution of discovery to the north-west or north-east by the English, or any other nation, was not precluded, although this point was obscured by the maps and globes showing the line of demarcation on which only the meridian, and not the related east-west line, was drawn.   The Treaty of Tordesillas [1] shifted the meridian westward, but it was the Pope's partition that suggested the principle to be observed.   That this interpretation is correct is borne out by the first Patent for Discovery granted after the Bull and Treaty, that of John Cabot in 1496. As Dr. Williamson has pointed out,[2] he was to go east, west or north, but not south, and the Spanish Ambassador could make no valid objection to the project.   Once land was struck, however, the English discoverers might follow it south, just as the Spanish might follow it north, so that much hinged on whether North America was a continent or merely an archipelago of islands.

Although six years elapsed between Eden's second translation and his third—namely, the *Art of Navigation*, published in 1561—the Preface to the latter suggests that he had, in the meanwhile, been officially employed as chronicler by the Muscovy Company, and in this capacity had made it his busi-

[1] Not confirmed by the Pope for several years.
[2] J. A. Williamson, *First English Voyages to America*, 1929.

ness to learn personally the details of the voyages of Stephen
Borough and Anthony Jenkinson. Eden's influence, joined
with Borough's anxiety to fill worthily the office of Chief Pilot,
and to make it one of dignity and importance, may have been
the impulses that carried the latter on a visit to the universally
admired Casa de Contratacion in Seville (described by Eden
in his second Preface), a visit that must have taken place after
Stephen's return to England from Lapland in 1557. In Spain
he must have obtained a copy of Martin Cortes' *Arte de Navegar*
(2nd Ed., Seville, 1556), which was then the most recent manual
of its kind, and it is to Borough's credit that on his return he
persuaded the Muscovy Company to bear the expense of its
translation by Eden for general use, instead of keeping the
knowledge of it to himself. He knew and quoted Medina's
earlier work on the same subject besides.

Eden's subsequent sojourn of ten years in France (1562–72),
besides putting an end for the time to his geographical work,
brought him under the influence of French writers and thinkers,
but before considering these, it is necessary to glance at the
work of other Englishmen up to 1561.

II

Two geographical books were dedicated (during his brief
months of freedom and Royal favour) to Edward Courtenay,
Earl of Devonshire, whose studies, during his imprisonment
since boyhood in the Tower, had included Cosmography.
These were Chaucer's *Conclusions of the Astrolabie*, amended
by Walter Stevens, which was never actually printed, and
Wyllyam Prat's *Description of the Country of Aphrique*
(1 January 1554) taken from a French version of Jo. Boemus'
extremely popular ' *Omnium gentium mores* ', which originally
appeared in 1536. The same work was also Englished in the
following year (1555) by Wm. Watreman, who dedicated his
translation under the title of *The Fardle of Facions* to the Earl
of Arundel, already mentioned as a patron of geographical
learning. Here it may be remarked that while the subject-
matter of what would now be called ' human geography '
interested the general reading public of the sixteenth century,
the absence of any realization of the significance of physical

phenomena (other than those that were violent and exceptional) meant that the branch of the subject now termed 'physical geography' was almost, if not quite neglected. 'Political geography' came, however, within the province of the historian, while its connexion with Astronomy assured the full consideration of 'mathematical geography'.

The latter branch now received assistance from the publication in 1556 of Dr. Record's *Castle of Knowledge*, containing 'the explication of the sphere', a volume which twenty years later formed part of Frobisher's ship's library. It was written directly to further the Cathay search, which commanded the services of the finest intellects of the day.[1] Dr. Record had an additional reason for being specially interested in the Northeast Passage : he was an Anglo-Saxon scholar, and familiar (as we learn from his own words) with the famous Norse narrative (added by King Alfred to his translation of Orosius) of Ochthere's voyage to the White Sea. This narrative, it will be recalled, was translated into English by Lawrence Nowell about 1564 when he was in Cecil's service, and was published by Hakluyt long afterwards. Humfrey Gilbert knew the translation in 1566 or thereabouts when it was still in manuscript.

In the *Castle of Knowledge*, Record states that he is planning a Cosmography, but actually the next book from his pen was another elementary mathematical treatise, *The Whetstone of Witte*, dedicated to the Governors of the Muscovy Company, November 1557. Here he writes, 'I will . . . shortly set forth a book of Navigation ', but death unfortunately prevented the fulfilment of his purpose, and the Company lost the services of a valuable adviser. Bale says of him :

'He made Arithmetic plainer than it had ever been before. He taught Astrology and expounded Cosmography, he illuminated Geometry and Music. He possessed great experience in the founding of gold, silver, brass, tin, lead and other metals. . . . He sought out antiquities, and rare chronicles with the utmost zeal.'

Robert Record's mantle-fell upon John Dee, but the temper of Dee's mind was such that he looked upon knowledge as the prerogative of the initiate only, and even when he published, he published in limited editions.

[1] See Chapter V,

Meanwhile the actual narratives of the Muscovy voyages, which were written by Richard Chancellor, Clement Adams and Stephen Borough, appear to have been left in manuscript form only, as were the charts of the far north prepared by Stephen Borough (which Dee examined) and the Chart of Northern Navigation prepared by his younger and subsequently more famous brother, William.

One book, however, appeared in print which proved of immense influence, even though its bearing on geography was indirect. This was Leonard Digges' *Tectonicon* (1556), which he had promised in his *Almanack and Prognostications* of the previous year. Leonard Digges was one of the landed gentry of East Kent, a keen amateur mathematician, and, like Dee and Eden, a disciple of Roger Bacon. According to his son Thomas, he was parted from home and family when Thomas was a schoolboy, and it is probable that he spent this period (which must have been the early '40's) in exile abroad as did William Thomas the translator, and so many others. However that may be, he became familiar with the growing body of continental writings (of which those of Apian and Phrysius were typical) upon the applications of geometry and astronomy to the survey of buildings and of lands. In the *Tectonicon* and in the more elaborate *Pantometria* published posthumously in 1571, his expressed aim was to make the conclusions and practice of these foreign writers available to the English reader.

The exile abroad of the English Protestants in Mary's reign was another factor which must not be overlooked as explaining the growing rapidity with which Geography and kindred subjects were influenced by continental thought. Strassburg, one of the headquarters of the exiles, must always be associated with the great series of editions of Ptolemy's Atlas, and of the *Margarita Philosophica*, which were issued there, while the latest publications in half a dozen noted German and Swiss Universities were immediately available to Strassburg residents besides. Facilities for obtaining foreign books in England, in spite of such London agencies as Birckmann's and Jan Desserans', were not great, and apart from those obtaining exceptional popularity, even important works might find their way into libraries only as a result of some student's visit abroad.

John Dee's gift of instruments and globes, together with his personal influence and that of Dr. Record, undoubtedly stimulated the study of Cosmography at Cambridge, the University that produced the first original English work on the subject—William Cuningham's *Cosmographical Glasse*, 1559, with its interesting *Map of Norwich*. Something, too, may be credited to Cuningham's own recent visit to Heidelberg and the Rhine Valley, where he made many learned friends and where he must have seen some at least of the half-dozen different editions of Ptolemy that he claims to have examined. His studies, however, like those of Leonard Digges, were directed in the first instance to Judicial Astronomy, and he had already published an annual *Almanack and Prognostications* since 1557. It is significant that he had enjoyed the patronage and support of Lord Robert Dudley, whose close association with John Dee was also based in part on his reliance on Astrology, and to Dudley the *Cosmographical Glasse* is dedicated.

' I am the first ', the author says, ' that ever in our tongue have written of this argument, and therefore am constrained to find out the path.' Naturally he follows closely the continental models provided by the Cosmographies of Apian and Orontius Finaeus (dealing mainly with the sphere), and the *Cosmographical Glasse* contains little of purely geographical interest, but it is notable for its exposition and illustration of the method of survey by triangulation, and for an incidental wood-cut of a military officer taking an instrumental bearing for gunnery purposes, this last serving as a reminder that the development of rapid survey methods owed much to military requirements. Considerable attention is given to the problem of longitude, the author having, by his own observations, fixed that of his native town, Norwich, as 22° 30' E. of the prime meridian. The method of calculation from observations of a lunar eclipse is treated as length, and is followed by an account of how to take a lunar distance from a fixed star by Jacob's staff (a method earlier described by Apian), with examples from Cuningham's own observations, made at Norwich, and compared with the Ephemerides for Antwerp. The third method suggested is by a timepiece. ' You shall prepare a parfait clocke artificially made, such as are brought from Flaunders, and we have them as excellently without Temple Bar, made of our countrymen.' 'Do you not mean such as we use to wear in the facion of a Tablet ? ' asks his pupil. 'Yea truly', is the reply ; and the method is commended for its universal applicability. The section on Hydrography and Navigation deals among other matters with tide-tables, with the Age of the Moon, and with the variation of the compass.

'They are of Jofrancus sette forth in this wyse. In the island called Insula Corvi (Azores) it declineth easterly 15 degrees. Also in the place which shipmen call Le cap d'espoir en terre neuve [C. Spera] it declineth toward the West 33 degrees and 45 minutes. Again at Deppe [Dieppe] (saith he) it pointeth easterly too much by 11 degrees well nie.'

These figures may be compared with those of Jean Rotz for 1542,[1] from which, however, they differ considerably. Like so many of his contemporaries, Cuningham realized that his theoretical knowledge of astronomical methods was superior to the instrumental accuracy he could obtain, and he promises to describe a new quadrant and astronomer's rings, besides writing a general treatise on instruments. Early in the book he examines his pupil (for the text is in dialogue form) as to whether he has the necessary foundation for studying his Cosmography, and on receiving the reply 'Yea, sir ! I have read the Ground of Arts, the Whetstone of Witte, and the Pathway' (i.e. Record's three books), he advises as further text-books, Orontius' Arithmetic, Scheubel's Algebra and Euclid (the latter only published in 1558), and Theodosius' Of Spherike Demonstrations. Such a demand meant, of course, that the *Cosmographical Glasse* remained a book for the University student only.

To complete this survey up to 1561, three translations must be mentioned. John Bale included an English version of Paulus Jovius' *Scotiae Descriptio* (1548) and one of Polidore Vergil's *Hiberniae Descriptio* (1534) in his *Scriptorum illustrium . . . catalogus*, Basle, 1558. George North, servant of the notorious Thomas Stuckley, presently to engage in the Terra Florida adventure, dedicated to his master a *Description of Swedland, Eastland and Finland*, taken chiefly out of Sebastian

[1] See Chapter IV.

Munster.   The translator had added to Munster from Johannes Magnus and Saxo Grammaticus, and makes a display of sympathy with the Protestant Gustav Vasa, as against the deposed King Christian II, perhaps to allay suspicion against his master, Stuckley, then in favour at Court, but later openly a traitor.

III

In 1562 Richard Eden's work of collecting records of the Muscovy voyages and generally furthering the cause of discovery had been interrupted by his acceptance of an appointment which kept him abroad for the greater part of ten years. His engagement, too, to translate Pliny, was set aside.   The English voyages, save for those to Guinea, of which he had already published an account as an addendum to the *Decades*, consequently remained unchronicled.   Those of a certain French Huguenot were more fortunate.

Jean Ribault of Dieppe, who had settled his colony in Charlesfort early in 1562, returned to France to find the Wars of Religion in progress.   Crossing to England as a refugee, he was made much of by the Queen, whose father and brother he had served many years earlier, and the joint venture with Thomas Stuckley was planned.   Meanwhile he had published (possibly in England) a narrative of his voyage in French of which all that can be learned is from the words of Thomas Hackett the printer :   ' There chanced into my hand a copy of the discovery of a West India called Terra Florida.' [1]   This copy Hackett translated into English and published in May 1563 (just when the vessels for the second Florida voyage were being fitted out), dedicating it to his patron, Alderman Sir Martin Bowes, and entitling it, ' *The whole and true discovery of Terra Florida etc.*'.

The joint English-French project (for Elizabeth had given Stuckley a licence to plant a colony) excited considerable public interest, and led to the publication of a tract which has not survived, entitled ' *A Commendation of the Adventurous Voyage*

---

[1] The words are ambiguous, and although Hakluyt in his *Western Planting* speaks of the relation as extant in French and English, the French version may have been in MS. only.

of *Thomas Stuckley and others towards the land called Terra Florida'*, by Robert Seall, 1563. Stuckley, it will be recalled, betrayed the venture to Spain, and this was probably the occasion of an anonymous ballad which appeared, entitled '*A ballad made by one being greatly impoverished by the viage prepared to Terra Floryday'*.

An account of Ribault's voyage and death in 1565 was written by Nicholas le Shalleux of Dieppe in May 1566, and published in France. This work, too, was translated by Thos. Hackett, and published in England the same year : finally he completed his group of important translations from the French by that of André Thevet's ' Les singularités de l'Amerique ' (1558) under the title of *The New found World or Antarctike.* This volume (1568) was dedicated to Sir Henry Sidney, and formed part of Frobisher's ship's library.

Of great interest is the fact that Thomas Hackett paid the then quite considerable sum of twenty pence ' for his lycense for printing of the unyversall Coosemographe Apyane in Engleeshe '. This occurred between July 1561 and July 1562, but there is no record of the volume (of which there was now a French version) coming into print in English, and there is little doubt that the elaborate diagrams and figures (some with movable parts) that illustrate the original, proved an insurmountable obstacle. Eden met with the same difficulty as regards woodcuts in producing one of the sections added to the English *Decades.* A second licence for Apian's book was taken out in 1567-8 by Thomas Purfoote, but again it was abandoned. It does not, of course, follow because no copy of a book has survived, or because there is no record of actual publication in the Stationer's Register, that it was never printed. The conclusion in this case rests on the absence of mention of such a work in contemporary reference catalogues, e.g. that of Maunsell of 1595.

In 1562-3, Gyles Godhed had licence to print ' *The Carde of London* ', and ' *The mappe of England and Scotlande* ', of which only the former is known. The year 1562 is also the date of the *Russiae Tabula* of Anthony Jenkinson, dedicated to Sir Henry Sidney, and used by Ortelius in the *Theatrum.* It seems probable that the actual drawing of the map was done by

William Borough, who had some knowledge of cartography, on information supplied by Jenkinson. Writing in 1581, Borough speaks of ' my map ' of Jenkinson's journeys to Boghar and Persia (1557–62), which he says Mercator used in drawing his Universal Map of 1569.

The years 1567, 1568, 1569, 1570 were important ones in the history of geographical science. In 1567 William Bourne added to his *Almanack and Prognostications ' Certen Rules of Navigation '*, which were the prelude to a series of works popularizing scientific methods of Navigation and Survey which are treated in a later chapter. In 1568, Humfrey Lhuyd sent his topographical and cartographical material to Ortelius. In 1569 Hawkins published the narrative of his Third Slaving Voyage, while in 1570 Dee wrote his influential *Preface to the English Euclid*. The last-named, too, is dealt with in detail in a later chapter.

It remains to speak of Hawkins and Lhuyd, their works representing two contrasting aspects of geography, the travel volume and the academic treatise.

' *A true declaration of the troublesome voyage to the parts of Guinea and the West Indies in 1567 and 1568 '* was published in 1569, the year of Hawkins' return. Brief, and not very informative, it is notable as the first official account of an expedition to be published by its leader, i.e. it was a diplomatic document. In the previous year one Robert Baker had published a tract, ' *The briefe Dyscourse of Roberte Baker in Gynney, India, Portyngale and France '*, which has not survived. It does not appear to be the same document as the account of the Guinea voyage of the *Primrose* and the *Minion* in 1562, written in verse by the same Robert Baker, and published by Hakluyt in the 1589 edition only of the English voyages.

Humfrey Lhuyd had by 1568 been working on the history and topography of Wales for at least ten years, and wrote as follows (in Latin) to Ortelius from Denbigh on his death-bed :

' I hope to send you not only a very exact description of Mona [Anglesey], but also of all Cambria, with ancient and modern names, and a geographical chart of England with additions out of Ptolemy, Pliny and Antonine of the ancient names, so as to expose the falsehoods of Hector Boethius. I have also a very exact description of the maritime features of Scotland [probably the Rutter in Lord Arundel's library], all of which I will send you when I come to London, when the errors of many learned men will appear, who depict sites of places, cities, rivers, in their geographical charts very incorrectly.'

One of the ' many learned men ' criticized is Mercator, who in 1564 had engraved a map of Britain which has strong points of resemblance to certain manuscript maps of Lawrence Nowell, which have not yet been thoroughly examined. The documents of Lhuyd's that eventually reached Ortelius were the *De Mona Insula*, printed in the first edition of the *Theatrum*; the *Cambriae Typus*, printed in 1571 (as may be inferred from the Ortelius correspondence printed by Hessels) ; the *Britannicae Descriptionis Fragmentum*, printed by Birckmann at Cologne in 1572, and reissued as the *Breviary of Britayne*, in a translation by Thomas Twyne in 1573 ; and the *Angliae Regni Tabula*, printed by Ortelius in 1573.

Thomas Twyne, a friend of John Dee's, had in the previous year published a translation of the greatly esteemed *Periegesis* of Dionysius of Alexander, under the title *The Survey of the Worlde, or Situation of the Earth, as much as is inhabited.* Of much greater importance and interest was another translation of the same year. This was Richard Rowlands' *Post for divers parts of the world : to travaile from one notable citie unto another.* Rowlands was an Englishman of part Dutch descent, resident in Antwerp, and translated this useful roadbook from the High Dutch, but he remarks that it is to be found also in French and Italian translations. The dedication is very appropriately to the great merchant prince, Sir Thomas Gresham.

During the six years that have just been reviewed, i.e. 1566–72, Sir Henry Sidney, whose interest in geographical matters was unfailing, held the post of Lord-Deputy of Ireland, and took steps to collect and preserve its records both past and present. The excellent map of Ireland by John Gough, now at the Record Office, was made in 1567, and full details are preserved of the more detailed survey for a large-scale map made by Robert Lythe, 1569–71. Sidney personally accompanied Lythe over a part of the ground, and it is an interesting coincidence that his secretary at the time was Emery Molyneux, who twenty years later as an elderly man made the first English globe at Wm. Sanderson's expense. Here also may be mentioned Daniel Rogers' ' *Description of Ireland in Verse* ', written about this date and sent to his kinsman Ortelius. Rogers promised at the same time to send over a very accurate geographical map of that country for the next edition of the *Theatrum* (Hessels No. 42, October 1572), and this may have been a reduced copy of Lythe's map, which was drawn on a scale of about three miles to the inch.

The question of surveying methods of the period is discussed in a later chapter, but it must be recalled that Saxton's work was now well under way, and that Reyner Wolf, the Royal printer, was busy on his ambitious scheme for a world history, fully illustrated by maps. That some of the maps were actually published by 1572 is suggested by a letter (Hessels No. 43) to Ortelius from Nicholas Reynolds, written between the date of publication of Mercator's Map of Europe (1572) and Wolf's death (1573). Reynolds (who was the engraver of Saxton's Map of Hertfordshire) writes as follows : ' Quod si chartas nostras vendibiles apud vos fuerint velim scribas ad Reginaldem ipseque me, cum opportunem fuerit, certiorem facit.' One of these maps (chartae nostrae) may have been the ' Map of this Shyre ' referred to by Wm. Lambarde in the MS. of the Perambulation of Kent, 1570, and existing in a unique copy in the example of the first edition of the Perambulation (1576) in the Library of the Royal Geographical Society. Such difficult points, however, cannot be discussed in a general review, and must be reserved for later examination.

IV

So far nothing has been recorded from the pen of the elder Hakluyt, mentioned as one of the men whose intelligence was behind the Cathay voyages. The first authentic picture we have of him, however, that drawn by his young cousin, shows him as a man deeply versed in Cosmography, with his maps and geographies around him in his Chambers in the Temple. The historic scene between the schoolboy and the lawyer cannot be dated much later than 1567–8, and it is probable that an undated letter from the elder Hakluyt to Ortelius (Hessels

No. 172) belongs to approximately the same period. Ortelius was a map-mounter and dealer long before he prepared the *Theatrum*, and his kinsman, Daniel Rogers, the diplomat, was the link between him and a large English circle which included the two Hakluyts and Dee.

The letter in question [1] was a request for a world map mounted on vertical rollers for use in a limited space, and Hakluyt was supported in his request by John Asheley, a London merchant. This man was part owner of the ship *Castle of Comfort* until 1569 or 1570, and so would himself be interested in the map of Guinea, but as the letter shows, the area that chiefly interested Hakluyt was that where the North-West Passage might be found. Discussion had raged afresh round a possible strait since 1565 at least, and the writer was anxious to have a map showing, as Gemma Phrysius' globes plainly did, a ' Fretum Trium Fratrum ' in this quarter. This ' fretum ' had been dropped out of maps, e.g. that of Vopel, current in the '60's, and from Mercator's later globes, but Hakluyt supports its existence by the argument of the ship-wrecked Indians, an argument used equally convincingly by Dee in favour of a passage by the North-east. Gilbert, too, used the same argument in his *Discourse*,[2] and a comparison between the latter and Hakluyt's letter shows that the argument written by Hakluyt is actually the source of Gilbert's Chapter IV. The only point to be made here, however, is the lawyer's preoccupation with the possible discovery of Cathay, and as it will presently appear that his object was the improvement of British industry at home, and of British trade overseas, and not any spectacular discovery of gold or revelation of mysteries, it is interesting to recall the fact that he had speci-fically drawn his young cousin's attention to trade relations in the geography lesson at his Temple Chambers.

Hakluyt was a landed proprietor, and a gentleman of some social importance, the correspondent of Burghley and well known to Walsingham. The earliest document concerning him in the younger Hakluyt's collection is a long relation of the commodities of Nova Hispania, drawn up at his request in

[1] See Document 9, Letter iv.
[2] Published 1576, but written ten years earlier.

1572 by Henry Hawks, a middle-aged Seville merchant who had resided there for five years and whose acquaintance with the pilot Diego Gutierrez allowed him to add some useful notes on recent Spanish voyages in the Pacific to his carefully considered account of the country, its products and trade. One of these notes refers to a Spanish search for the North-West Passage from its supposed south-western end, and mentions that it is known in New Spain as the ' Englishmen's Strait ', and lies not far from China. Drake's visit to New Albion was to test just such a view, and for one such document as this preserved and printed, Hakluyt must have collected many more.

By this time the younger Hakluyt was studying and teaching Cosmography at Oxford, and the tide of English interest in the subject was rising strongly. That there was such an interest, backed by no corresponding training in the subject, is shown by the appearance in 1573 of a little tract, *Brief rules of Geography for the understanding of Maps and Charts*, which deals in elementary fashion with the circles, parallels and meridians, and other conventions of the map. The initials of the author, D. P., probably stand for David Powell, Sir Henry Sidney's domestic chaplain.

Standing in a class by itself, and closing the period to 1575, is Jerome Turler's *Traveller*, a philosophical guide-book to continental travel, written by a man who had lived much abroad, and who wished to induce others to seek the pleasures and enlightenment that travel has to offer.

Before turning to the remarkable output of geographical writings which coincided with the search for the North-West Passage, some reference is necessary to the advances in geographical education that the last twenty years had seen. Books, globes and maps, although still almost entirely of foreign origin, had multiplied in the houses of the well-to-do, and a well-educated young man like Humphrey Gilbert could quote a list of thirteen of ' the best modern geographers ' as confirming his opinion. His *Discourse*, sketched out in 1566, and gradually worked into shape during the next ten years, does not, however, prove its author so erudite as at first glance might appear. Some of his authorities could not have been actually examined, since they contradict him, while the majority of them are quoted at second-hand from the compilations of Eden and Ramusio. Arguments, too, were undoubtedly furnished to him by the elder Hakluyt (as in the case mentioned above) and by Dee. Nevertheless, the *Discourse* indicates the resources which a man interested in geographical problems could now readily command, and the important service rendered by Ortelius in gathering a selection of the best maps into the single volume of the *Theatrum* is aptly illustrated by the use Gascoyne made of that monumental work in revising Gilbert's *Discourse* for the press. It is a striking fact that, apart from a confused knowledge of Sebastian Cabot's voyage, based on Eden, Ramusio, and a map at Whitehall, Gilbert knew nothing of any English attempts at western discovery. Nor can he mention a single English authority on cosmography, or an English map. He devotes much care to elaborating the argument for a strait based on the general east to west circulation of the ocean which was earlier used by Peter Martyr. Taking as his starting-point the strong Cape Agulhas current, which has a volume obviously too great to find passage through Magellan's Strait, he held it proved that it did find its way right round the earth, because of the existence of the baffling north-equatorial current in the Pacific Ocean, encountered by Bernard de Torre in 1542, and flowing westwards towards the Moluccas. A broad open western passage commencing in the unexplored section of America between 62° and 72° north latitude seemed to afford the best solution of the current problem (since the Atlantic current did not appear to flow back towards Europe), and the only doubt that arose was as to the feasibility of a return voyage by this route against the ocean stream.

By way of comparison with Gilbert's sources of information, the geographical library of Sir Thomas Smith, the Secretary of State, may be examined. Sir Thomas Smith, Eden's revered tutor, may be taken as a typical Cambridge scholar and public man of the older generation. His library catalogue (as preserved by Strype) is dated 1566. He has but three modern works dealing with the New World—Munster's *Cosmographia*, Eden's *Decades*, and Barros' *Asia*, with in addition Eden's

Art of Navigation, which contained the small map of America found in the Spanish original. He has a fair collection of works on the less known parts of Europe—those by Olaus Magnus, Saxo Grammaticus, Wolfgang Lazius, and Albert Krantzius— besides the French *Description d'Afrique* (1556) from Leo Africanus. He has three copies of Ptolemy's Geography, one in Greek, one in Latin, and one in Italian, and the usual classical works, Herodotus, Strabo, Pliny, Diodorus Siculus, Dionysius of Alexandria, Solinus and Macrobius, dealing directly or indirectly with Geography.

His mathematical library, though excellent, proves (as do indeed his surviving private papers) his interest in Judicial Astronomy rather than in Cosmography, in spite of Eden's repudiation of such a belief on his behalf. Here he has the works of Apian and Gemma Phrysius, of Stofler and Reinhold, of Cardanus and Regiomontanus, even of Copernicus ; but taken as a whole, his library is geographically poor and suggests, as we should indeed expect, that a man like Gilbert growing up in the early years of Elizabeth's reign had a geographical out-look and geographical interests very notably wider than that of a man, like Smith, who had grown up in the reign of Henry VIII.

Nevertheless, in view of this improvement in geographical education, it is impossible to pass over without comment the poverty of Frobisher's ship's library, got together for his journey in 1576, although the expedition was admirably fur-nished with instruments, made by the greatest of all Eliza-bethan instrument-makers—Humphrey Cole. Record's *Castle of Knowledge* and Cuningham's *Cosmographical Glasse,* both of which were carried, were certainly adequate reference books for such astronomy and mathematical geography as was neces-sary to understand the principles of these various instruments, while (provided Spanish could be easily read by the Master) Medina's *Arte de Naviguar,* which was taken in the original, was likely to be more useful either than Eden's *Cortes* or Bourne's *Regiment* (mainly a paraphrase of Cortes). There was, moreover, no English text-book of Cosmography in which the explorers might hope to find a summary of what was already known of the North of America ; they took, therefore, Thevet's work, since it was published only the previous year, and so might be expected to be up to date. Thevet was a man of some practical experience (although only in the Levant and in Brazil), and he held the office of Cosmographer Royal in France, a fact which probably accounts for the inclusion also of his *Singularités de l'Amérique* both in the original and in Hackett's translation. The only English travel book included was *Sir John Mandeville*—presumably for the sake of its account of the Far East, which was the ultimate goal of the expedition.

Bookishness was, of course, an attribute not to be looked for in a Martin Frobisher or a Christopher Hall, and we may surmise on their part even some impatience during the lengthy and learned conferences with Michael Lok and John Dee, arranged for them by the Muscovy Company. By such men a library of seven books might be reckoned even excessive, and in point of fact there was not a single volume published at that date in England by which it could have been usefully supplemented.

V

The period from 1576 to 1583 was so rich in geographical output that to survey it within brief compass is a task of some difficulty. The Massacre of St. Bartholomew (1572) had brought Richard Eden back to England, and to a residence in London, where he took up his former work with a mind enriched by contact with the French school of geographical thought and practice. He had enjoyed the friendship of the ingenious inventor Jacques Besson (who became a refugee and died in England) ; he must have met Thevet and Nicholas de Nicolai ; he had read Fernelius ; and among the works which he brought over was a treatise on the magnet and on perpetual motion by John Taisner. This he translated as a pendant to a proposed new edition of Cortes' *Art of Navigation* under the title of *A very necessary and profitable book concerning navigation*, although a series of accidents delayed its publication until 1579, three years after his death. He took up besides his former task of gathering records of the English voyages, particularly those into Muscovy and Persia, and made a translation from the Latin (Madrignano's) version of the

Travels of Varthema. His death in July 1576 cut short these activities, and the task of carrying out his plans (which had included a new edition of the *Decades*) fell to his literary executor Richard Willes.

Very little can be learned about Willes, but in his *Poematum Liber*, published by Tottell in 1573, he prints a testimonial from the University of Perugia, where he had been Professor of Rhetoric until June 1572. The poems are dedicated to Burghley, who appears to have been attached to Willes' dead brother William, and they are accompanied by a treatise on Poetry addressed to the masters and boys of the writer's old school, Winchester. From the poems it may be gathered that Willes had a wide circle of friends not only in Italy, but in France and Germany, and in the 'Travels' he speaks of the famous Jesuit traveller and writer, Petrus Maffeius, as his old acquaintance. A letter to Francis Walsingham, written in July 1574, is dated from the Court, and while references in the poems point to an old connexion with the Russell family, it was to Bridgit, third wife of Francis Russell, Earl of Bedford, and formerly wife of the diplomat Sir Richard Moryson, that Willes owed a position in the household of Drake's godfather. The edition of the *Decades* was his first work in the English tongue, but he had for a long time, he says, had some other important geographical work on hand, while he also mentions a work on the coins of all nations as one he hoped to publish if his life were spared. Willes makes a very notable claim for Geographers as men whose services to the community were of first importance (Document 3), and it is clear that his description of himself as a Professor of Cosmography (although, as he says, there were neither Chairs nor Readerships in that subject) was amply justified. He rearranged Eden's material in a logical sequence, cutting away all the sections and notes that appeared to him irrelevant, besides omitting the Dedications which would offend Protestant taste. The whole work was now divided into four parts, of which the first was devoted to the West Indies, while the second, written entirely by Willes, has every appearance of having been originally designed as a separate publication, and set up as such in type. The title runs : ' For M. Cap. Furbyshers Voyage by the north west of

China in Cathayo, situated in the east syde of Great Asy. Of the Iland Giapan and other little Iles in the East Ocean, by the way from Cathaya to the Moluccaes.' The famous Discourse with which the pamphlet opens, reprinted (with considerable editing) by Hakluyt, was written at the request of the Earl of Bedford's daughter Anne, wife of Ambrose Dudley, the principal promoter of the voyage. The date, 20 March, must refer to the year 1577, since Willes had already seen the charts of the voyage of 1576 and discussed them with Frobisher. The Countess of Warwick was herself an investor in the second voyage, and was naturally anxious to hear the arguments for its success. Willes displays in his discourse a wealth of learning and a wide familiarity with globes and maps (including, as was natural, a majority of Italian origin), which bears witness to a prolonged study of cosmography.[1] It is here, too, that he discusses that Cabot map in the Earl of Bedford's possession, which seems to prove unmistakably a passage by Sebastian Cabot through Hudson's Strait, presumably in 1508-9.

The sections on the Far East are prefixed by a letter to Mistress Elizabeth Moryson, daughter of the Countess of Bedford by her first husband, with whom Willes had read Italian, and the date 21 February 1576 may indicate that these particular translations were first made in 1575. It is clear that Willes anticipated that Frobisher would pass safely to the Moluccas, doubtless because he had heard the explorer assert that he had already reached a point where he saw the Capes of America and Asia on either hand, at the entry to Mar do Sur.

Parts three and four of the volume are entirely from Eden, the one containing all that he had formerly printed on the North-east, the other the unpublished material which he had collected upon the Persian Voyages (1561-8), together with the Guinea Voyages, his unpublished translation of Varthema, and the account of Magellan's Voyage. Willes himself merely added (to fill the last few pages) a brief summary of the remaining *Decades* of Peter Martyr, with a rather fuller account of the Conquest of Mexico. He mentions that the English

---

[1] Willes appears to have used one of the collected sets of maps that are referred to as 'Lafreri Atlases'.

translation of Gomara's *History of the Conquest* was in preparation, and this must have been the version by Thomas Nicholas, published in the following year, which was dedicated to Sir Francis Walsingham, a personal friend of Willes.

It is difficult to estimate the state of feeling in England when the rumour went round that, as Philip Sydney wrote to Hugh Languet, Frobisher had discovered a new Peru. Languet's sobering reply was justified as the event proved, but meanwhile everything about the East, and everything about the earlier Spanish conquests was of interest. Hence arose the series of translations, produced almost, it would seem by their respective dates, in a spirit of rivalry by two elderly retired Spanish merchants—John Frampton and Thomas Nicholas.

Both these men were well known in Seville and the Canary Islands in the '60's, and both had suffered under the Inquisition. Frampton enjoyed the steady patronage of Edward Dyer, the courtier and close friend of Dee ; Nicholas had had a long business connexion with the family of Michael Lok. Frampton's output included : *Joyful Newes out of the New Found World* (Monardes) ; *A Description of the Portes and Havens of the West Indies* (from the work of de Enciso translated nearly forty years earlier by Barlow) ; *The Most Famous Travels of Marcus Paulus* ; *A Discourse of the Navigations which the Portugals do make* (Escalante) ; *A Discovery of Tartaria, Scythia and Cataia by the north-east* ;[1] and *The Art of Navigation* (Pedro de Medina) : six in all during six years. Thomas Nicholas produced : *News from the great Kingdom of China* (from the Castilian) ; *The Conquest of the West Indies* (Gomara) ; and *The History of Peru* (Zarate). He also wrote an original book, *A Description of the Forunate Isles* (the Canaries), which he knew at first hand.

A point worthy of special note, since it indicates the attitude of mind, and the purpose that lay behind all the great collections of travels of the sixteenth century, is Willes' reiteration of the first principles of Geography as laid down by Ptolemy :

---

[1] This translation was specially made for the renewed search for the North-East Passage of 1580 : MS. copies were given to Pet and Jackman. The subsequent printed edition was dedicated to the Governors of the Muscovy Company.

' The first principle and chief ground of all Geography, as great Ptolemy saith, is the *history of travel*, that is, reports made by travellers skilful in Geometry and Astronomy, of all such things in their journey as to Geography do belong. Lib. I. Geog. cap. 2.'

This sentence is the key to the travel literature of the period, and incidentally to the title of Willes' collection, *The History of Travell*. Of Willes himself nothing further is heard, and it must be presumed that death interrupted his labours, as he seemed to fear it would.

The voluminous output from Dee's pen at this period is dealt with in a later chapter. The elder Hakluyt's notes, reprinted by his cousin, show that the ideal he was working for was the planting of a colony in America which should enable the Mother Country to command supplies of essential commodities at present purchased from France and Spain ; his inquiries as to Newfoundland, directed to Anthony Parckhurst, were to this same purpose.

The Frobisher voyages themselves were, of course, thoroughly reported, both unofficially by Settle and Ellis, and officially by George Best, whose General Discourse on Cosmography, not reproduced in its entirety by Hakluyt, is not without interest as illustrating the geographical attainments and views of an ordinary educated man. The continued popularity of Honterus' little rhymed cosmography, which Best quotes, argues no very high standard even yet.

Some curious minor publications arose from the voyages, as for example ballads in praise of Frobisher, and ballads in welcome and farewell ; of these only those by Thomas Church-yard, soldier of fortune and court rhymster, now survive. Churchyard once served under Sir Hugh Willoughby, and knew Chancellor, whom he aptly describes as ' the odde (i.e. out-standing) man of his time for matter touching the sea '. Another of the topical tracts was *A discription of the pour-trayture and shape of those strange kind of people which the worthie Martin Ffourboiser brought into England in anno 1576 and 1577*. The Mongoloid appearance of these Eskimos gave colour to the suggestion that the north shore of the fancied Straits was Asia, and they were actually referred to as men of Cathay.

Interest in events overseas had not lessened the growing interest in England itself. Lambarde's *Perambulation of Kent* (largely written in 1570) was printed in 1576, and Holinshed's Chronicles (or rather Reyner Wolfe's, as John Stow [1] continued to call them) were published in 1577. William Harrison, who had worked for Wolfe until his death, compiled for the Chronicles a ' *Description of Britain* ', taken from manuscripts of Leland (borrowed from Stow), and from Saxton's still unpublished county maps (with Sackford's permission); for Scotland he had Bellenden's translation of Hector Boethius, which he rendered into English, and for Ireland a description begun by Edmond Campion, the Jesuit, and finished by Richard Stonyhurst. The great Saxton *Atlas* appeared in 1579.

Meanwhile William Bourne was continuing to publish his popular manuals, encouraged by the patronage of Lord Burghley, and his *Treasure for Travellers, Inventions and Devices*, and *Art of Shooting in Great Ordnance* all appeared in 1578, while a second edition of the *Regiment of the Sea* (1580 ?) containing the *Hydrographical Discourse of the Five Ways to Cathay* was inspired by the Frobisher voyages.

Standing quite in a class by itself was the first original English work on the magnetic compass—Robert Norman's *New Attractive* (1581), to which was attached a tract on the *Variation of the Compass* by William Borough. It is significant that both these authors were practical men and not students ; Norman had settled down after years on shipboard and in Seville, and was an instrument maker, working for Borough, who had lately received a naval appointment. It was over eighteen years before an original academic treatise on the same subject appeared, Dr. Gilbert's ' *De Magnete* ' of 1600.

Another work indicating original thought was the *Politic Plat for the Honour of Princes*, published by Captain Robert Hitchcock on New Year's Day, 1580. This ' plat ' had been formulated some four years earlier, and had been brought before Parliament by Thomas Digges. Its subject was one bearing on economic geography ; the author had ascertained that there was a large import of fish into England from France, and that whereas the Dutch and French sent out large fishing

[1] John Stow, *Survey of London.*

vessels to the Dogger Bank, the English fishermen, in vessels of inferior size, hugged the shore.   A well-equipped fishing fleet would make England self-supporting as regards this commodity, and he sought for Government aid in obtaining funds for its establishment.   An interesting map of the North Sea accompanies the booklet.

It is remarkable that the great exploit of Drake, 1577-80, left no impress whatever on current geographical literature (although the reasons for silence are probably political), but it is a curious coincidence that on 26 September 1580, the very day of his return, the publisher Thos. Purfoote obtained a licence to print *The voyage of Fferdinando Maganasses* (*sic* for Magellan) *into the Maluccos*.   Was this to cover also the story of Drake ?

All the writings centring on the Pet-Jackman voyage of 1580—the notes of the elder Hakluyt, Borough's and Dee's Instructions and maps, besides the two narratives of the voyage, remained in manuscript until printed by Hakluyt the Preacher.   Again the lawyer's mind was bent on the establishment of trade, as a solution to the pressing problem of unemployment at home, ' for in finding ample vent of everything that is to be wrought in this realme, is more worthie to our people . . . than Christchurch, Bridewell, the Savoy, and all the Hospitals of England ', i.e. than any palliative of charity. His instructions in the previous year (1579) to Master Hubblethorne, the Dyer, sent over to Persia ' at the charge of your city ', i.e. London, are designed to the same effect, and the tone of all these documents is that of a man acting in an official capacity as the economic adviser to those furthering the voyages. Hakluyt was an expert on the subject of woollens, vegetable dyes and oils, and rightly regarded the expansion of the woollen manufacture and of an export trade in cloth as of first importance.   His detailed notes on the subject are contained in the last of his writings to be preserved—the *Remembrances for a principal English factor at Constantinople* 1582.   Here he set out, quite in the style of a modern text-book, the geographical advantages for England for manufacture : the climate allowing work to be carried on throughout the year ; the abundance of cheap labour and cheap food ; the water-mills on the swift rivers, lacking in Flanders ; the uniform flow of the rivers, which are neither dried up in summer like those of Spain, nor frozen in winter as in the north ; all these in addition to the high quality of the raw wool and the abundance of certain dyes.

If the elder Hakluyt assisted also in the preparation for Gilbert's 1583 voyage, there is no record of it to-day. A *Prayer* for Sir Humphrey licensed in 1578, and Thomas Churchyard's 'Commendation' in verse mark the abortive start in the September of that year, while the *Carmen* of the ill-fated Steven Parmenius of Buda, and the map prepared by Dee, which has only just come to light, form the prelude to the actual voyage. The *True Report* upon this adventure, written by Sir George Peckham, closes this record, for although Florio's translation of the Cartier Voyages, Lichfield's translation of Castanheda, the anonymous translation of las Casas and the *Divers Voyages* itself, all fall within the date specified, they are the prelude to the immense undertaking of the younger Hakluyt now leaving Oxford. By 1583 Richard Eden was dead, William Bourne was dead, probably Richard Willes likewise. Barlow was dead and forgotten, though Thorne was remembered. John Dee was following a chimera in Bohemia. The page was turning to open a new and still fuller chapter in English Geographical Thought.

That new chapter will not be dealt with here. It is time to turn back and examine more closely the work of certain representative and influential men who have so far been barely named—among them Roger Barlow, Jean Rotz, John Dee and William Bourne—whose lives cover the century under review.

CHAPTER III

ROGER BARLOW AND CABOT : 1526–1542

AMONG the manuscripts from the Royal Library, now preserved at the British Museum, is one, docketed *Geographia Barlow*,[1] dedicated to King Henry VIII in a style which belonged to him only subsequently to 1535. Bishop Bale glanced at this work, when compiling his *Catalogue of British Writers*, and ascribed it to his contemporary William Barlow, the aged Bishop of St. David's, an ascription tentatively repeated in the *Dictionary of National Biography* (*Art*. Wm. Barlow).

In the dedication of the *Geographia*, however, it is clearly stated that the author is one Roger Barlo, and in the printed catalogue of the Royal Manuscripts (1921) this Roger is correctly identified with the Englishman of that name who is known to have accompanied Sebastian Cabot's expedition to La Plata in 1526. This identification is placed beyond doubt by the *Geographia* itself, which contains a vivid account of the topography of the Parana Basin, and of the character and customs of the various Indian tribes encountered there. As the book is not primarily a record of travel, there is naturally no mention of Sebastian Cabot or the members of his expedition, and little light is thrown on the controversial aspects of his voyage ; nevertheless, Barlow's Geography, as the first English work of its kind written after the Great Discoveries, marks a stage in the development of English Geographical thought, and the circumstances of its appearance form the subject of this chapter.

It will be recalled that Hakluyt, in his *Principal Navigations*,[2] gave prominence to the fact that two Englishmen went in 1526 to La Plata, his authority being the famous letter from Robert

---

[1] Royal MSS. 18 B. XXVIII.
[2] Hakluyt : *Princip. Navig.*, 1600, vol. 3, p. 726.

Thorne to Dr. Lee which he himself had printed for the first time in the *Divers Voyages* of 1582. Thorne had merely mentioned the men as ' two friends of mine ', but their names—Roger Barlow and Henry Latimer—are repeatedly found in Spanish documents dealing with the 1526 venture.[1] Thorne and his partner, as he himself relates, had invested a large sum in this voyage (destined originally for the Moluccas) in order to secure places among the company for Barlow and Latimer : this they did, not so much for profit, as in order to secure information bearing on a possible English route to the Spice Islands, which had been Thorne's dream since as a child at Bristol he had seen his own father sail and return with John Cabot from the New Found Land. Both Barlow and Latimer, according to Thorne, were ' somewhat learned in Cosmography ' ; a statement that is confirmed by Barlow's book, and by the esteem in which Latimer was held, according to the Spanish documents, as ' the English pilot '. Their specific, though naturally secret, intention was to study the navigation and navigating charts of Far Eastern waters, and to inquire as to the seas north and north-east of the Moluccas, that is, towards the ' backside ' of the New Found Land.

Now, not the least important chapter in Barlow's Geography is an appeal to King Henry VIII to prosecute northern discoveries, couched in terms which are in places almost identical with those of the address to the King which Hakluyt prints with Thorne's letter to Lee. It becomes necessary therefore to elucidate the history of the Address and the Letter. As far as Hakluyt himself was concerned, he tells us that they were ' friendly imparted ' to him by Cyprian Lucar, into whose hands they had come from his late father, Emanuel Lucar, who is described as ' executour ' to Thorne. Actually the elder Lucar had been apprenticed to Thorne, had been with him in Seville, and was very generously remembered in his will. He rose to be a prominent London merchant (Master of the Merchant Taylors Company), and his eldest son was educated at Oxford, and entered at Lincoln's Inn. Cyprian Lucar, as his later published work shows, was keenly interested in mathematics and its practical applications, while his cousin, a second

[1] Harrisse : *John and Sebastian Cabot*, 1896, Syllabus lvii, 1530.

Emanuel Lucar, had sailed with Francis Drake, and it was this twofold interest, possibly, that made Cyprian aware of the labours of the great mathematician and geographer, John Dee. The latter, in 1577, was busy on the third volume of his *magnum opus, General and Rare Memorials Pertaining to the Perfect Art of Navigation* (to be considered later in detail), for a chapter of which he was collecting material bearing on Queen Elizabeth's title to the northern lands which Frobisher was actively exploring. It was to Dee, then, in the first instance, that Cyprian Lucar brought the Thorne papers, as is clear from a note to Dee in his handwriting, endorsed by the recipient, ' To Mr. John Dee, 1577 '.[1] The purport of this note is to request that in making use of the papers credit shall be given to the elder Lucar for their preservation, and the same request was no doubt made to Hakluyt in 1582, since he is careful to mention Emanuel's name. The text of the note is as follows :

' It may please your honour at your curtesye to remember my father Emanuel Lucar for that he preserved Dr. Thorne's book and card of the viage to Cataia at the humble request of me his sonne Cyprian Lucar. Dr. Thorne was a marchant adventurer and borne in Bristowe my father was also a marchant adventurer and sarvant to Dr. Thorne at the time when Thorne did write his letter to the King and his ambassitor.'

The fragment is preserved with the oldest extant MS. version of the Thorne documents, apparently the copy which Dee caused to be made on this occasion, to judge from the title and marginal notes. Confirmation is afforded by the paper used, which has a watermark corresponding to one dated 1577 in Beasley's Collection.[2]

The discrepancies between this MS. of the Thorne documents in Vitellius C. VII, that in Lansdowne MSS. 100 [3] and the printed versions in Hakluyt, prove that no one is a copy of the other, but each from a common original, i.e. Lucar's, which was in places faulty or difficult to decipher. It seems to have had no title, for Dee and Hakluyt added each his own. Dee's

---

[1] Cotton MSS. Vitellius C. VII, fol. 344.

[2] Additional MSS. 38637 and 38638.

[3] This MS. is the work of a professional copyist : the only clue to date is afforded by the watermark, which is of a type common about 1580, but not known earlier.

contains a phrase clearly indicating the work he had in hand :
' wherein is conteyned matter very needfull, to be now considered of : As well for discovery to be made : As for the
Recovery and enjoying of our Right and interest in some lands
allready by Englishmen discovered.'

It may be mentioned in passing that Hakluyt made minor
alterations in each of the three versions which he printed,
while no MS. copy of the map has been preserved. The
printed map has been both carelessly copied and deliberately
altered, and the Latin note attached to it concerning Ophir [1]
affords some clue to the material that Thorne himself used.
It is a summary statement of the position relative to the respective spheres of Spain and Portugal, and the references to longitude are in accordance with Thorne's text, whereas the longitudes on the map as printed by Hakluyt are quite wrongly
numbered. The note, however, is in a language which Thorne
does not use, and it has reference to Ophir and Tharsis, which
Thorne nowhere mentions, although their position is indicated
(also in Latin) on the map. Now in the Preface, written in
1518, to his *Suma de Geographia*, Fernam de Enciso sums up
the view of cosmography that resulted in Magellan's voyage,
namely, that the Portuguese in reaching Malacca had already
covered 180° E. longitude, and consequently that all the still
undiscovered lands, which must include Ophir and Tharsis, lay
in the Emperor's half-sphere. While no map was published
with Fernam's book, he expressly states that he had prepared
one, and it was to this map, or a like one prepared for the same
argument, that Thorne had (probably surreptitious) access.
Dee (who had a copy of Fernam's *Geographia*) wrote a long
discourse on Ophir in the spring of 1577, identifying it with the
same area as on Thorne's map, the loan of which must therefore
have been especially precious to him.

We must turn now to the circumstances in which the Thorne
documents were originally composed. Dr. Edward Lee,

---

[1] '. . . . Et sic, licet insulae Tharsis et Ophir videntur attingere
Portugalenses, tamen insulae Capo Verde dictae, quae intra supra dicta
signa x + cadunt, videntur omittere. Et sic dum insulas Capoverde
retinere volunt Portugalenses, illas Tharsis et Offir non possunt
attingere.'

Henry VIII's almoner, and later (1531) Archbishop of York, was sent in December 1525 to Spain, where one of his commissions was to collect a debt owing from the Emperor Charles V to the King. The spring of 1526 saw him at Seville on the occasion of the Emperor's marriage, and it was here that he made the acquaintance of Robert Thorne. Under date of 15 April 1526, he writes to Wolsey : [1]

'I had good hope to have had redie payment heer of the 150,000 crownes, and for the indemnitie of themperor had devised with two marchants heer (the toone called briges the aldermans brother the tooder a right toward young man as any lightlie belongeth to England called thorne) divers sufficient ways for anie man willing to pay. These two hath shewed themself in all things redie to doo the kings highness service and be heere of great credence.'

The Alderman here referred to was Sir John Briggs, or Bridges, the draper and Levant merchant who in 1520–1 was Lord Mayor of London : [2] Thorne had many personal links with London as well as with Bristol.

Less than a fortnight before this letter was written, and a few days before the arrival of the Court at Seville, Barlow and Latimer, Thorne's friends and agents, had sailed with Cabot : but the financial and general arrangements for the expedition had been made as early as 1524 (presumably after the meeting of the Judges and Cosmographers on the bridge of Caya), while the idea must have been mooted soon after the successful return of Magellan's ship, the *Victoria*, with a cargo of spices, in 1522.

A similar expedition had already been dispatched by the Emperor in July 1525 under Garcia de Loaysa. Both ventures had as their prime object the establishment of a Spanish Spice Trade, in rivalry with the Portuguese, and hence it is somewhat surprising to find that in 1526 the Emperor was already secretly negotiating the sale of his claims to Portugal (a sale actually completed in 1529). Such was the statement of an unnamed informant who approached Dr. Lee in Granada, somewhere about the New Year of 1527, with the suggestion that the

---

[1] Vespasian C. III, fol. 232 (Cotton MSS.).

[2] He had been a subscriber to the proposed North-West Passage venture of 1521.

English king, and not the Portuguese, should become the purchaser. Lee wrote to Wolsey on the subject on 20 January 1527,[1] recounting the interview in full. He had been asked to write to King Henry VIII, but had insisted that he must first have the offer confirmed by the Emperor himself ; meanwhile he had interrogated the secret agent as to the state of the trade, the Emperor's profits, the part of the spiceries he had in peaceable possession, the charges incurred, and finally, the price offered by the King of Portugal. ' He said ij millions. I said he offered verie mutch for a thing yet being in hope and little in hand.'

After two long colloquies nothing further eventually came of the matter, but there can be no doubt that this affair was the occasion of the submission by Dr. Lee to Thorne of that series of questions to which his letter is a categorical answer, ' a summary declaration of that which your Lordship commanded', as he himself writes. These questions all refer to the very points which the English ambassador had raised at the secret interview : What did the Emperor's spiceries produce ? What was his profit ? What was his title to the spiceries ? and further, did the English discoveries (i.e. of the New Found Land) give King Henry any title therein ? In his answer Thorne revealed his own plan of discovery by the north, and the part his two friends were taking to make it feasible : it was a plan which would make any purchase of the rights of the ' Emperor's Spicerie ', and the route thereto, quite unnecessary.

In spite of the uncritical assumptions of Hakluyt to the contrary, there can be no doubt that the direct address to Henry VIII was not written at the same time as this letter, namely, in February or March 1527. Thorne asked Dr. Lee to keep silence about the matter of an English discovery until the writer should return to England, when he would adduce further arguments. He would obviously await Barlow's home-coming with the expected fresh information from the Moluccas, and this did not take place until October 1528, while Latimer only reached Seville in July 1530. Moreover, the mention in the Address of an unsuccessful English attempt by a route other

---

[1] Cotton MSS. Vespasian C. IV, fol. 3.

than that proposed by the Seville merchants can only refer to John Rut's voyage, from which the surviving ship could not have returned until late in 1527.   Lee was still in Spain in 1529, but the period of difficulty which arose for the English merchants in Spain subsequent to that date, owing to the royal divorce, decided both Thorne and Barlow to return to England (probably in 1531 after Latimer's return from La Plata), and there we hear of them both, in the March and February respectively of 1532.[1]

The most probable date for the composition of the Address is between Latimer's return to Seville and the departure of the merchants for England, i.e. 1530–31.   There is no evidence for any association between Thorne and Barlow once they reached home,[2] although their previous business relations are confirmed by the fact that Barlow was a debtor to the Inventory of Thorne's goods made after the latter's death on Whitsunday 1532.   It will be noticed that the Address is unsigned (' The rest is wanting ', says a footnote to the MS. version) and its style differs very markedly from that of Thorne's letter, while resembling that of Barlow's Geography.   It is possible, then, that while the idea expressed was Thorne's, the composition was Barlow's.

That any opportunity arose for its presentation to Henry VIII in Thorne's lifetime seems doubtful, and the more so in that Barlow embodies a version of it in his Geography less than ten years later,[3] without any reference to Thorne, or to such a suggestion having been already laid before the King.   A further point confirms this view : Barlow's Geography, as will later be shown, can be dated confidently as completed in the winter of 1540–41, while in March 1541, as we learn from a letter from Chapuys to the Queen Regent of Holland, quoted

---

[1] Gairdner, *Letters and Papers of Henry VIII*, Vols. IV and V. Thorne went so far as to purchase a ship, the *Saviour* of Bristol, which was offered for sale in Spain : this he proposed to use on the voyage of discovery.   S.P. Henry VIII, 238, ff. 13 and 14.

[2] But Barlow was executor of the will of Nicholas Thorne, Robert's brother, in 1546.

[3] While engaged on the book, Barlow presented an Address, and possibly a map, to the King, outlining his purpose.   S.P. Henry VIII, Vol. 239, fol. 106.

90942

by Harrisse and Williamson,[1] the Privy Council had debated sending out an expedition to Tartary by the very route which Barlow advised, and a pilot of Seville (and if he were not Cabot, Barlow must have known many others) had been provisionally engaged to conduct it. This certainly looks as though a new suggestion, and not an old one already rejected, had been made.

Before turning to examine the Geography itself, a few words must be said about Barlow's life on his return to England, so far as it can be gathered from contemporary documents. Like Thorne, he was a Bristol man, and had two brothers who held ecclesiastical preferment at Westbury, while a third brother, that William Barlow to whom the *Geographia* was wrongly attributed, was for some time Prior of Haverfordwest. All the brothers were friends of the Reformation in its extreme form, and active agents of Thomas Cromwell. The sometime Prior, on the dissolution of his House, was made Bishop of St. David's, and we find Roger Barlow settled as a large landowner at Slebyche (Shebech), near Haverfordwest, on estates formerly belonging to the Priory. Thomas Cromwell made use of his services in a matter of shipping in July 1535, and the coincidence that Barlow presented his Geography to the King in the winter following Cromwell's disgrace and execution, suggests that he was a little anxious about his position. He was employed, however, by the Privy Council in April and March 1543, to investigate a suspected embezzlement of gold from a Spanish prize in Milford Haven by the Mayor of Pembroke (John Rastell being on the same commission), and was making further large purchases of Crown Lands in June 1547, when he was a sheriff of the County of Pembroke.[2] He died in 1554.[3]

The date of the Geography, as has been said, was 1540–41, for in the text the expedition of Charles V to Tunis, which took place in the summer of 1535, is mentioned as occurring ' 5 or 6 years since '.[4] That this date is correct, and that we have the MS. as it left Barlow's hands, is confirmed by the three different

---

[1] J. A. Williamson, *Maritime Enterprise*, p. 265.

[2] This account is compiled from Gairdner, *Letters and Papers of Henry VIII*, Vols. IV–XXI.

[3] Inquisitions Post Mortem, Chancery Series II, Vol. 101, No. 100.

[4] i.e. *between* 5 and 6 years, according to current usage.

watermarks on the paper used. Two of these are identical with, the third almost identical with, examples in Beasley's collection dated 1540 and 1541.[1]

In the Preface to the King the scope and purpose of the book is outlined :

' As one most desirous to occupie himself in some service that myghte be acceptable into your royall majestie under your gracys favour and suffraunce I have set foorthe a brief somme of geographia which dothe treat of all partes and provinces of the worlde and specially of contreis latelie dyscovered by your majestie and by themperor Charles of that name Vth and of the kynges of Portugall and Spayne which I humblie present unto your majestie for that your grace maye commande it to be corrected and amended and to give your auctoritie to be put fourthe in prynte for that it may be agradable to the readers and also profytable to such as intende to have knolege of the navigation to dyscover straunge countreis . . . wherfore at the beginning I have put [2] a little declaration of the sphere with the regiment of the northe pole and the sonne with their declinations the longitude and latitude of all the worlde & also the costes of the lands with their derotas (i.e. bearings) and altitudes showing every place in how many degrees it stondeth . . . whereof parte I have travelled and sene myself by experiens and those parties which I have not sene I have had knowledge of them by such credible persons as have labored that countries and also have written of the same . . .'

Actually the basis of the book is a fairly literal translation of the already mentioned *Suma de Geographia* of Martin Fernandes de Enciso [3] which was first published in Seville in 1519, and of which a second edition appeared in 1530, although Barlow used only the first. The English writer's original contributions include a long account of the Parana-Plate region,[4] his version of Magellan's voyage, some personal notes on the Canaries, Azores and Morocco, the greater part of the section on Britain, including a full notice of South Wales,

[1] *Loc. cit.*

[2] In the *Address* presented to the King (*loc. cit.*) Barlow writes, ' I doo entend to put . . . ', but the *Suma* itself was already complete.

[3] Fernandes is described in the Privilegio Real to the first edition as ' El bachillar Martin Fernandez de Enciso alguazil major de castillia del oro '. He had been the companion (and enemy) of Balboa in Darien, and his book is valuable for its account of the West Indies and Terra Firma, a section also translated by Frampton in 1578.

[4] For further extracts, see Document 4, Appendix III.

an account of Calicut taken from the Italian of Varthema, and the appeal for northern exploration. In addition there are occasional minor omissions, interpolations and alterations.

The nautical tables of the Spanish original are brought up to date and extended, Barlow adding to the solar declinations the daily position of the sun in the Zodiac for four years. The whole of the first section dealing with the sphere, the fixing of latitude, and the rhumb lines, forms a compact manual of contemporary sea practice, and its close correspondence with the preliminary matter in Jean Rotz' Book of Hydrography presented to King Henry VIII in 1542,[1] i.e. just a year later, shows that such manuals were already more or less stereotyped. Rotz gives declinations for one year only, while Barlow (following de Enciso) gives them for four, ' the first yere after the Lepe yere ', ' the second yere ', and so on. Thus Barlow's tables are most probably calculated for the years 1541-4, and those of Rotz for 1542, the second year after the Leap Year, which most nearly represents the average. Taking the figures for the first day of each month as found in Barlow's second year (probably 1542) and Rotz' single year, and correcting an obvious error of transcription in Barlow, the two agree on an average within 2'. According to the Deputy-Superintendent of H.M. Nautical Almanac, who kindly looked over a part of Barlow's tables, they are consistent among themselves and are subject to an error of the order of 5' or 10'.

The Regiment of the North Pole (Fig. 3) is made clear by comparison with the similar figures in Rotz and Vallard. The guiding stars (called ' guards ') are not the pointers, but the three stars in the handle of the Dipper, i.e. ε, ζ and η in Ursa Major. Their successive positions, corresponding to Barlow's figure, are given roughly in Fig. 4. The maximum correction, $3\frac{1}{2}°$, is certainly too high, although its value was greater in the sixteenth century than it is to-day, namely, $1°$ 5'. In 1726 it was taken as $2\frac{1}{4}°$, while it was slightly reduced in the 1530 edition of de Enciso, where the figure given is $3°$ 20'. The line of zero correction (Fig. 3) is found only in Barlow.

The Geography proper, which follows the section on navigation, is written in portulan or ruttier style, detailed description

[1] Royal MSS. 20 E. ix.

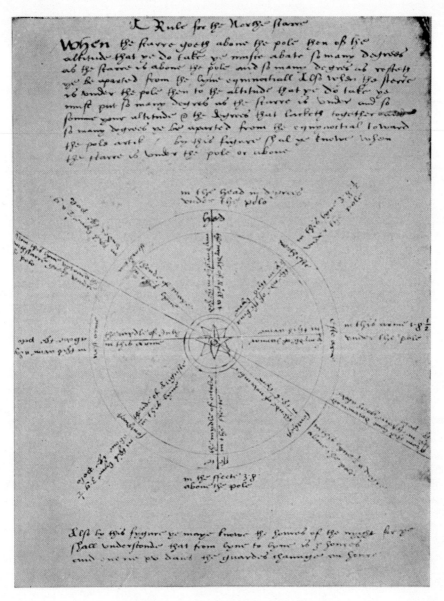

FIG. 3.—THE REGIMENT OF THE NORTH POLE

Barlow's Briefe Somme of Geographie, MS. Brit. Mus.

being limited to coasts and havens, with more general accounts of the chief countries by river basins. Both style and content may be judged by a quotation or two from the region that Barlow knew best, namely, South Wales and the Severn.

'Mylfordhaven (is) one of the best and goodlieste portes for shippes that is in the worlde for at all times thei may come in and owt without dainger and though thei brought nother cable nor anker thei maye save themselfes in krykkes. . . . From Gloucester to Brigstowe west is 10 legis which is a noble towne of grate trate and many shippes belongyng to hitte/but hathe a goodlie haven that cometh through the towne and a sumptuouse bridge ower it of lyme and stone after the maner of the bridge of London. The shippes and bots cometh in to ij portes of the towne the one is called the barke the other the keye and ij leges from the towne is the river of Severne ther is a goodlie rode called kyngrode and an other within that called hungrode wher ryde the shippes that list not to come before the towne . . .'

St. David's Head is placed in 52°, an error of only 6', but while the two little islands of Rhamsey and Skalney off the coast of Pembroke are minutely described, one line suffices for the whole coast northward to Scotland, where Barlow follows his Spanish authority. He is better instructed as regards the non-existent 'Iland of Brasyll', which he places in 52° N., 70 leagues west of Ireland, than he is as regards Scotland.

The route to Brasil proper from the Canaries, and the principal landmarks all along its coast to the River Solis, are taken direct from de Enciso, who clearly already had a good general chart and ruttier of the area in front of him in 1518. Barlow adds a note as to the latitude where the North Star is lost, and that where the South Star is picked up ; he also gives details of the seasonal alternation of the Trade Winds and consequently of the currents along this coast. His description of the cannibal Tupys and Guaranis (correctly named and located) is very full and accurate,[1] and he is able to contrast them with the hunting and fishing tribes on the north coast of the Plate estuary, and with the Pampas Indians, who were much taller, and were not cannibals.

A sketch map prepared solely from the indications given in Barlow (Fig. 5) is in complete harmony with the Spanish docu-

[1] It is interesting to compare Barlow's account with that of Hans Staden.

ments quoted by Harrisse and with Sebastian Cabot's map of 1544. Careful study of the hints in the documents, and some clear indications in a letter of Ramirez,[1] one of his fellow-travellers, allow of the conclusion that Barlow (and therefore almost certainly Latimer too) was on the flagship of the little fleet, and after the shipwreck at Santa Catalina on the newly built galley, with Cabot himself. He is referred to as the lieutenant of Herando de Calderon, Treasurer of the expedition, and was sent home with the latter in advance, to carry to the Emperor specimens of the gold and silver found among the Indians. Latimer, coming home later with Cabot, had among his companions the famous cosmographer Alonzo de Santa Cruz, while more than one of the company who had been on the *Victoria* in 1519–22 took part in this expedition. Hence both the Englishmen had every opportunity for collecting valuable geographical and nautical information.

Since Sebastian Cabot's motive for abandoning the voyage to the Moluccas for the sake of an exploration of the Plate Basin was probably to follow up the rumour of precious metals, what Barlow has to say about the latter is of interest :

' On the west part of the river, within the land towards the mountains 150 leagues off, is a Serra or mount, whereas they say is a king where is a great abundance of gold and silver. And all his vessels and stools that he sitteth on is of gold and silver, and among these Indies by this river's side we had gold and silver which the women wear upon their breast and about their arms and legs, and by their ears. This land and the land of pirro (Peru) which is in the southside that the Spaniards have discovered of late is all one land, whereas they had so great riches of gold and silver.'

Space will not allow of quotations from Barlow's descriptions of birds, beasts, and fishes (including the humming-bird), which show remarkable powers of observation, and a tenderness and love of nature unusual at this period. The whole account of Brazil, however, as the first to be written in the English tongue, is of great historical interest, and will shortly be printed *in extenso*.[2]

[1] Ternaux-Compans : *Nouvelles Annales des Voyages*, Vol. III (Paris, 1843).
[2] In the Hakluyt Society's Publications.

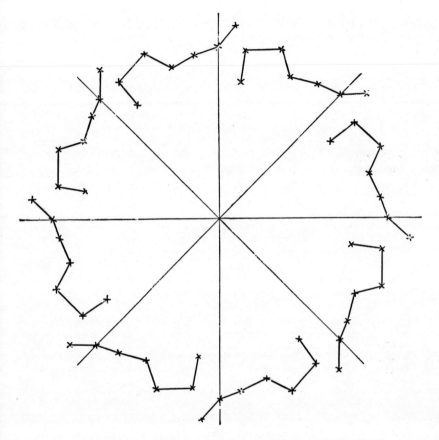

FIG. 4.—DIAGRAM TO SHOW SUCCESSIVE POSITIONS OF THE GUARDS

De Enciso's book closed with a brief paragraph on Labrador and Baccalaos, as forming the fourth quarter of the globe, and by following this arrangement Barlow was able to make his appeal for the pursuit of northern discoveries the close and climax of his volume. The opening passage of this section must be transcribed in full :

' Now that I have spoken of that parte of the worlde from the ilond of ferro toward ponyent and austro we shall speke of the part of the lond that is in the second parte called septentrion, which is called the newe founde lande. Which was fyrst discovered by marchants of Bristowe where now the Bretons do trat thider everie yere a fyshing and is called the bacaliaus. It lieth westnorthwest of galisia and hath many goode ports and ilonds and northwest of it hath the lond of laboradoris which standeth in 57 degrees. What commoditie is within this lond as yet is not knowen, for it hath not been labored, but it is to be presupposed that ther is no riches of gold spyces nor preciose stones for it stondeth far aparted from the equinoctiall where as the influens of the sonne doth norish and bring fourth gold spices, stones and perles, but where as our English marchants of Bristowe did enterpryse to discover and discovered that part of the land, if at that season they had followed toward the equinoctiall no doubt but thei shulde have founde grete riches of gold and perles as other nations hathe done sence that tyme.[1]

Here we find two references to the Bristol merchants as discoverers, and none to the Cabots, while there is also that hint of a wonderful opportunity missed in not sailing south that we come across in contemporary literature elsewhere. Had John Cabot's plan been followed in 1498, Mexico and Terra Firma might have been English instead of Spanish.

Students of the ' Thorne ' Address to Henry VIII as printed three times by Hakluyt, as transcribed for Dee, and as found in the Lansdowne MS., will recollect that all alike contain a meaningless, garbled passage relative to the three ways in which exploration had already been accomplished. In Barlow's version the rendering is correct, so that the error must have originated in Lucar's copy. A second erroneous reading in Hakluyt and Dee is also elucidated by comparison with Barlow. In dealing with the distance on either side of the Pole which must be reckoned dangerous, Hakluyt has ' 2 or 3 leagues ', Dee, ' 3 or 4 ', both being nonsensical. Barlow has

---

[1] The remainder of this passage is quoted in Document 4 (b).

' Moche more passing this little space of navigation which is counted dangerous maie be 3 ☾ leges before thei come to the pole and other as moche after thei have passed the pole it is clear from thens forwards the sees and land is temperat as it is here in England '.   In the copies the symbol for ' hundred ' has evidently been omitted.   Three hundred leagues is about 17½ degrees of latitude, and hence the dangerous zone is north of 72°–73° N.   This fits in with the *Geographia*, where Iceland and the north of Scandinavia, to which the waters were known to be open and safe, are placed in 71°–72°.[1]

As has already been stated, Dee endorses the Thorne MS., which he caused to be copied, as being incomplete.   Apart, however, from a superscription (which probably never existed), there can be missing no more than a line or so, as appears by comparison with Barlow, whose closing paragraph runs :

' And beside all this yet the comoditie of this navigation by this waie (i.e. across the pole) is of so grete avantage over the other navigations in shorting of half the waie, for the other must saile by grete circuites and compasses, and this shal saile by streit wais and lines.'

Here, quite abruptly, the manuscript comes to an end ; King Henry, for reasons that we cannot guess, did not allow it to be ' put forth in print ', and this precursor of Eden and Hakluyt—Roger Barlow—has been forgotten until to-day. No direct result (apart from the mooting of a voyage by the north in 1541, and, as will presently be shown, in 1551) can be traced either to his personal knowledge of Brazil, or to his *Geographia*.   Yet it is not irrelevant to note that the English voyages to Brazil (in which Barlow's patron, Thomas Cromwell, took some interest) fall within the period 1530–1542, as does that strange venture of the gentlemen of the Inns of Court led by Master Hore, which has already been mentioned.

[1] The Lansdowne MS. has ' two or three hundred leagues ', i.e. this copy is correct.

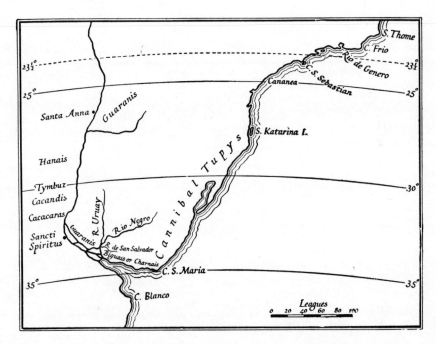

FIG. 5.—SKETCH-MAP ILLUSTRATING ROGER BARLOW'S VOYAGE TO LA PLATA

CHAPTER IV

FRENCH INFLUENCES: 1542–1547

THE story of the oldest Scots Rutter or Pilot-book, fair-written to commemorate a Royal Progress, given by an English admiral to a French painter, translated immediately from the Scots tongue to guide a French fleet through Scottish waters, and finally, some forty years later, published in Paris in its French version by the same painter turned cosmographer, reads like a romance, and its examination serves as an occasion for studying the general question of the influence of France on English geographical thought.

There can be little doubt that the coasting pilots of Britain, like those of France, had their stereotyped written sailing directions and rough charts in the early sixteenth century.[1] Only under special circumstances, however, did these documents come into the possession of educated persons, and so chance to be preserved. Such an occasion was the circumnavigation of his kingdom by James V of Scotland in the summer of 1540, under the conduct of the noted pilot Alexander Lindesay. Alike as a consideration of prudence and to commemorate so interesting an event, the detailed Rutter and the Chart of the route were put into readable form, and it is natural that the English Admiral, Lord John Dudley, Viscount Lisle, should have obtained a copy of the two documents.

A special mission—the ratification of peace—took the Admiral to France in the summer of 1546, and there he met the young traveller Nicholas de Nicolai, Sieur d'Arfeville, who had recently made a tour of the northern countries of Europe.

---

[1] See above, p. 4, and Harleian MSS. 6207, fol. 23. Such written rutters derived from directions handed down from pilot to apprentice by word of mouth, and the illiterate majority must still have relied on the latter.

Nicholas the Painter, as he was called from his early training
as an artist, had found employment for his brush in making
charts and harbour plans, and Dudley was told, says Nicholas,
' d'une Carte et description Géographique de l'Isle et Royaume
d'Angleterre en laquelle j'avois observé plusieurs choses notables et non vulgaires '.[1]   The Englishman did not rest until
he had obtained this map, and had finally also persuaded
Nicholas to return with him to England, where the painter
remained for nearly a year, being well received at Court.   The
manner of his employment is clear, for on 7 March 1548, Dr.
Nicholas Wotton complained to the Privy Council that a
French painter named Nicholas had taken to France plans
of all the English ports, which, we may infer, were copies of
those made for Lord Dudley.   The Admiral had disclosed to
Nicholas several important matters relating to his office, and
' pour mieux m'attirer à ses desseins, me communiqua un
petit livret escrit à la main en langage escossois, contenant la
navigation du Roy d'Escosse Jacques cinquième . . . faicte
autour de son royaume . . . ensemble la Carte marine assez
grossement faicte '.[2]

Of the double game that Nicholas was playing we learn
from the French Ambassador at that time in England, Odet
de Selve, who writes to France [3] that Nicholas is getting him
information as to the port of Rye, and, a fortnight later,
that he has shown him this very book of Scottish navigation.
Unfortunately, says the Ambassador, he (de Selve) has only
been able to arrange for a translation by a Scotsman whose
French is very poor, and the translation cannot be checked,

[1] See *Navigation du roi d'ecosse Jacques V. autour de son Royaume* . . .
*recueillie et redigee en forme de description hydrographique, avec les addi-
tions du dit Nicolay touchant l'art de naviguer.*   Paris, 1583.   The
quotation is from the Dedication.   An English translation was published in *Miscellanea Antiqua,* 1710, since reprinted in *Miscellanea
Scotica,* 1818, Vol. 3.   Nicholas's words suggest that a visit to England
had been included in his earlier tour, when he had obtained material
for the map.

[2] From the Dedication as above.   The Earl of Arundel had an
English version of this Rutter, no doubt identical with that in the
beautiful contemporary MS. Seaman's Manual, Add. MSS. 37,024.

[3] *Correspondance d'Odet de Selve,* edited by Germain Lefevre-Pontalis.
1889.   Quoted in Document 9, No. i.

for the painter has carried off the original. Nicholas, however, had his own plans. He returned to France about this
time, May 1547 (for Henry VIII and Francis I alike were
dead), and had a translation of the Rutter made by a famous
scholar, Johannes Ferrerius, a Piedmontese ecclesiastic, who
later wrote a supplementary chapter to Hector Boethius' *History of Scotland*, and who, through long residence at the Abbey
of Kinloss, was familiar with the Scots tongue. Nicholas
collated the Rutter and the Chart, and then, being careful to
keep a copy for himself, presented the documents to the French
King, who handed them to his Florentine Admiral, Leo Strozzi,
at the same time ordering Nicholas to accompany the latter
when the fleet sailed to besiege St. Andrews. Subsequently,
with the help of the Rutter, the French ships passed right
round Scotland, and carried Mary Stuart to France from
Dumbarton by way of St. George's Channel.

The French printed version of the Rutter, not published by
Nicholas in Paris until 1583, is dedicated to the French Admiral,
the Duc de Joyeuse,[1] at whose studies in navigation the painter,
by that date Premier Cosmographer of France, had assisted.
It is accompanied by a well-executed map of Scotland in
portolan style, which is probably one made by Nicholas many
years earlier. At a date unspecified, but after the execution
of Northumberland (formerly Lord Dudley), he had made a
hand copy of the Rutter, together with a new Chart, for the
great Cardinal of Lorraine, Charles of Guise, who had much
to do with the education of his young kinswoman, Mary Stuart.
The date must have been before 1566, the year when Nicholas
began his series of survey maps of the French Provinces, for
he refers only to having made a new map of the Boulonnais,
the reception of which by the Cardinal encouraged him to
further work of a similar kind.[2] The Cardinal's MS. copy of
the Rutter is preserved at the British Museum [3] and includes a
section on Navigation written by Nicholas himself, and derived

---

[1] Document 5, ii.   [2] Document 5, i.
[3] Harleian MSS. 3996. *Navigation de la Mer . . . alentour du
Royaume d'Ecoce . . . Premierement composee par Alexander Lyndesay,
Ecossoy . . . avec augmentation par Nicolas de Nicolai . . . Geographe
du Roy.*

in part from his own French edition of Pedro de Medina's *Arte de Naviguar* (1545), which he had translated about 1549 and published in 1554. This section is elaborated in the later printed Rutter of 1583, which contains, too, a general description of Scotland.

It is, however, the content of the Scots Rutter itself that is of the greatest interest. The Navigation is divided into four parts, from Leith southward to the Humber, from Leith northwards to Dungesby (Duncansby) in Caithness, from Dungesby to the Mull of Kintyre, and from the Mull of Kintyre to the Mull of Galloway and the River of Solway. Each of the four navigations is dealt with under five heads : 1. The course of the tide ; 2. The time when the tide flows and ebbs ; 3. The features of the coast ; 4. The *veues* (i.e. ' kennings ' or runs of 14 miles)[1] between one point and another ; 5. The harbours, roadsteads, soundings and dangers. A few quotations will illustrate the kind of information supplied :

" Dedans le mylieu de Pantheland Firth entre Dungesby et Orknay, il ya un grand dangier au tems de basse marée, qui est nommé le bar. Et pour l'eviter vous prendrez votre course Nort oest, de Dungesby jusques à ce que vous parviendrez au Nort, tirant à l'Est, de Stroma. Au bout de Stroma au Nort gist un aultre grand danger nomme Soulle, lequel est causé par quatre ou cinq marées contraires, avecques grande circulation d'eau, causant un profond et bruyant goulfre, le mylieu duquel est dangereux pour toutes navires grandes et petites. . . .

' Entre Scarba et Dura (Jura), ya la plus dangereuse marée qui soit cognuee en Europe, à cause des diversitez des marées, lesquels courant entre la Mulle de Kynteir et Illa (Isla), passant parmi l'estroit canal, et en passant, court avecques si grande violence sus la coste de Scarba, qu'elle est rejette a la coste de Dura, avecques bruit si espouventable qu'elle fait à son retour un profond et bruyant goulfre, qui garde et empesche les navires d'y entrer, et n'ya aultre refuge sinon à Dieu et à la mort : neantmoins, le tems plus convenable pour passer ledit danger est quand la marée est plaine, ou quand elle est du tout basse Ce passage est vulgairement appellé Correbreiken.' [2]

It will be seen that this Scots pilot-book was very much more detailed and exact than the well-known *Rutter of the Sea*,[3]

[1] The English ' Kenning ' was reckoned as 20 miles : see Add. MSS. 37,024.

[2] Quoted from the MS. version.

[3] *The Rutter of the Sea and the Laws of the Isle of Auleron.* Translated by R. Copland. London, 1528.

mainly a guide for Channel shipping, which was first published in London in 1528. The translator of the latter explains that the original was brought to him, printed in the French tongue, by 'a sad ingenious and circumspect mariner of the City of London', who obtained it in Bordeaux. This original was by Pierre Garcie, a ship-master of St. Gilles sur Vie (Vendée), and it is to be noted that a card, compass, rutter, and dial are named by the translator, but not by the earlier author,[1] as the necessary furniture of a ship-master, even though only coastwise sailing is dealt with. Naturally, neither the astrolabe nor the mariner's staff is mentioned. The Laws of the Isle of Auleron (Oleron), a code of sea-laws and customs which the book includes, are dated 1266, i.e. they go back to the period when Aquitaine (with Auleron) was an appanage of the English Crown. Hence they became the common heritage of French and English sailors, and are to be found in the English ' Black Book of the Admiralty ' (where they include an ordinance of King John), although Copland translated them from Pierre Garcie.

Nicholas de Nicolai and Pierre Garcie are not the only French contributors to English knowledge of navigation. The Ambassador, Odet de Selve, was distressed to find that there were no fewer than sixty French pilots and mariners in the service of Henry VIII in 1546. Among these was Jean Roze (Rotz),[2] who had been appointed salaried Hydrographer in 1542, after presenting the King with an elaborate meridional compass (or Differential Quadrant, as he termed it) and a Treatise on Nautical Science.

Jean Rotz' manuscript, written in archaic French, is sometimes difficult to decipher. The translated title runs : ' Treatise on the variation of the magnetic compass and of certain notable errors of navigation hitherto unknown, very useful and neces-

---

[1] The extremely crude woodcuts of landmarks (not printed in the English version) suggest that the *Routtier* was first published in France very early in the century, although the oldest French edition extant appears to be that of 1542.

[2] Document 6. While little is known of the career of Jean Rotz, save for the material here collected, it is significant of the esteem in which he was held in France, that Nicholas de Nicolai, writing of distinguished French navigators in 1567, places his name in a list including Jacques Cartier, Villegagnon, Jean Alfonce, and Ribault.

sary to all pilots and mariners. Composed by Jan Rotz, native of Dieppe, in the year 1542.'

In a long and flattering preface to the King, the writer says that he comes before him not empty-handed, but bearing a book and an instrument for his acceptance : the book composed for all those who wish to taste the pleasant fruits of Astrology and Marine Science. It is not written, he adds, in the common tongue of the (English) people, although the author, having spent part of his life in England, has some knowledge of the language, but he knows the King's love of the French tongue, while his Grace may, besides, choose whether to keep the book for himself and so be the superior of his subjects in science, or whether to have it translated for the instruction of his mariners. 'Laquelle seroit cause comme j'estime qu'on trouveroyt en pou de temps autant ou plus de bons et parfaictz pillottes et astrologues de marine en Angleterre quen aultre lieu du monde.'[1] Rotz excuses himself for not presenting also a nautical chart, but does not doubt that the King has already received examples as fine as any he has made or will make. Further, he begs his Grace not to notice the workmanship of the Instrument, since it is the first of its kind to be made.

The book itself is divided into three parts, of which the first treats of the spherical shape of the Earth, with emphasis on the proof by experience on long voyages. The second part deals with the imperfection of the marine chart and its causes :

'. . . la maniere et facon du compas aymante, la difference du regard de son north (sic) envers le pole, et la plus commune oppinion sur ce tenue, avec la premiere maniere et facon de la carte marine, emoins par les modernes, observee ; et par consequent de la difficulte et faulte de ladicte carte procedant de ladicte difference de regard du north du compas envers le pole.'

The third part treats of the construction and use of the instrument, which the inventor calls a Differential Quadrant (see Fig. 6). Actually it is one of the precursors of the theodolite, and a very elaborate one. The large magnetic compass

[1] A majority of the mariners and pilots on the King's ships at this period were foreigners—Ragusans, Venetians, Genoese, Normans and Bretons—notes the French Ambassador Marillac, writing in 1540. E. T. Hamy : *Etudes Historiques et Géographiques*, No. X.

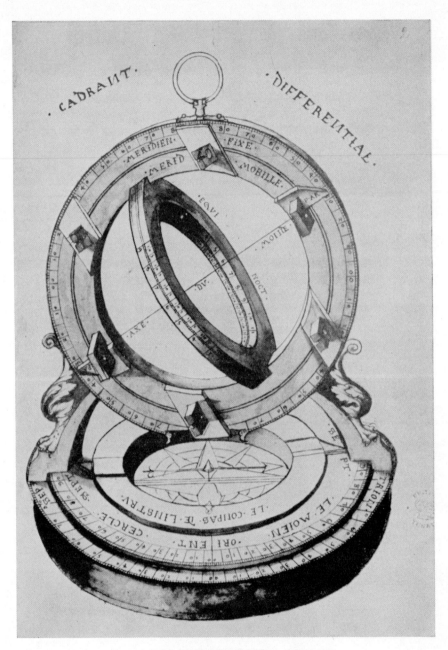

FIG. 6.—JEAN ROTZ' DIFFERENTIAL QUADRANT
MS. Brit. Mus.

set in the horizontal circle suggests a marine origin, and it may
be compared with the contemporary instruments designed for
taking horizontal bearings by such landsmen as the brothers
Arsenius, which were orientated by tiny compasses inset
on the margin. Like Waldseemüller's *Polimetrum*, Rotz'
instrument could take a combined altitude and azimuth,
but its prime purpose was for the accurate determination of
the variation of the compass. Thus the title of Part III
runs :

' La composition et usaige de linstrument que nous avons praticque
pour lobservation des differences du compas declarez en la precedente
partie. Et la maniere de prendre toutes latitudes et eslevations polaires.
Avec la maniere et usaige de praticquer la longitude par la lune et une
etoile fixe selon la doctrine des cosmographes. Et aussi lusage pour
scavoir les heures egalles du jour artificiel en toutes regions et finable-
ment une brefve doctrine pour prendre toutes longitudes, latitudes et
profunditez de geometrie par la moyen dung Instrument.'

The making and assembling of the instrument are described
with great care, separate working drawings being given of each
part. These reveal that the general sketch given in the figure
is faulty in some important respects, notably as regards the
fitting of the vertical and horizontal circles. Actually the
horizontal part of the instrument is in three concentric sections.
The innermost is the mariner's compass, the needle very deli-
cately poised, and protected by a sheet of glass. This box
compass carries an alidade, the fiducial line corresponding with
the N.–S. line on the compass rose, and extending across the
angular graduations on the second section, the mobile circle.
It is into this latter that what Rotz calls the orthogonal circle
is mortised, so that it can be rotated into any desired position.
The outermost base circle is rigid.

The vertical portion is also threefold : the outer and rigid
graduated circle embraces a mobile circle carrying sights.
These are joined by a thread (*fil*) representing the axis of the
Earth. The mobile circle carries a ring in a third plane which
is graduated to serve as an equinoctial or universal dial. An
important feature not shown in the figure reproduced was
the levelling device. This consisted of three metal knobs
screwed at equal distances into the rigid base : by twisting

these knobs farther in or out the base could be levelled with the help of a plummet. A suspensory ring was provided for use at sea, and the inventor points out that to avoid the instrument's swaying in the wind the base must be weighted with lead at discretion.

Like Pierre Crignon [1] and some other intelligent men of his day (including Sebastian Cabot), Jean Rotz believed that he should find in the variation of the compass a solution of the problem of longitude. Reasoning from insufficient data, his conclusion was faulty, but none the less interesting. The facts he set out are these : he knew that the deviation at his native town Dieppe was 10° E., while he had himself determined a deviation of 8° E. in Guinea, and 10° W. in Brazil ; and he learned from those who frequented the navigation to Terre Neufve (Newfoundland and Canada) that there it was as much as ' half a run of the wind ', or 22½° W. He records further that two ships of Dieppe, sailing to ' Taprobane ', i.e. Sumatra, found the deviation there to be 35½° E. He is uncertain, however, whether there was a steady increase to this value throughout the voyage, or whether the deviation had not passed through a maximum and was decreasing, since the distance in longitude traversed exceeded a quarter of the circumference of the world by 35°, i.e. ' Taprobane ' lay 125° E. of Ferro. The reference is undoubtedly to the voyage of 1529 to Sumatra made by the Parmentier brothers of Dieppe, on which Pierre Crignon accompanied them, and the deviation of 35½° E. and the longitude 125° E. (less than 8° out) are some of the data upon which Pierre Crignon must have based his own theory of longitude : his work [2] was evidently known to Rotz.

The latter's revelation of travel, too, is interesting. It is the Guinea-Brazil route he knows, returning by the Azores : he gives the date of one Brazil voyage, the autumn of 1539, while he also mentions being at sea in 1529. This is just the period of the English Brazil voyages, and as Rotz mentions

---

[1] For the life of this poet-navigator, see *Recueil de Voyages*, Vol. IV. 1883.

[2] His lost *Perle de Cosmographie* was written in 1534 and dedicated to the Admiral Philippe de Chabot. Crignon took the line of zero declination as his prime meridian. *Recueil de Voyages*, Vol. IV.

his residence in England, he may have been employed as pilot by the elder Hawkins or his confrères.[1]

To return, however, to the observations. Leaving aside the ' Taprobane ' figure, Rotz compared the other deviations with the linear (not angular) distances from the prime meridian, on which, so he stated, the deviation was nil. Thus Cap Raz was 480 leagues W. and the deviation there $22\frac{1}{2}°$ W. ; this gives a deviation of $1°$ for every $21\frac{1}{4}$ leagues. The other observations gave varying values up to 24 leagues, but the differences were put down to errors of the charts from which the distances were taken, and $21\frac{1}{4}$ was accepted.

It is clear from his diagrams that Rotz considered that the needle, wherever it was carried, remained parallel to itself, and to a plane drawn through the prime meridian. Hence if it was taken west, the convergence of the meridians would produce an (apparent) deviation to the west, and similarly, if it were carried to the east, a deviation to the east. At $90°$ E. or W. the deviation would pass through a maximum, hence the rejection of the Sumatra figure. Sebastian Cabot appears to have had a somewhat similar theory, although he placed his zero line west of the Azores.

That Jean Rotz, even when at fault, was ahead of his contemporaries, is clear when we compare his work with the extremely popular Spanish Navigating Manuals of Pedro de Medina (1545) and Martin Cortez (1551). Pedro de Medina, an experienced West Indian pilot, held that the ' north-westing and north-easting of the needle ' (as it was called) was of little moment, and was associated with the movement of the Pole Star round the pole. He remarks also that since the ' virtue ' of the compass resides in the needle and not in the rose (i.e. card), it is to be regretted that compass makers do not make the north point of the needle tally with that on the card. This emphasizes a further cause of confusion on which Jean Rotz also dwells. Just as the compass-clock makers of the fifteenth century cut the magnetic deviation on the dial as a matter of course, so the marine compass-makers allowed for it, and as the rose or card was attached *above* the needle, and adjusted so that the north point or ' lilly ' pointed to the north star,

[1] J. A. Williamson, *John Hawkins*, Ch. I.

the deviation was not brought to the pilot's notice. Sailing, too, was only to 32 points, and consequently any small variation was likely to escape notice or be dismissed as accidental, e.g. the variation as between Dieppe where the deviation was 10°, and London where (according to Digges in 1571) it was 11¼°, or just one point east of north.

As and when, however, navigation became more cosmopolitan, a new difficulty was introduced : a compass made in one port, with the local deviation allowed for, did not tally with a compass made in another port, when both were taken overseas. Columbus, for example, refers to the contradictory readings of his Genoese and Flemish needles respectively on his Second Voyage. On this point Rotz furnishes interesting details. The Portuguese, for the navigation to Guinea, made compasses corrected for a deviation north and quarter northeast. The Italians, for the Mediterranean navigation, made no correction. The French, Scots, English and Flemings made needles practically alike, corrected for a deviation north and half a quarter north-east. For transoceanic voyages the French compasses were very variously corrected, and Rotz considered that all such methods were at fault, for since there was a continuous variation from point to point, the only method of determining the true direction of the ship's course was to make frequent comparison between the geographical and magnetic meridians. As exemplifying the errors of current practice, he states that it was the usual experience on the return from Brazil for the master to find himself 70 leagues farther west of the Azores than his reckoning showed, notwithstanding the exactness with which both Brazil and these islands were, so he says, laid down on the charts, as a result of being frequented by sailors of many countries. Such errors were put down to currents and faulty seamanship, but were actually due to faults of the compass.

Rotz reiterates that the variation of the compass and the sphericity of the Earth alike determine that the rhumb lines, forming a parallel network, in the marine chart, do not represent true bearings. Hence errors arise in using the charts, and it is very necessary that positions should be fixed astronomically, although he recognizes that not only are the operations difficult in themselves, but the computation requires more knowledge of astronomy than the ordinary ship-master can command.

He gives two supposititious examples of longitude determination, as follows : ' je dycts que le 15° de Janvier 1529, moy estant dessus la mer voulus scavoir la distance de mon meridien au meridien dulme.' At sunrise, then, which occurred at 8 o'clock, he took his astronomer's staff, ' dict par les mariners esbalester ', and measured the distance between the sun and moon, finding it 41°. Two folios of complicated calculations follow, and finally, taking Ulm to be in 47° N., 30° 20' E., the required longitude is found to be 180° E. of Ferro, i.e. somewhere east of the Moluccas. Using in the second example the moon, and a fixed star, he says, ' Moi estant sur la mer veulant scavoir la distance de mon meridien de Dieppe, premierement je rectifies mes ephemerides ou tables dalphonse au meridien de dieppe et puis je regard le vrai lieu de la lune pour ung certaine de la nuyt,' namely, ten o'clock, when he finds it 16° in Taurus, and determines its declination. He also finds the right ascension of the star Aldebaran ' aprez toutes rectifications faictes destiez ' 2° 18' in Gemini, and its declination 15° 55' N. ' Et notte ycy ung poinct cest quil est necessite que tu rectifies ton heure par en moyen des equations des heures mis aux tables dalphonse ou aux ephemerides.' Again, a couple of folios are occupied by computations, and the longitude works out as 229° 30' E., or somewhere in mid-Pacific. Rotz does not, unfortunately, give any examples of the observations he would make for determining the variation of the compass, although it was for this that his instrument was specially designed.

It appears, from several direct references, that Jean Rotz was a student of the deservedly popular writings of Peter Apian, and especially his Cosmography. It is not surprising, therefore, that in the last section of his book he refers to the method of map-making by triangulation, due to Gemma Phrysius,[1] and found in his editions of Apian from 1533 onwards. The title of his Chapter 8 runs : ' De la mensuration pour practicquer les longitudes et quantitez des espaces qui seront enter tous les lieux a lenviron de toy, et desquels tu veulx avoir lesdits espaces et mensurations, voyre pour lieu que tu les puisses

[1] See Chapter VIII, below.

veoir, et ce par angles sans calcul et par deux stations seulement.'

After describing the method of triangulation and drawing
the diagram as in Phrysius-Apian (although without reference
to particular places), Rotz adds :

' Et davantage tu doits scavoir que ceste maniere de faire seroit tres
necessaire et utille pour la composicion de quelque carte terrestre, tant
pour la scituation de tous les lieux, places villages, chasteux, et villes
et citez que lon voudroit escrivre en icelle selon la latitudes par lesquels
seroient trouvez les unes et les autres.'

This Dieppe seaman had no reason to complain of his personal
reward at the King's hands.   He was taken into royal service,
and described himself as ' servant of the King ' in the well-
known *Boke of Ydrography*, the preparation of which was his
first official duty.   This beautiful volume consists of a Navigating Manual and a set of charts which appear to have been
copied from a large world map of the ' Desceliers ' type, since
they can be fitted together.   The text is in English, but with
certain Lowland Scots forms which suggest that Rotz had lived
across the Border at some time.   At Michaelmas in 1542, the
author received a payment of £20, being one-half of an annuity
of £40, then a very considerable sum,[1] while on October 7 of
the same year [2] he was granted papers of denization for himself,
his wife and children.   Here he is described as ' native of Paris ',
and as he speaks incidentally of having given two years to the
study of nautical problems, he may have retired to that city
from Dieppe in 1540.

In 1544 Rotz was granted a licence for the export of wool
beyond the Straits of Morocco, but soon after the accession
of Edward VI, his salary was halved, and he came to the
Ambassador, Odet de Selve, with offers of harbour plans and
other information, besides a promise of maps of Scotland and
England in his possession, on condition of being allowed to
return to France in spite of having become a naturalized
Englishman and engaged in war against his country.   De Selve
secured the necessary permit, and it is to be presumed that
Rotz returned to Dieppe.

[1] *Letters and Papers of Henry VIII*, Vol. 17, g. 880, fol. 426.
[2] *Loc. cit.*, Appendix A, 20.

An equally well-known figure in England at this time was Jean Ribault, also of Dieppe, later the Huguenot colonist of Florida, who had been appointed to serve by sea under the Admiral (Lord Dudley) on 7 April 1546.[1] De Selve's letters reveal him as in close personal association with the Admiral, but under the new régime he was given his *congé* in March 1547, and in July he was offering information as to operations in Scottish waters to the Ambassador. He pleaded that only poverty and misfortune had forced him into the service of a foreign King, but he seems to have had no genuine desire to return to France, and found it an excellent excuse that the ports were being watched, since the English authorities had no wish for these well-informed Frenchmen to cross the Channel. Later in the year Ribault went to the Scots wars, and returned to tell de Selve the story of the battle of Pinkie.

The last notable Pilot and Cosmographer to be named by de Selve as serving in England was Sécalart. This was the man ' well skilled in his craft ', as the Ambassador writes, who had earlier been associated with the famous Captain Jean Alfonce, who piloted the Sieur de Roberval to Canada. Sécalart added his signature and the date, November 1545, to the important manuscript treatise on Cosmography which Jean Alfonce completed not long before his death in 1544, although the extent of the actual contribution of the former to the work is a matter of dispute.[2] It was to Sécalart, evidently a man of authority, that de Selve entrusted the task of persuading or compelling his compatriots to return home, but his success (and the only evasion was Ribault's, who subsequently was made prisoner in the Tower) must have been partly due to the fact that in France, as in England, a new monarch had come to the throne early in 1547.

Besides the services of these distinguished men of action, Henry VIII might have enjoyed those of a man of letters, one who described himself as ' calligrapher, cosmographer and mathematician ', Jean Maillard. Maillard, who was appointed poet-royal to Francis I in 1530, had been outshone by a rival, and offered himself to Henry as Court poet, ' as one Marot is

[1] Acts of the Privy Council, Henry VIII.
[2] *Recueil de Voyages*, Georges Musset, Vol. XX.

to the King of France '; this dates his offer as not later than 1543, when Clément Marot, the poet in question, accused of heresy, left the French Court. Like Jean Rotz, Maillard did not approach King Henry empty-handed. His gift [1] was a metrical version of part of a Rutter by Captain Jean Alfonce which he must have seen in manuscript, since although written by 1536, it was not printed until 1559. The title given to the printed version of this Rutter, *Voyages Avantureux de Jean Alfonce*, is a misleading one, for it contains little that is personal, being largely a French rendering of the *Suma de Geographia* of the Spaniard de Enciso, published in 1519 and 1530. Maillard calls his version *Le premier livre de la cosmographie en rethorique Francoyse*, and doubtless the more attractive title was coined by the poet and courtier, Mellin de Saint Gelays, who was responsible for the publication of Alfonce's manuscript in 1559. Saint Gelays had, it seems, a gift for titles, for it was he who invented the name ' Holometre ' for the plane-tabling apparatus of Abel Foullon.[2] No map accompanies the *Voyages Avantureux*, but Maillard had made one to embellish his manuscript,[3] which for its originality has been reproduced here (Fig. 7). The novel division of the hemispheres is appropriate, since the poem is confined to a description of the circuit of the Atlantic Ocean from Trafalgar Bay to Magellan's Strait.

The question arises as to why those Frenchmen who were eager for a share in the rapid expansion, alike of material and mental horizons, which took place in the early sixteenth century, turned in the 'forties to Henry VIII rather than to Francis I. The answer is to be found in the restrictions which the French King sought to place on native overseas enterprise, owing to the offence it gave to his ally Portugal, and also in the Huguenot sympathies of so many men of action and men of letters, which led them to seek a welcome from a Protestant King. Their brief sojourn in England could not have been without effect,

---

[1] Royal MSS., 20 B. xii. The poem was originally composed for Francis I, and a copy is preserved, under a different title, in the *Bibliothèque Nationale, fonds français*. No. 13,371. Here he praises Pierre Crignon side by side with Jacques Cartier.

[2] See Chapter VIII, below.

[3] No map appears to be known with the French version.

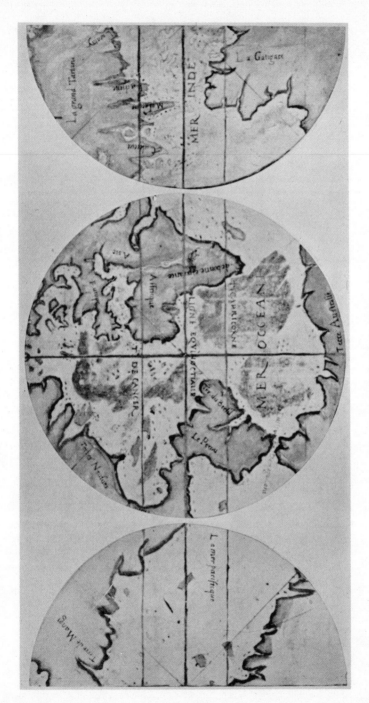

Fig. 7.—JEAN MAILLARD'S WORLD MAP

MS. Brit. Mus. circ. 1543

if only in stimulating young Englishmen to study Navigation
and Cosmography.   The year that saw the repatriation of the
Frenchmen saw young John Dee at Louvain, making his first
acquaintance with Gemma Phrysius and Gerard Mercator.
Dee was, at this time, the close associate of the young Dudleys,
of whose education their father, the former Admiral Lord Lisle,
was so solicitous.   Mary Dudley married Sir Henry Sidney in
1550, and it was as a member of Sidney's household that Richard
Chancellor, the first great English pilot, made (in John Dee's
company) those astronomical studies that fitted him for the
task of 1553, the Search for a North-East Passage.

Dee's influence on geographical thought will presently be
traced in detail.   Here it will be convenient to characterize
briefly the French output of geographical literature up to the
middle of the century, since it was a further channel of French
influences.[1]   Works on Cosmography included an edition of
Waldseemüller's *Introductio* (Lyons, 1517), an edition of Apian-
Phrysius (1544), a descriptive work (confined to the Old World)
by J. Signot (1539) and the mathematical treatises *De Cosmographia* of Orontius Finaeus (1532 *et sqq.*).   The New Discoveries were represented by a version of Vespucci's *Navigations* (1515 ?) ;   the *Travels of Haython the Armenian* (1517 ?) ;
Pigafetta's *Narrative* of Magellan's voyage (1525) ;   *Letters* from
the East and West Indies (1532) ;   the *First Three Decades* of
Peter Martyr, with which was included F. Cortes' narrative
of the *Conquest of Mexico* (1533) ;   an account of Pizarro's
Conquest of Peru (1534) ;   a *Brief Récit* of Jacques Cartier's
voyages (1545) ; a translation of Oviedo's *Historia* in the same
year ; a letter from Francis Xavier concerning *Japan* (1546) ;
and a translation of the letter from King Manuel of Portugal
announcing to the Pope his success in Abyssinia in the same
New Year.   All these works were in the vernacular, and so had
an English public, for the French tongue was familiar to many
men of the English merchant class, as well as to English courtiers
and scholars.   As the list shows, the books cover every part
of the newly discovered world, and this output emphasizes the
poverty of English geographical literature during the same
period, in which overseas discoveries are represented merely

[1] A complete bibliography has been published by Geoffrey Atkinson.

by the wretched tracts printed by John of Doesborowe, by Rastell's *Interlude*, and by John More's translation of the *Legacy or Embassate of Prester John*.

The deficiency was, up to a point, to be remedied within a few years by Richard Eden, who had left Cambridge and come to Court in 1544, but his studies in Cosmography, like his studies in Alchemy, owed nothing to his University ; Protestant Theology and the pronunciation of Greek were the subjects that filled the minds of learned men in England.

CHAPTER V

JOHN DEE AND THE SEARCH FOR CATHAY:
1547–1570

I

SHORTLY before his death in 1568, Humphrey Lhuyd, historiographer and cosmographer, himself a Welshman, wrote of his fellow-countrymen as follows :

' They be somewhat impatient of labour, and overmuch boasting of the nobility of their stock, applying themselves rather to the service of noblemen than giving themselves to the learning of handicrafts. So that you shall find but few noblemen in England but that the greater part of their retinue are Welshmen born. . . . There is no man so poor, but for some space he setteth forth his children to school, and such as profit in study sendeth them to the University, where for the most part they enforce them to study the Civil Law. Whereby it chanceth that the greater sort of those which possess the Civil and Canon Laws in this Realm are Welshmen.'

John Dee was just such a Welshman as is here described—tracing his descent from Kings, boasting of the five Emperors whom he might have served. His father, Roland Dee,[1] had a petty appointment about the Court of Henry VIII, and managed to send his son from Chelmsford Grammar School to Cambridge University. It was not, however, until he went from Cambridge to Louvain that the brilliantly endowed youth took up the study of Civil Law, for his genius lay in the direction of Mathematics ; yet it was perforce rewarded by a Readership in Greek, since there were at that time no Readers or Professors of Mathematics either at Oxford or at Cambridge.

[1] A Roland Dee, probably the same man, is mentioned in a Grant of 1550 (Patent Rolls, Ed. VI) in a list of city Mercers. John Dee's first marriage (*circ.* 1565) was into the city, his wife Katherine Constable being the widow of a grocer.

In claiming for the mathematician John Dee an important place in the history of sixteenth-century English Geography, it is sufficient to state that he numbered among his teachers and consultants the five greatest of his geographical contemporaries : Pedro Nuñez, Gemma Phrysius, Gerard Mercator, Abraham Ortelius, and Orontius Finaeus. These men were not merely his teachers and his critics, they were his chosen and close friends, although as far as Gemma Phrysius was concerned, the friendship was cut short by premature death. To establish the fact of Dee's influence in England, it is again sufficient to state that he was the technical instructor and adviser of Richard Chancellor, Stephen Borough, William Borough, Anthony Jenkinson, Martin Frobisher, Christopher Hall, Charles Jackman, Arthur Pet, Humphrey Gilbert, Adrian Gilbert, John Davis, Walter Raleigh and probably, but not quite certainly, Francis Drake. Among the influential men who are known to have valued his learning and judgment are most of those who played a leading part in promoting the great enterprises of discovery : the Duke of Northumberland and his sons the Dudleys, Sir Henry Sidney, the Earls of Arundel, Pembroke, Lincoln, and Bedford, Sir Francis Walsingham, Sir Christopher Hatton, Sir James Crofts, Sir William Winter, and Sir William Pickering, while, in writing to Burghley, Dee could refer to himself as ' il favorito di vostra Excellentia '.[1] The learned men who sought his company included all those who are themselves distinguished in the annals of English Geography : Dr. Record, Leonard and Thomas Digges, William Lambard, John Stow, William Camden, William Bourne, Thomas Blundeville, Cyprian Lucar, Abraham Hartwell, Thomas Harriot, and, foremost of all, both the elder and the younger Hakluyt.

Such a rapid survey of Dee's friends would be incomplete without a reference to his relations with the Court. The ladies of the Privy Chamber formed part of his intimate domestic circle, and he took as his third wife a gentlewoman in the retinue of Lady Howard ; Lady Sidney (formerly Mary Dudley) showed him marked favour, as did Lady Katherine Crofts, while the poet and courtier Edward Dyer—

[1] Document 9, vi.

a man to whom Hakluyt pays striking tribute for his services
to geography [1]—was his closest personal friend. More important still, Queen Elizabeth made frequent demands upon
him for personal service and personal attendance, and came
herself with Raleigh, Leicester and others to his house, in
order to see his great library, of which the cosmographical
section is catalogued in an Appendix. Add to this list of
English men and women an enumeration of the host of Dee's
noble and learned friends upon the Continent [2]—the Emperors
Maximilian II and Rudolph, Henri II, M. de Monluc, M.
Babeu, Prince Lasky, the younger Baron von Herberstein,
Gaspar à Mirica, Postellus, Goropius, Goupyl, Fernelius,
Ramus, Gogava, and many others, in addition to the great
geographers already named—and the picture is one of a man
whose geographical record deserves careful examination.

The fact that John Dee was a practitioner of Judicial
Astrology has, however, created such prejudice against him,
and has led to such a one-sided estimate of his place in history,
that it is here necessary to state emphatically that a close
examination of the evidence leaves no doubt of his intellectual
honesty and genuine patriotism. His fame as an astrologer
lent Dee prestige among the vast number of his contemporaries who believed, with him, that there was a legitimate
as well as an illegitimate exercise of that art ; while his preoccupation with the search for the Philosopher's Stone and
the Elixir of Life lent urgency to his desire for a discovery
of the way to Cathay, since it has been a constant tradition
that Initiates and Adepts are to be found among the learned
of the Far East. That such was the case, nevertheless, does
not detract from the value of his geographical studies or his
geographical teaching.

Dee's own great debt to his geographical contemporaries
will first be examined, and this will involve a brief summary
of the claims of each to importance, and the general tendencies
of their teaching.

After a brilliant academic career at St. John's College,
Cambridge (which was Lord Burghley's College), commencing
in 1542, and crowned in December 1546 by a Foundation

[1] Document 7, c. iv.   [2] Document 8.

Fellowship of Trinity, Dee betook himself to the University of Louvain (termed by him ' the fountain-head of learning '), in May 1547, not long after the accession of Edward VI.[1] The teacher under whom he placed himself was Gemma Phrysius (1508–55), the great Flemish Mathematician, Cosmographer and Cartographer, whose first globe, accompanied by a text dealing with the principles of Astronomy and Geography, had been published in 1530. A year earlier, when only twenty-one, Gemma had published the first of the Antwerp editions of the Cosmographia of Peter Apian of Ingoldstadt, a work which had originally appeared in 1524. In subsequent editions he added important sections of his own to this cosmography, and the Phrysius-Apian versions became the standard general textbooks of the age, as countless references by contemporaries make clear. A second terrestrial globe, designed by Gemma in 1537, was engraved by two fellow-workers : Gerard Mercator, his pupil and friend, later his assistant and colleague, and Gaspar à Mirica, an older man than Mercator, and himself an astronomer and mathematician of note. A privilege precluding the publication of a like globe for ten years was granted by the Emperor Charles V, while the globe itself was dedicated to the Imperial Secretary, Maximilian Transylvanus, whose early published account of Magellan's voyage indicated the valuable services he could render as the patron of a geographer.

Gemma's position as Cosmographer to the Emperor, who kept his Court at Brussels, gave him, indeed, unique opportunities for geographical synthesis, since it placed at his disposal documentary resources as wide as the Empire itself, German and Flemish academic theory thus being balanced by Spanish practical experience.

The celestial globe of 1537 bears the names of the two engravers Mercator and Gaspar à Mirica, in this case joined with that of Gemma as authors also of the design. This, then, must have been the pair of globes which Dee, after a first short visit to Louvain, took back to Trinity College,[2] for although before that date Mercator had made his first terrestrial globe (1541), he did not complete its fellow until

[1] Document 6. [2] Document 8.

1551. Nevertheless, at a later date, the two Mercator globes, and not those of Gemma, were used by Dee in his own library, and were critically used, as his own account reveals.

It was many years, however, before Mercator's work superseded that of Gemma Phrysius with the general public, and the latter's globe, together with his world map made in 1540, and also dedicated to Charles V, became the standard authorities in the Low Countries and Western Europe generally. Their influence is clearly traceable in the writings of such men as Eden, Gilbert, and the elder Hakluyt, i.e. men who were behind the English voyages, and hence certain of their special features must receive attention.

While it had been accepted as axiomatic by classical and medieval writers that the Tripartite World was encompassed on all sides by sea, the fourteenth-century invasion of the Norse Greenland colony from the north by hordes of Eskimos, raised a difficulty of interpretation. All mankind had spread from one cradle ; these invaders, therefore, had come from Eurasia, they were to be identified with the ' infidel Carelians ' of the east of Finland, and their passage involved a land-bridge across the Polar Regions connecting Greenland with the Continent. Such is the sense in which we must understand the inscriptions on the map of Claudius Clavus, 1427.[1] To trace the influence of Clavus' map on cartography in general is outside the scope of the present work ; it is sufficient to say that the problem faced by the Danish geographer presented itself to the learned world at large with the discovery of the New World. Thenceforward academic cartographers (as opposed to chart-makers) exercised their ingenuity in devising land-bridges which would bring into harmony accepted theories and observed facts. The alternative solutions are shown diagrammatically in the accompanying figures, and their bearing on the practical question of discovery by the north will be briefly indicated.

Diagram I (Fig. 8) shows the pre-Columbian world of Claudius Clavus, with the land-bridge to Greenland ; such an interpretation is the foundation of the Cantino Chart, where Greenland is a ' Point of Asia '. Should this land

[1] Document 14, ii.

connexion exist, clearly any north-east passage to Cathay is blocked at some point east of the White Sea.

Diagram II shows a connexion of Greenland with the opposite extremity of Asia. The Arctic Ocean is merely a great Gulf (as Cardanus maintained), and a ship sailing by the north-east would simply sail round the shore of this gulf, without finding a short passage to Cathay. According to this view, the New World consisted of 'islands and terra firma' separated from north-east Asia by a strait which led to the South Sea. On the north shore of this strait was Asia, on its south shore America. Such was, broadly speaking, the solution adopted by Gemma Phrysius.

Diagram III again shows the Arctic Gulf, but the New World is now a great peninsula extension of Asia, partly separated from it by Ptolemy's Sinus Magnus. This is the view associated with Franciscus Monachus in 1526, and adopted in one or another form by Orontius Finaeus, Vopellius, Ruscelli and Moletus. It entirely precludes any discovery of Cathay by the north, whichever direction is taken.

Diagram IV shows an interpretation which has much in common with II. America, however, is no longer a group of islands, but a great continent, having open water to the north, and separated from Asia by the Strait of Anian in the extreme west : such was the view of Mercator in 1569, when no longer greatly influenced by Gemma Phrysius, and Ortelius agreed with him.

Diagram VI shows a view which is a blend of II and IV : there is a strait between Asia and America, which has its entry to the north of Labrador, but its exit somewhere not far from latitude 40°, for it trends to the south-west, and widens in the same direction. The views expressed in Diagrams II and IV, but especially that in Diagram VI, favoured a search for Cathay by the north-west, while it is to be noted that the latter harmonizes with the text and description of the Cabot map preserved at Chenies, and may explain the particular route followed by Francis Drake on his way to the Moluccas.

The dotted line across Asia in Diagram V roughly expresses

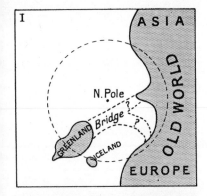
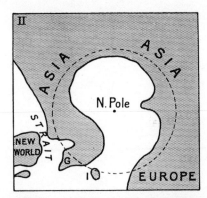
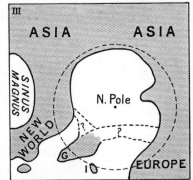
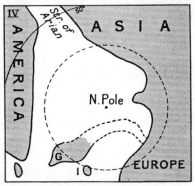
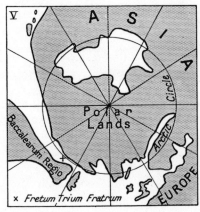

Fig. 8.—DIAGRAMMATIC SKETCHES OF VARIOUS CONCEPTS OF THE POLAR REGIONS AND PASSAGES

Dee's idea (based on a faulty interpretation of the Arab geographer Abulfeda), that Cathay had a north coast, with a trend such that discoverers by the north-east (e.g. Pet and Jackman) could easily and quickly reach the South Sea in latitude 40° N., and might thence pass to America and make rendezvous with a discoverer (e.g. Drake) coming from the opposite direction. This view was individual to Dee, and excited considerable opposition, as will be seen later.

A return must now be made to Gemma Phrysius' globe, of which but one example has survived, and of which a complete set of photographs are not available. A description and transcripts in Averdunk & Müller-Reinhard's *Mercator*, together with a small photograph of the critical portion of the globe in Björnbø's *Cartographica Groenlandica*, have therefore been used here as sources. Gemma's *Principia* of 1530 also throws light on his views.[1] The globe is based on Marco Polo, the records of Gaspar Cortereal's voyage, the Cantino or a similar Chart and some unspecified Spanish and Portuguese sources. Gemma definitely dissociates himself from the view that the New Lands are a part of Asia, while admitting that Marco Polo's evidence is obscure, and consequently he places a ' Fretum arcticum sive Fretum trium fratrum ' between ' Cortereati ' (Newfoundland and Labrador) and the north-eastern polar extension of Asia (Diagram V). On the north shore of the strait he has ' Quii Populi ', i.e. a branch of the Lequii, Lequio or Lu-Chu of the Portuguese narratives. Here he has also an inscription (the origin of which has never been discovered) which attracted very wide attention ; it runs : ' ad quos (i.e. the Quii) Joannes Scoluus Daneus pervenit circa annum 1476 '. This is possibly one of a number of, at present, very faint clues to a joint Portugo-Danish expedition from the Azores, with which the father of Gaspar Cortereal was associated. Gemma was favourably situated for learning of such a voyage if it took place. Be that as it may, the inscription afforded strong evidence of a navigable strait, and this was further confirmed by Gemma's view (derived apparently from the Cantino Chart) that Gaspar Cortereal

[1] Document 13, i, ii, iii.

had passed through the strait as far as the coast of Cathay.[1]
There he places a *Promontorium Corterealis* beside Polo's
Polisacus River. This unique combination of names, used
by Humfrey Gilbert in his Discourse, proves that Gemma
Phrysius' globe was the one he used. Eden, too, used this
globe, for he remarks in his Preface of 1553, that should the
search by the north-east fail, there is a way by the '*Fretum
trium fratrum* sufficiently known to such as have any skill
in geography'. It was by this very strait, too, that Gustav
Vasa, hearing of Willoughby's expedition, asked the young
traveller Hugh Languet to lead a Swedish voyage of discovery, a fact that Languet reveals long afterwards in a letter
written to his patron, the Duke of Saxony, on the subject of
Martin Frobisher. Martin Frobisher, in his turn, believed
the configuration of the globe to be as indicated on Gemma
Phrysius' globe, or as in the modified view of Diagram VI.
This explains his vehement declaration that he had the head-
land of Asia on his right, of America on his left, quoted in
Document 12, v, as also the belief of many people that the
Eskimos he brought home were men of Cathay.

No reference to Sebastian Cabot's passage of Hudsons Strait
in 1509 (for which Dr. Williamson adduces strong evidence)
is to be expected from Gemma Phrysius, for the explorer
preserved strict silence in Spain upon that point.

The influence of Gemma's views as expressed in his globe
and map were given even wider range by their adoption by
Sebastian Munster for the world map in the Basel Ptolemy
of 1540. This shows a widely opened arctic strait, with the
inscription : ' Per hoc fretum iter est ad Mollucas.' Archbishop Cranmer had a copy of this edition of Ptolemy which
passed at his death into the possession of the Earl of Arundel,
and thence to Lord Lumley's library, while it is now in the
British Museum. Dee had a copy of the 1545 edition.

Not only did John Dee introduce Gemma's globes into
Cambridge University, he brought over a number of instru-

---

[1] It is just possible that the inexplained name ' *Fretum trium fratrum* '
was coined to commemorate the three brothers Corte Real, although
only two actually made voyages to the north, or was it a reminiscence
of Sebastian Cabot and his two brothers ?

ments of the master's devising, some, no doubt, of the workmanship of his nephews the brothers Arsenius.   The importance of such instruments, leading as they did to improvements in astronomo-geographical observations, cannot be overestimated.   Gemma Phrysius, as will later be shown, was the first to publish details of the method of survey by triangulation. Nor did his influence cease here.   It was one of the accepted generalizations of the age that precious metals and spices alike were generated from the sun's heat, so that they were to be looked for only in the torrid zone : this led to the complementary view that lands of the far north were necessarily worthless, and merely to be passed by, in the search for the tropics.   Gemma did not hold this view, and his favourable description of Baccalaos [1] was read and approved by Eden among others, and the latter paraphrases it in his Preface to the *Decades*.

The appended catalogue of Dee's library shows that he brought to England many of the books of this, his earliest geography teacher, to whom he always refers with the deepest respect.   He could not have failed to recommend these books to others, especially at the time of the preparation for the earlier Cathay voyage.

II

The second of Dee's cosmographical friends and teachers, the great Portuguese mathematician and cosmographer, Pedro Nuñez (Petrus Nonnius), was born in 1502, and lived to be seventy-five years of age. Cosmographer Royal in 1529, he held the Chair in Mathematics at Coimbra from 1544.   The pre-eminence of the Portuguese mathematicians from the time of Prince Henry the Navigator in respect of the application of their science to the problems of Navigation needs no emphasis.   Pedro Nuñez followed in an excellent tradition, and numbered among his pupils the Infante Luiz, and the great navigator and Vice-Roy João de Castro.   The most famous of his practical treatises was the *Tratado da Sphera*, written in 1537, and the outcome in part of conferences with the Portuguese navigator Martim Affonso da Sousa, who had

[1] Document 13, ii.

returned from Brazil after a three years' voyage in 1533. As Jean Rotz points out,[1] masters returning from Brazil commonly found themselves as much as 70 leagues further west of the Azores than their reckoning showed. The sources of error were the variation of the compass, and the use of charts making no allowance for the convergence of the meridians, and the latter was the point Nuñez took up. The *Tratado da Sphera* contained new vernacular translations of Sacrobosco, and of Peuerbach's *Theory of the Sun and Moon*, together with two original pieces, the *Tratado sobre certas duvedas de navigacaõ*, and the *Tratado em defensam da carta de marear*. The use of the vernacular was appropriate to the subject, but in 1526 Nuñez published his views also in Latin, *De arte atque ratione navigandi lib.* 2, which could be read by the whole learned world. These original tracts contained the first discussion of his most important contribution to nautical science, the demonstration of the relation of the rhumb lines to the great circles of the globe, and in particular to the meridians. By 1541, Mercator, borrowing from Nuñez, had placed these 'tortuous helique lines', as one puzzled mariner described them, upon a new globe published by him at Louvain—the globe subsequently used by Dee : it was Mercator, too, who presently solved the problem of devising a plane projection on which the rhumbs could be ruled as on the old navigating charts. A second important contribution to science made by Pedro Nuñez was contained in his astronomical treatise *De Crepusculis*, 1542 : this was his device for reading subdivisions of the scales on astronomical or other instruments, known after him as the ' nonnius '. The work and views of Pedro Nuñez must have been much under discussion at Louvain, and at Paris too, whither Dee presently betook himself, for the Portuguese cosmographer had just published a polemical book, *De erratio Orontii Finaei*, i.e. on the errors of Dee's Paris teacher, while his own views had been attacked by Diego da Saa.

There is no direct evidence that Dee's relationship with Pedro Nuñez was other than by correspondence, but it reached such a point of intimacy that, when in 1558 the Englishman, worn out by illness, and by the anxiety bred of his brief

[1] See p. 68.

detention under suspicion of heresy, believed that he had not long to live, he made the Portuguese his literary executor. This is related in a long letter to Mercator, quoted in Document 9, ii, and Dee's declaration that he can rely on Pedro to carry out his wishes, ' for he loves me faithfully ', argues an intimacy of no slight order.

The work that Dee himself did, in developing Pedro Nuñez's teaching as to the rhumb lines, will be related in its place : this brief note is merely to show the connexion between the two men.

The third great cosmographer with whom Dee was linked, Gerard Mercator, matriculated at Louvain University in 1530, and remained there until 1552, when he removed to Duisburg. He was some fifteen years older than Dee, but so close a friendship arose between the two during the period of Dee's second visit to Louvain—June 1548 to July 1550—that, as the Englishman assures us, they were scarcely ever three days apart.

Mercator's first independent geographical publication, a map of Palestine, appeared in 1537, followed in 1538 by a world map based on Gemma Phrysius', but drawn on a twin-heart projection. The ' fretum arcticum ', so important for the theory of a North-West Passage, is shown, but the name ' Fretum trium fratrum ' is dropped. The popular globe of 1541, having the spiral rhumb lines of Pedro Nuñez, was very similar to this map. Mercator was not only a globe-maker and a cosmographer, but a very skilful mechanician, designing and making astronomical and surveying instruments. In this rôle he was employed by Charles V, to whom he had probably been introduced by Gemma Phrysius, for the latter was often called to the Court at Brussels. Dee had in his library a number of instruments specially made for him by his friend, as well as the pair of globes already mentioned.[1] The debt was not all on one side. Dee had occasion to go from Antwerp to Vienna in the new year of 1564, when his route lay past Duisburg, where he could hardly have failed to visit Mercator. He is likely, therefore, to have been the ' English friend ' who supplied the manuscript for the map of Britain engraved by Mercator in April of that year, and it is tempting to think that the original was Lawrence

[1] Document 8.

Nowell's, for Nowell was writing to Cecil in 1563 about a matter of English maps.

The great Mercator world map of 1569, and the Europe map of 1572, were often discussed and referred to by Dee, but he inclined to the view that the great distortion of scale, which the projection of the 1569 map introduced, militated decidedly against its usefulness. It certainly proved unsatisfactory to mariners, for the simple reason that they failed to understand the principle upon which it was constructed. William Borough (who represented the instructed class of sea-masters) so far misunderstood it as to cite it in defence of the old-fashioned navigating chart of which he believed it an example.

It is significant that it was Gerard Mercator, together with another Louvain mathematician, Anthony Gogava, who influenced Dee to take up seriously the study of Judicial Astrology ; the high character of Mercator alone should be sufficient to acquit Dee of the charges of sorcery and conjuring —interpreted to-day as charlatanism—brought against him by the fanatical English mob, a charge which he frequently and earnestly repudiated.

Orontius Finaeus, Regius Professor of Mathematics at the Collège de France, and the fourth of Dee's great teachers, is less well known as a cosmographer than he deserves. Nevertheless, he did for France what Gemma did for the Low Countries, and Mercator at a later date for Western Europe at large, he prepared maps and texts synthesizing the vast mass of conflicting material which the discoverers brought home more quickly than the public could digest it. Like the two men referred to, he also performed the important service of applying his great mathematical knowledge to geographical problems, particularly the fixing of position and surveying. A notable contribution was his manuscript *l'art de trouver certainment la longitude*, etc., dedicated to Francis I in 1543, while examples of his surveying instruments are described in the work *Della fabrica et uso de diversi stromenti*, compiled by Gallucci in 1597. He published an edition of Reisch's *Margarita Philosophica* (1523 and 1535), and prepared a world map for the Paris edition of *Novus Orbis*, besides maps for editions of Glareanus' Geography, and Pomponius Mela. His larger world maps on the twin-

heart and single-heart projection attracted considerable attention, and the latter was re-engraved in Italy. As has been
mentioned, he took the view of the land connexions indicated in
Diagram III (Fig. 8), which precluded a route to Cathay by the
North-West. He came into contact with Dee, and formed a
friendship with him while the latter was studying in Paris, after
leaving Louvain in July 1550. It so happened that many
prominent Englishmen were at the Court of Henry II during
1550 and 1551, so that the public lectures on Euclid which Dee
was invited to deliver at the Collège de Rheims had an over-
flowing audience, and made a great stir beyond the limits of the
University world. Both Record and Cuningham show the
strong influence of the cosmographical and astronomical works
of the French teacher Orontius, and Dee's library contained a
very large number of his writings.

Exactly when Dee came first into touch with Ortelius is
not clear. The great Antwerp Cosmographer was in early
life engaged merely in mounting and selling maps, and the
prelude to the *Theatrum* was a collection of maps made to the
order of a rich Flemish customer, a merchant. His period of
influence in England was from 1564 (the date of his first world
map) until well into the seventeenth century. That he was so
well known on this side of the Channel was not due to the
merits of his work alone : Antwerp, the headquarters of the
Company of Merchant Adventurers, had a considerable resident
English population, and the example of Humfrey Lhuyd, who
was brought into personal touch with Ortelius through Sir
Thomas Gresham's Antwerp factor, Clough, illustrates the
intercourse thus promoted. Antwerp, too, was a favourite
port for English travellers proceeding either to the Low
Countries or to the Germanic lands, and there was constant
coming and going between the Flemish city and London.
More important, however, than either of these two connexions,
was the fact that Ortelius had English kinsfolk with whom he
kept in very close touch, besides a Flemish cousin and nephew
who were prominent members of the foreign merchant community, and of the recently formed Dutch Church in London.
These family connexions must be briefly examined.

A cousin of Ortelius, Adrienne van der Weede, had married

John Rogers, an English Protestant, who was to become the first martyr of the Marian persecutions. The widow remained in England with her children, and her son Daniel (who had been educated at Wittenburg) married a daughter of Nicasius Yetswiert, a Dutchman who, since the reign of Henry VIII, had held the office of Royal Secretary of the French Tongue. Daniel Rogers, thus introduced at Court, was constantly employed on diplomatic and other missions, and crossed the Channel very frequently. The friend of the elder Hakluyt, of William Camden and of John Dee, he served to knit very closely the Ortelius circle with that of the geographical pioneers in England. Emanuel Van Metern (Demetrius), the Dutch cousin in London, and Jacob Cole, the nephew, both intimates of the younger Hakluyt, were other links with the great Flemish cartographer ; nor must it be forgotten that the Ortelius circle included Mercator, who was thus brought more closely in touch (as correspondence proves) with English affairs than his more remote situation at Duisburg would have warranted. When to all this it is added that Rumold Mercator, who followed his father's profession, was much in London and Antwerp between 1569 and 1575 (and possibly for a longer period), as the employee of the Cologne publisher, Arnold Birckmann, and that he formed a friendship with the younger Hakluyt, the whole network of interrelationships is seen to be very firm indeed. The impetus given to the propagation of the great Flemish teacher's works and views by a personal visit is a point that need not be laboured, and evidence of exchange of visits between Dee and Ortelius, and of the meeting of Ortelius with the younger Hakluyt, is afforded by Documents 12, via, and 12, vib. Details of the consequences of this intercourse will be furnished in their place.

III

Sufficient has now been said of the opportunities, and the stimulus, which Dee's personal connexions afforded him in his approach to geography. His travels into Italy, Austria, Bohemia and Poland, to say nothing of Germany and Flanders, gave him further opportunities, which he did not neglect, both of conferring with the learned and of acquiring a fine library of foreign books. The appended catalogue [1] of the cosmographical section of his library is sufficient to show his equipment in that direction, and no man in England was better fitted for the office of technical adviser to the Cathay voyagers than Dee, when he returned to London from Louvain and Paris late in 1551. Richard Eden, it is true, was well read in cosmography, and had an openness of character which Dee lacked, but, as he himself confessed, he had no skill in mathematics, a pre-requisite for the solution of problems in navigation and astronomy.

Dee's sensational intellectual triumph in Paris had been witnessed by the English Ambassador, his old friend and sometime pupil, Sir William Pickering, whose hobbies included astronomy, cosmography, and optics ; by young Henry Sidney, Gentleman of the Privy Chamber ; and by the latter's brothers-in-law, Robert and Henry Dudley. To this list must be added Sir Thomas Smith, Eden's old tutor, who, like Dee, when in Paris, sought the society of the brilliant philosopher, Peter Ramus. When back in London Dee renewed his acquaintance with Sir John Cheke, who had admired his work at Cambridge, and who gave him an introduction to Cecil and so to Court. Here he had the opportunity of cementing those friendships in the Duke of Northumberland's family (including that with his son-in-law Sidney) which were of such great importance to him then and later in life. At this period it was John Dudley, the eldest son, a young man close to his own age, with whom he was most intimate, teaching him the application of mathematics to the arts of warfare, and in the Preface to the English Euclid, Dee pays touching tribute to the worth of this young nobleman, who died in 1554.

The Duke of Northumberland, who only a few years earlier was utilizing the services of the leading French cosmographers and navigators, had considered with Sebastian Cabot a possible raid on Peru in 1551 ; from this he turned to the promotion of the discovery of Cathay by the north-east, the particular venture which—from the promise it held of new markets for English woollens—had gained the support of the great London merchants. Sir Henry Sidney charged himself with the

[1] Appendix II.

maintenance of the young sailor whose brilliant parts ensured his unanimous selection as chief pilot of the coming voyage, and Dee placed his own mathematical skill at this young man's disposal.

Of Richard Chancellor, the man referred to, little is known. From Eden it may be gathered that he was Bristol born and went early to sea ; from his demeanour at the Emperor's Court, that he had no lack of breeding ; and from his reference to having seen the French King's Pavilion, that he had been in France, probably sent there as a youth to learn the language. His first authentic appearance is as a member of the ship's company on the bark *Aucher*, which made a memorable voyage to Chios in 1550–51. His presence on board could have been no mere chance ; to make the Levant voyage was the best practical training that the English merchant fleet could then afford a novice, and that particular voyage will bear a little examination.

The bark *Aucher* belonged to Sir Anthony Aucher, Victualler of Calais (whose heiress Humfrey Gilbert married), and the captain was one Roger Bodenham, a Bristol man of some consequence both then and later. He had, however, only at the last moment superseded James Alday in that office. Alday was the 'servant', i.e. apprentice or assistant of Sebastian Cabot, and there is evidence that his master, the veteran Spanish Pilot Major, had imparted to him that nautical and cosmographical knowledge for the sake of which he himself had been brought into England. It was Cabot who procured from Edward VI an embargo on Alday's sailing, and this was one of the incidents which drew upon Alday the cloud of suspicion which hung about him through life. If the *Aucher* was meant to have something of the character of a training-ship, Cabot's action was well in accordance with his known character, and such a supposition alone can lend any point to Bodenham's own remark about the voyage :

' And all those Mariners that were in my sayde shippe, which were, besides boyes, threescore and tenne, for the most part were within five or six years after, able to take charge, and did. Richard Chancellor, who first discovered Russia, was with me in that voyage, and Matthew Baker, who afterward became the Queenes Majesties chiefe ship-wright ' (Quoted from Hakluyt).

That Chancellor was more than an ordinary seaman with rule of thumb training is a point needing emphasis. He was a mathematician of such an order that Dee worked with him on equal terms, and he had a further talent, one which always commanded Dee's deepest respect : he was a mechanician, and could make, and indeed improve, the necessary instruments for navigation. Together the two men set about a series of observations on which they could base a new table of Ephemerides for 1553, using to ensure accuracy, instruments of very unusual size, with scale divisions, according to a device of Chancellor's (resembling that of Nuñez), which allowed of fractional readings. From his own words it is reasonable to infer that Thomas Digges sometimes made a third observer at these meetings : Digges was Dee's friend from College days through life,[1] and was not slow to acknowledge his debt alike to the friend who had been his tutor in mathematical science, and to Richard Chancellor, ' peritissimus et ingeniosissimus Artifex Mathematicus ', whose sole memorials were the instruments of his making, and the tender recollections of his friends. To Dee he was ' the incomparable Richard Chancellor ', and ' my dearly-beloved Richard Chancellor ' long after his death, and the *Volume of Great and Rich Discoveries*—part of Dee's *magnum opus* of 1576–7—provides abundant evidence, if evidence be needed, of the conferences held between the friends for the discussion of the results which the first Muscovy Voyages afforded. Since both Cabot and Eden took part in the active preparation for these voyages, and so often conferred likewise with Chancellor, John Dee must necessarily have come into contact with both these men, although there is no direct evidence on the point.[2]

While the outcome of the geographical discussions of the reign of Edward VI was a first voyage in search of a North-East Passage, there is plenty of evidence of divergent views and rival plans, in the light of which Richard Eden's remark about the alternative way to Cathay, sufficiently known to such as have any skill in geography,[3] takes on a new significance. Sebastian Cabot on his arrival from Seville remained quietly at

[1] Document 9, xii.   [2] See Document 7, a, i–vii.
[3] See above, p. 82.

Bristol until May 1549, when on Admiral Seymour's recommendation he was sent for by Protector Somerset.[1] His pretence that he was an old man merely seeking his rest did not deceive the Spanish Ambassador, and attempt after attempt was made to get him back to Spain.[2] By June 1550 he had plans under way; Jean Ribault, in whom Northumberland still had confidence, was brought out of the Tower to assist him, and it was then that he secured a copy of the Letters Patent of 1496. On 26 June, two days after the Ambassador, Jean Schefve, had written to the Queen-Dowager as to the rumours of plans for discovery that were afloat, he was the recipient of the large sum of £200, ' by way of the King's Majesty's award ', over and above his annual pension.

According to the Ambassador's letters [3] there were to be two voyages, one to the East, i.e. by the Portuguese route to the Indies ; the other *by way of the Arctic Pole.* The voyage ' to the East ' was undoubtedly merely the Barbary voyage which took place in 1551, and which Cabot's servant or assistant John Alday (who had doubtless been kept back from the Levant voyage of 1550 for this very purpose) was to have commanded. With him were associated Cabot's son-in-law, Henry Ostrich, and Sir John Lutterell, who had entertained the survivors of the voyage of 1536. Lutterell and Ostrich were seized with the sweating sickness and died, while Alday was too ill to proceed, so that a navy man, Captain Thomas Wyndham, who had just been granted a handsome annuity, actually took charge. The voyage ' by the Arctic Pole ' can have been none other than the old Thorne-Barlow scheme : it was (according to Jean Schefve) to be led by Ribault, who was to be accompanied by ' certain Englishmen, experienced in navigation who have been with Cabot '. Now only Barlow and Latimer fit in with this description, and, considering they were middle-aged men, it is little

---

[1] Spanish Calendar. Letter of Van der Delft to the Emperor May 28, 1549. His first work was probably the supervision of an English edition of his World Map. Clement Adams, who prepared the block (?), received his Court appointment, doubtless through Sir Henry Sidney, in May 1552.

[2] Spanish Calendar, 1549, 1550, *passim.*

[3] Spanish Calendar, 1550–51.

wonder that the project came to nothing. It would seem possible that the first part of the voyage was to have been taken in company with the Iceland fleet, for on 24 March 1551, the Lord Admiral was commanded by the Privy Council to license that fleet to depart, 'and not to stay them any longer'.[1]

The next year (1552) Jean Ribault, still nominally a prisoner, is named by the Ambassador as right-hand man to Vice-Admiral Henry Dudley, Northumberland's cousin, while Thomas Wyndham carried out a second successful Barbary voyage. These voyages were looked upon by the Portuguese as an encroachment upon their privileges, and they made it known in London that they intended to take reprisals. To one of them, however, the English enterprise appears to have suggested a mode of personal advancement. This was Anthony Anes Pinteado, a notable seaman, who had been entrusted with the task of keeping the African and Brazil coasts clear of French intruders. A glimpse of him thus engaged is afforded by the well-known narrative of Hans Staden,[2] the German adventurer who was subsequently captured by South American cannibals, for Staden voyaged to and from Brazil in Pinteado's ship in 1548-9.

It must have been soon after this that Pinteado fell into disgrace with the King of Portugal, and made up his mind to put his knowledge of the Guinea trade at the disposal of the English adventurers. His defection was viewed with concern by his master, who sent a messenger after him to England with letters of pardon. The use he made of these, according to the Spanish Ambassador, who also put forward his best efforts to get Pinteado out of England, was to display them to those who were about to employ him, in order to enhance his reputation and importance. Richard Eden, whom he naturally met as a member of Cabot's circle, was one of Pinteado's most sincere admirers, and printed these papers, which the Portuguese had left behind him when he took what proved for him a fatal voyage to Guinea with Wyndham in 1553.

Eden was not the only admirer of the Portuguese pilot. Thirty-three years or more after these events, an anonymous

---

[1] Acts of the Privy Council, Ed. VI.
[2] *The Captivity of Hans Staden*, Hakluyt Soc. Pub.

advocate of the search for Cathay by the North-West [1] adds to his discourse transcripts of the letters of one Jon, a reputable merchant, who appears to have been consulted in 1586 about the Passage (possibly in view of Davis' third attempt). Jon claims that 'upon the encouragement of Mr. Chancellor that first found for us the Musco, and Doctor Recordes conference in my house, and speciallie the noble pilott Pintiago the portugale encouraged me ', he himself equipped a ship and a pinnace to search by the north-west for a strait into Mar del Sur, since it was thought that the north of Asia stretched to 77°. He further declares that a 'plott of the West India' submitted to him 'doth agree with the opinion of Doctor Recorde, Mr. Bastian Cabotta, Harry Estrege, his sonne in lawe, Mr. Chancellor that founde the Muscovia, and noble Pintiago, the Portugal pilott that was with Windam in Guinea '. The voyage set out by Jon was a failure and the whole story is obscure, but it is in harmony with the picture of the reign of Edward VI as a period of anxious consultation and discussion between cosmographers, navigators and merchants. It lends colour, too, to the view that while the hope of finding a market for woollens in Scythia and Tartaria determined the Muscovy Company to look for a passage north-eastwards, the very men who acted as the Company's technical advisers, having Ptolemy's map (with Cape Tabin) and Gemma Phrysius' globe and maps in mind, were inclined to think that the north-west route was the more hopeful.

Further confirmation is to be found in the letter of Jean Schefve to the Emperor Charles V, written from London the very day after Willoughby's fleet had cleared from Greenwich, i.e. on 11 May 1553. Some say, he writes, that the vessels are to go to the north-east ; while some say they are for the north-west. If they go by the latter route, he adds, they will enter the *Strait of the Three Brethren*, a point on which Gemma Phrysius discourses 'in his last chart published in 1549 '. This reference appears to be all that is known of this new map, published while John Dee was at Louvain : it adds yet another piece of evidence witnessing to the wide influence and import-ance of the Emperor's Flemish Cosmographer.

[1] Harleian MSS. 167.

IV

To follow the fortunes of the voyages of discovery forms no part of this study, which is concerned solely with their intellectual background. The untimely death of Chancellor was a great blow to English navigation : he had, however, already sent the man who served under him on the first voyage, Stephen Borough, to make an independent venture in 1556 ; Stephen Borough, in his turn, was training his younger brother William. The Boroughs, however, though not uneducated men, had no mathematical or technical knowledge ; hence the request of the Muscovy Company that Dee should give them necessary instruction. The two great problems, from the theoretical standpoint, which faced the navigator in the far north, were in the first instance the rapid convergence of the meridians, with the resultant rapid spiral curvature of the rhumb lines, and in the second instance the very great variation of the compass from point to point. The current *carta marina*, with parallel meridians, was, of course, quite useless under such circumstances, and some fresh technique for setting and plotting a course was necessary. To this end Dee invented an instrument or device, about which, although he several times refers to it, he was extremely reticent: his Paradoxal Compass. A very careful study of all the inventor's own references, together with those made by the last of his pilot-pupils, John Davis, leads to the conclusion that this Paradoxal Compass enabled the master to lay a course along a succession of rhumbs which would make an approximation to great circle sailing. It was, in fact, a practical development of the teaching of Pedro Nuñez on this subject, and its invention belongs to a period when Dee is known to have been in personal touch with the great Portuguese.

As to the exact date of this invention Dee himself is not clear : the relevant written account listed in his MSS. is dated 1556, which agrees very well with the ' 20 years ago ' of which he speaks in 1576. Elsewhere, however, he says, ' of me invented 1557 ', and again, ' 1559 '. It is probable, however, that the confusion arises as between the time when Dee first considered the device, and that when it actually took practical shape in a form suitable for use by the two brothers Borough.

After Chancellor's death in 1556, these two pilots wintered in Lapland, and were not home until the late summer of 1557. It was some time in 1557–8 that Stephen went as an honoured guest to the House of Contracts in Seville, and Dee's period of instruction probably fell within the same dates, in preparation for the Muscovy Voyage of 1559.[1]

Dee's invention of ' Compasses of Variation ', to which he twice refers, was probably to the same purpose and at the same period as his Paradoxal Compass : such instruments were, of course, already numerous in Spain and Portugal, and Jean Rotz' *Quadrant Differential* lay neglected somewhere in the Royal Library. Stephen Borough's charts and records of his voyage to the Ob were carefully discussed with Dee, and it is clear that this successor of Richard Chancellor took a serious view of the responsibilities of a Pilot's office. One outcome of his visit to Spain, it will be recalled, was the procuring of Eden's translation of Cortes' navigating manual at the Muscovy Company's expense, and the net result of his training under Chancellor, his instruction by Dee, and the lessons he learned at Seville was to bring home to him the profound knowledge, the subtlety and the high degree of skill which a mastery of the art of navigation required. All this he set out (Lansdown MSS. 122) in a petition to the Queen and Council in 1562, asking for the establishment in England of the office of Chief Pilot on the lines of that in Spain, i.e. with the prime object of securing a supply of thoroughly instructed English pilots. ' We have had ', he says, ' to go to Spain and France for pilots ', and by Spain he refers to 'the old and famous man S. Cabot'; he further quotes ' Pedro de Medina in his book of Navigation ' as saying that the special inspiration of God is needed for the right handling of sea causes. His eloquent plea for official action in a matter that was indeed urgent, went unregarded, but it is surprising that this keen sailor, explorer and thinker was relegated to an unadventurous naval post in the Medway in 1563. His brother William, however, remained in the service of the Muscovy Company, and drew up the plans for the proposed Bassendine voyage in 1568, by which date he was an expert chart-maker. That he was prime-mover of the expedition is

[1] See Document 10, Nos. i–iv.

made clear by the heading to his instructions preserved in Lansdown, 10, No. 35. ' W^m. Borough's voyage for discovery of the sea and coast beyond Pechora, and to find an open passage to Cathaye, 1568.' The explorers were told very explicitly not to enter the Ob, but to search beyond it, where it was hoped that the coast tended southwards. This, as has been mentioned, was Dee's view, drawn from his reading of Abulfeda, as it was also Anthony Jenkinson's, and it was strongly challenged in the following year by Mercator's mapping of a north-stretching Tabin Promontory. To save expense, the Bassendine voyage was cancelled by the Company's agents, and alternative proposals made for a north-eastern reconnaissance from the White Sea in a Russian coasting vessel, of which, however, there is no further record.[1]

William Borough, as a practical man, appears to have resented rather strongly the mathematical teaching, as applied to navigation, of such men as Dee, Record and Digges (for both the latter also attempted to reform current seafaring practice). In a partly autobiographical address to Queen Elizabeth, written in 1578, he says :

' None of the best learned in those sciences Mathematical, without convenient practise at the sea, can make just proof of the profite in them : so necessarily dependeth art and reason upon experience. Albeit there are divers both learned and unlearned, little or nothing experienced, which in talke of navigation will enter deeply and speak much of and against errours used therein, when they cannot reforme them.'

Digges met the charge of being unpractical by actually spending fifteen weeks at sea, when he was able to demonstrate to the mariners on the spot the ' gross errors ' of the cards, instruments and rules commonly in use : but when and where this took place we do not know : he records the fact in the Preface to his *Stratioticos* in 1579.

The discovery of the new Muscovy trade, and of the route to Persia, led in the early '60's to a practical abandonment of the search for Cathay by the Muscovy Company itself, although the Company held a monopoly for undertaking voyages by the north, north-east and north-west. This was a cause of discon-

[1] Document 9, No. iv.

tent, and while Anthony Jenkinson petitioned the Queen (30 May 1565) [1] to further a new attempt by the north-east (which he wished to lead), Humfrey Gilbert was put forward as spokesman for those who had better hopes of an attempt by the north-west. These hopes were based on the new world-map drawn and published by Ortelius in 1564, a map which embodied the results of the Cartier voyages, and showed a north-west passage even more freely open than did Gemma Phrysius' Globe, while interposing a north-stretching peninsula across the passage by the north-east. Gilbert and Jenkinson, who had 'sundry times discoursed together' according to the latter's letter to Cecil, debated the project publicly before the Queen and Privy Council, apparently in the winter of 1565–6, but without practical result, save that in 1566 Gilbert began to put the material he had gathered together into writing, including a précis of this debate, and adding to it a sketch-map derived from the *Typus Orbis* of Ortelius.[2]

Jenkinson's address is especially interesting because it is clear from the identity of phraseology and the similarity of the arguments employed that he had before him the similar Thorne-Barlow address to King Henry VIII, and Thorne's letter to Dr. Lee, which were in the possession of Emanuel Lucar, by that time a prominent member of the Merchant Taylors Company. Jenkinson's own arguments were based on careful inquiries made alike of Cathayans in Boghar and of Samoyeds in the far north, to which Gilbert in his reply does less than justice. The 'unicorn's' head which he saw at the Emperor's Court in 1564 had been found on Vaigatz Island, and confirmed Jenkinson's view that the general trend of the coast east of the Island was east-south-east as far as Cathay, where such animals (rhinoceroses) were reported.

This discussion was probably the occasion of the elder Hakluyt's letter to Ortelius,[3] asking for a map on rollers which

---

[1] Document 11, No. iii.

[2] Ortelius placed Quinsay exactly opposite the Sierra Nevada, and under 400 miles away, hence Gilbert's suggestion of an entrepôt near the Sierra. In his sketch-map he lessens the distance between the two points, and also brings the Moluccas slightly nearer his proposed base than in the original.

[3] Document 9, No. v.

should clearly show the *Fretum trium fratrum* : his arguments for the existence of that strait, giving chapter and verse from his authorities, form, as already noticed, the basis of Chapter IV of Gilbert's *Discourse*. As would be expected, Dee took his part in these discussions, at least privately : and at the request of his friend, Edward Dyer (then enjoying his earlier period of the Queen's favour), he wrote down his views in the form of a pamphlet. It was only when Gilbert published the *Discourse*, early in 1576, that Dee remembered his own ' Atlanticall Discourses to the self-same purpose at the said M. Dyer his request almost ten years since set down in writing ',[1] and commenced to revise them, as will presently be described. A word should be said as to the title ' Atlanticall ' : Dee held that the term West Indies was grossly misleading, and preferred the classical ' Atlantis ' to that of America, as a name for the new lands. Hence ' Atlanticall ' meant pertaining, not to the Atlantic Ocean, but to Atlantis.

The public interest taken in this question of a new search for Cathay in 1566 is curiously illustrated by the ledgers of the Plantin Press, which record the sale to English booksellers of unusually large numbers of world-maps. In the three months 13 November 1566 to 20 February 1567, eighteen copies of Ortelius' map were sent over, and thirteen of that by Vopellius, the latter, it will be recalled, being of the type that showed no Arctic passage whatsoever. In the period April to July 1568, six copies of Vopellius' map were sold, but only one of Ortelius'. During the same two periods a dozen copies of Mercator's map of Britain (1564) were sold, and two copies of a map by him of Europe. A pair of Gemma Phrysius' globes was sent over on 15 April 1568, and an interesting letter from Plantin to his customer shows that as between Gemma's globes and the more recent ones of Mercator, the question considered was rather that of price than of content ; the earlier and smaller pair were a little cheaper, and so continued to sell.[2]

Further evidence of the widespread eagerness at this time for the Cathay discovery is afforded by a letter to Cecil from Thomas Champneys, a well-known ' pirate ', who had been

---

[1] *General and Rare Memorials*, 1577.
[2] Document 11, No. vi.

sending home harbour plans of Malta and Goletta, and was temporarily resident at Naples. This letter, written in 1566, is quoted in Document 9, No. iii. The writer has planned a new attempt on Cathay, and he refers to an unnamed individual who is waiting to start at the word of command, apparently by the land route across Asia. From this route Anthony Jenkinson had not long since returned baffled, but it was one which Dee planned secretly to conquer. No answer to this letter has survived.

Several notes on schemes for voyages of discovery, illustrating the same eagerness, are calendared in the State Papers under 1576, but almost certainly belong to this earlier date. Two examples are quoted in Document 11, Nos. i and ii. The first is based on deductions from the common type of map which linked the original Labrador (South Greenland) with Baccalaos, now called Labrador, while dissociating it from Greenland proper, and so indicated a great gulf to the south and west of Cape Farewell in 60°, and a coast running west in 67°. The name of this Gulf—Dusmendas—is a corruption of ' das maluas ', one of the early Portuguese place-names. The argument is for a north-west passage by a strait which has its mouth in 67°–68°, and its far end near Sierra Nevada, where Coronado met the supposed Cathayans in 1541. The main sources of the document are Gemma's globe, with fragments from Ramusio and Gomara as translated by Eden. The views expressed about the ice difficulty and the current (from east to west) sweeping the strait clear, are new, for on those points there was great diversity of opinion,[1] and widely differing inferences were drawn from the rather contradictory and scanty facts of observation.

The second document contains the very sensible proposal that a reconnaissance of the passage might be effected by way of Iceland, by utilizing one of the fishing vessels normally engaged there. Two or three observers could be placed on board with the crew to bring back any information obtained, and the passage westward from Iceland would take no more than 8–10 days. It is possible that some such plan was in Charles Jackman's mind when he disappeared with the ship *William*,

---

[1] Cf. Document 12, No. vii.

going ' towards Groenland and Iceland ', after the failure of the
1580 voyage.   In this document, as in the previous one, the
mouth of the Strait is placed in 67°,[1] a little north of its position
on Gemma's globe.   The argument is directed not only towards
an Iceland route, but against that by Magellan's Strait.
This suggests a date in the early '70's, for it was only then that
(as a result partly of Hawkins' voyages and partly of the new
political orientations) it had ceased to be taken as an axiom that
discovery must not be attempted by way of the South owing to
the Spanish monopoly.   The Iceland-Greenland route had,
however, already been suggested during the debates of 1566–7,
for the Spanish Ambassador, De Selva, writing to Philip II
under the date 15 March 1567, says : ' There is an English
gentleman here (Gilbert ?) who is said to be a great cosmographer, and thinks he can discover a shorter route to the East
Indies than that taken by the Portuguese.   He goes on to
mention that two alternative routes are proposed, one from
London by Norway, Iceland, and the north coast of Labrador,
the other from Bristol, by the Irish Sea, to Labrador, doubling
Cape Frio.   Either Mangi or Japan is to be visited *en route* for
China or the East Indies.   A third document (Lansdown, 100,
No. 21), not quoted in full, argues at length for the abandonment
of the Arctic route altogether in favour of that presently to be
taken by Drake.   It is endorsed by Burghley ' Mr. Grenfeylde's
voyage ' (i.e. Richard Grenville's), and must be dated about
1574–5, for it belongs to the interesting group that includes
the ' Petition of divers gentlemen of the west part ',[2] dated
22 March 1574.   The Grenville tract is distinctly polemical,
being entitled : ' A discourse concerning a straight to be discovered towards the north-west passing to Cathaya and the
Orientall Indians, with a confutacion of their errour that
thynke the discovery thereof to be most conveiently attempted
to the north of Baccalaos.'   The drawbacks of the fog and the
short summer season in the north are held to more than counter-

[1] The anonymous writer of the late sixteenth-century argument
already cited (Harleian MSS. 167) insists, like Jon, on the point that the
Strait has usually been missed by attempts in too low a latitude, and
John Davis seems to have taken this view.
[2] Document 13, No. v.

balance the shortness of the route as compared with that by the Strait of Magellan, and the point of interest here is the emphasis laid on the opinion that any northern island discovered could yield nothing of value save furs such as the Muscovy Company already brought from Russia, whereas from any land discovered on a southern voyage the adventurers were ' assured to expect gold, silver, pearls, spices, and other precious merchandise '. This view was still very strongly held by the general public, and it was the unexpectedness of the event that accounts for the wild excitement aroused by the discovery in high latitudes of the (supposititious) gold ore of 1576 : Hugh Languet, writing of the finding of the original fragment, says that Frobisher put it aside as worthless, because of his foregone conclusion that cold lands could breed no precious metals. It should not be overlooked that the title of the Grenville tract, quoted above, implies that a voyage by the Magellan route has still as its object not a direct journey across the Pacific, but the discovery of the North-West Strait leading to Cathay, although the discovery is most conveniently to be attempted by its western extremity, supposed, as must be remembered, to lie well to the south. A number of slight indications, and some quite definite statements by those who recorded the voyage (e.g. Hakluyt and Camden), make it clear that Drake's route was planned in part with this end in view, a point to be developed later.

It is further to be noted that all discussions after 1569 were influenced by Mercator's great map, and by that in Ortelius' *Theatrum* of 1570, which closely resembled it. Mercator had set the seal of his authority on the supposed Strait of Anian, while he had also accepted the pseudo-Zeni narrative and map, which, first published in 1558, had been given a wider circulation by Ramusio and Gastaldi. The tendency of the resulting interpretations of the continent of America was to make discovery by the West more attractive than discovery by the East, and the strongest argument remaining for the North-East Passage was that Stephen Borough in 1556 had already got half-way through it.

Before, however, examining in detail the geographical ideas of the '70's, some consideration must be given to an important work of John Dee published in the first year of the new decade.

CHAPTER VI

JOHN DEE, FROBISHER AND DRAKE: 1570-1579

I

BOTH Gilbert's and Jenkinson's projects had been shelved in 1566, and although the latter returned to Muscovy as Ambassador in 1571-2, he retired the next year into private life ; Gilbert, meanwhile, was in Ireland with Sir Henry Sidney, and Borough was engaged in the Baltic. Only Dee was left to keep Cathay before the public mind. So far, his published works, e.g. his *Propaedeumata*, and *Monas*, had been on subjects remote from Geography, save for an edition of Record's useful *Ground of Arts* in 1561. His practical treatises, two astronomical books for Edward VI's schoolroom, a book on tides and one on astronomy for the Duchess of Northumberland, the Ephemerides for Chancellor, the Paradoxall Compass, two books on the Astronomer's Ring, and a *De Nova Navigatione Ratione* in two books, written when he was instructing the Muscovy Pilots, were all deliberately kept in manuscript, and not made common to the public. So, too, was a work *De itinere subterraneo* in two parts, written in 1560 for two gentlemen who, having adjoining properties, and being engaged in a mining venture, were concerned to know the position of the workings relative to their boundaries.

In 1570, however, Dee wrote, in the form of a Preface to Henry Billingsly's *English Translation of Euclid*, a magnificent exposition of the relationship and application of mathematics, especially arithmetic and geometry, to the practice of various skilled arts and crafts. It was, in fact, a plea for scientific method, and owed much to the great Schoolman of whom Dee was so devout a disciple, Roger Bacon. In the *Opus Majus* of Bacon, Dee found his inspiration, as did Leonard Digges, at least in that fragment of it which came by chance into his hand.

From the point of view of this study, the most important sections of the Preface (apart from its autobiographical details) were those dealing with mathematics as the essential foundation for the practice of Surveying, of Navigation, of Cosmography and of Hydrography.　With regard to the latter, Dee writes:

' And many other points are belonging to perfect Hydrographie, and for to make a Rutter by, and of the describing in any place, upon Globe or Plaine, the 32 points of the Compasse truly : (whereof, scarce four in England have right knowledge, by cause the lines thereof are no right lines nor circles) : Of making due projection of a sphere in plaine. Of the variation of the compass from the true north.'

These, it will be noticed, were all matters on which he had instructed the Boroughs, but in default of a school for pilots, no general advance in sea-practice had been made.

As to surveying, in spite of the work being done by such men as Christopher Saxton, Robert Lythe and Ralph Agas (the subject of a later chapter), the general practice was far from scientific, as reference to the most popular text-book of the time, that of Valentine Leigh, will abundantly show.　Hence Dee's strictures were fully justified :

' Of these feates [i.e. of geometry] (further applied) is sprung Geodesie, or Land Measuring ; more cunningly to measure and survey lands, woods, and waters *affarre off* [i.e. by triangulation].　More cunningly I say : but God knoweth (hitherto) in these realms of England and Ireland (whether through ignorance or fraud, I cannot tell in every particular) how great a wrong and injustice hath (in my time) beene committed by untrue measuring, and surveying.'

The money thus lost, he goes on to say, would suffice to endow a Mathematical Readership in each of the two Universities, where at present there were no such Readerships, although Paris University had two.

It was hardly by chance that Dee's friend and disciple, Thomas Digges, brought out in the following year his late father's *Pantometria*, a book dealing with practical measurements of all kinds, borrowed admittedly from continental sources : while as to William Bourne's debt to Dee's Preface, he himself makes no secret of it.

The twofold aspect of mathematics, as a pure and an applied science, was constantly in Dee's mind, and in a treatise supplementing the books of Euclid, written in December 1569, and embodied in the Billingsly edition of 1570, he declares that his additions are ' to aid and show the way to declare your discourses mathematically or to invent and practice things mechanically '.

The discussion of Navigation, and its obvious grounding in mathematics, gave Dee his opportunity of reminding his countrymen of their duties and privileges in the matter of discovery.

' In Navigation none ought to have greater care to be skilful than our English pilots. And perchance some would more attempt, and other some more willingly would be aiding, if they wist certainly what privilege God had endued this island with, by reason of situation most commodious for navigation to places most famous and rich. And though of late [Margin, 1567] a young Gentleman [Margin, S. H. G.] a courageous Captain, was in good readiness, with great hope and good cause of persuasion, to have ventured for a discovery (either westerly to Cape Paramantia, or easterly above Nova Zemla and the Czeremisses), and was at the very time of attempting called and employed otherwise (both then and since) in great good service to his country, as the Irish rebels have [Margin, 1569] tasted : yet, I say, (though the same gentleman do not hereafter deal therewith) some one or other should listen to the matter : and by good advice and by discreet circumspection, by little and little win to the knowledge of that trade and voyage ; which now I should be sorry (through carelessness, want of skill and courage) should remain unknown and unheard of. Seing also we are herein, half challenged by the learned, by half request, published [i.e. committed]. Thereof verily might grow commodity to this land chiefly, and to the rest of the Christian Commonwealth, far passing all riches and earthly treasure.'

The phrase ' half challenged by the learned ' refers to the views expressed by Ortelius and Mercator, who considered it was the duty of the English to finish that unveiling of Northern Asia that they had so successfully begun. The two ' landmarks '—Cape Paramantia and the Czerimisses—are those on Ortelius' map of 1564, used also by Gilbert (' S. H. G.'). The final phrase as to the commodity ' far passing all riches and earthly treasure ' is no mere hyperbole, but a reference to that secret hope which lay behind all Dee's efforts, the hope of a revelation of Occult Mysteries in the East.

By this date, Dee had already begun to dream of England as Mistress of a Northern Empire, based on the command of the seas, and at the request of Edward Dyer he had already committed his ideas to writing in a tract called *Synopsis Reipublicae Britannicae*; this, in his own list of his manuscripts,[1] is dated 1565, although in a reference made to it in 1576, he seems to imply for it a date not much before 1570. It would be easy, of course, to dismiss Dee as a fanatic and a megalomaniac, and it is true that he had, to use a homely expression, too many irons in the fire, but his eagerness and his enthusiasm were a stimulus to others, if not actually a driving force, and his symbolic picture of Queen Elizabeth at the helm of the Christian ship of Europe, devised as the frontispiece of his *Magnum Opus* of 1576, had in it an element of the prophetic.

The year 1571, however, saw Dee abroad, with the Queen's permission, on a visit to Lorraine, whence in company with her servant, Mr. Powell, he returned (after a severe illness) with supplies of material and apparatus for his laboratory. Either going or coming, Dee visited Ortelius in Antwerp on this occasion, and saw his library. This was the year in which Sir Thomas Smith incorporated a ' Society of the New Art ' with the object of transforming copper into gold, and three of Dee's friends, Dyer, Leicester and Gilbert, besides Burghley himself, invested money in the scheme. Humfrey Cole was employed by the Society to oversee the metallurgical work, but the alchemist Medley, who was to supply the necessary formula, proved a fraud, though for over four years his dupes failed to find him out, and he even then found a defender in Lady Sidney (Mary Dudley).

In 1572, Archbishop Parker, who had long interested himself and his circle in ancient records, founded the Elizabethan Society of Antiquaries. Practically all the members were Dee's friends or acquaintances, but although the collection of neglected manuscripts was one of his own special activities, he is not himself recorded as a member of the Society. The same year lifts the veil for a moment that hides the career of the elder Hakluyt ; he is seen carrying out a systematic collection of economic material relating to America, a country which he, at least, regarded as a theatre for colonization, and not merely as an obstacle lying in the path to Cathay.

[1] Appendix IA.

Of 1573 there is nothing to record, save that Dee's friend Dyer was restored to the Queen's favour, after two years of her displeasure, while another favourite, Christopher Hatton, was rising to a position of importance. These were the two men through whose influence Dee was presently urging his expansionist schemes. It is noteworthy that his friends were equally numerous among the group suspected of Catholic leanings, e.g. Leicester, Dyer, Hatton, Crofts, and those who were strongly Protestant, e.g. Walsingham, and the Secretary of the Privy Council, Robert Beale. The next year (that in which Richard Willes, Italian scholar and excellent cosmographer, was taken into the Countess of Bedford's service) Martin Frobisher, furnished with a letter from the Privy Council, and backed by the Earl of Warwick, Bedford's son-in-law, made an onslaught upon the supineness of the Muscovy Company, which still held its paralysing monopoly of discovery, whether by the north-east or the north-west. The following February, Frobisher had his licence, and a new chapter of intense activity began.

Leicester, Hatton, and the Queen herself, had shown Dee signal marks of favour in 1575, on the occasion of his second marriage,[1] and it is probable that this marriage, and the death of his wife in the following spring, distracted his mind somewhat from public affairs. According to his own account, it was Edward Dyer, whose own heart was set also on the discovery of Cathay, who first showed him Gilbert's *Discourse*, published in April 1576. Gascoyne, in his preface to the *Discourse*, had pointed out how a ' great learned man, even M. Dee ', had in his English Euclid publicly commended Gilbert's zeal, and this roused Dee to a realization that the Frobisher voyage was actually in an advanced stage of preparation. Sir Lionel Duckett, for the Muscovy Company, had already asked him to ' examine and instruct ' those who should take charge, and since so little time remained before the expedition was due to sail, Dee took up his residence at Muscovy House in

---

[1] Dee's first marriage, which took place about 1565, has not been noticed by his biographers. His first wife was Katherine Constable, widow of a London grocer. [Chancery Proceedings, Series II, Bundle 49, No. 44.]

Seething Lane. Michael Lok, who was a little anxious lest his own credit as the chief furtherer of the voyage should be diminished, says that Dee knew nothing of the plans until 20 May, when hearing the common talk of what was afoot, he came to see Lok. Be that as it may, Lok was glad to call a special meeting at his house, when he laid all his notes, charts, and other material before Dee for critical examination,[1] and Dee in return laid before the company, which included his old friend and pupil Stephen Borough, as well as Frobisher and Hall, the information which was in his own possession. Others unnamed were present, and the elder Hakluyt may have been among them, for he drew up notes for the voyage of the following year, and Michael Lok on this first occasion expressed the views that were also Hakluyt's, as to the possibility of opening up trade with America itself, even if there proved to be no passage.

Dee's instructions, given to Frobisher and Hall ' in the Rules of Geometry and Cosmography ', for their better instruction in ' the Use of Instruments of Navigation ', were not so successful as might have been hoped, for as the mariners hinted in a letter of thanks [2] sent from the Scottish coast after they had started, their grounding in mathematics was too scanty for them to profit by his teaching.[3] This suggests that the elaborate furniture of instruments which had been provided for the voyage, together with a goodly number of maps and charts and a library of books (the last already discussed), was likely to be of little use. Nicholas Chancellor, one of the little sons left behind him by Richard Chancellor, and now grown to manhood, was purser of the voyage, but he had not followed in his father's footsteps as a mathematician, since as soon as he could reckon up accounts he had been sent out as an apprentice to the Muscovy Company in Russia. William Borough, it may be noted, was not very enthusiastic about the chances of success, though he drew out a chart (with rhumbs in conventional

---

[1] Document 12, No. i.   [2] Document 9, No. xi.

[3] Christopher Hall made for Dee a very beautiful transcript of his log of the Third Voyage, adding a ' view ' of ' Dee's Pinnacles ', the name given to certain crags on the supposed Frizeland, actually Greenland. [Harleian MSS., Vol. 167.]

portolan style) on which the discoveries were to be plotted, and busied himself with the furnishing of the ships.   Dee had naturally introduced Frobisher and Hall to his Paradoxal Compass, and from his own deliberately obscure remarks it is possible to gather that Frobisher told him that its invention had been claimed twenty years since by someone else : Frobisher further suggested that Dee should establish his claim by publishing an account of the Instrument.[1]   The impudent plagiarist was probably James Alday, who had been trying to get employment with Frobisher, and who, twenty years earlier, must (as the assistant of the official Chief Pilot Sebastian Cabot) have been very jealous of the part of instructor played by John Dee.   As regards publication, it may be observed, Dee never got further than naming the Instrument in the title-page of his *General and Rare Memorials*, where he puts back its discovery to an earlier date than he claims for it anywhere else, namely, 1553.

It is from the Preface to his *Memorials* that we learn the details of Dee's activities in connexion with the Frobisher venture, and it is here that he relates how in May 1576 he carefully went through Humfrey Gilbert's newly published *Discourse* and ' did further for every article thereof, in the Margent note their value or imperfection.   And straightway, after that, made a new collection for the same voyage, very probable.   And thirdly, the same day, wrote *an other voyage of Discovery* : (in report of Safetie, Neereness and Com-moditie) nothing inferior to that which they now (they did set forth on the 12 June last) have undertaken '.

He then (he says) hurried off to Muscovy House (where he was to instruct Frobisher and Hall) ' intending to give those his 18 new and very strange Articles of Consideration, to him or them, whom he should deem apt or desirous to further the said Discovery '.   It seems most probable that these ' Articles ' contained the germ of the scheme which during the next twelve months was elaborated in the *Memorials*, and which was embodied in part in the plans of Drake, and in part in those of Pet and Jackman, who carried, as is well known, Dee's Instructions and Charts with them.

[1] Document 10, No. ii.

II

This raises the whole question of the objectives of Drake's voyage, on which new light has only recently been obtained, and it is necessary to re-examine the World Map as it appeared in the eyes of the contemporary English student of cosmography. The picture we have of Richard Willes, with a dozen or more maps and globes before him, comparing them carefully, one with another, and weighing up the evidence they afforded as to the feasibility of a discovery of the North-West Passage, is a picture also of the Hakluyts (the younger now also actively at work) and of John Dee. But there was a source of information more up to date and more detailed than the printed map or printed book, namely, the information to be obtained about the Spanish discoveries from the English merchants resident in Spain, or passing to and from the Spanish Indies.

Prominent among these were Roger Bodenham, Henry Hawks, and John Frampton : all were acquainted one with another, as extant correspondence shows, and all were in London about 1571–2. Roger Bodenham, Chancellor's old captain, now married and settled in Spain, was the correspondent of Burghley, Walsingham, Edward Dyer, and Michaël Lok, and gave to one of the Hakluyts (probably the elder) an account of his voyage to Mexico. Henry Hawks wrote a long account of New Spain at the request of the elder Hakluyt in 1572, while Frampton, a few years later, began his important series of translations from the Spanish under the patronage of Edward Dyer. Roger Bodenham went out to the Indies from New Spain in 1563 (not in 1564 as he says in the account given to Hakluyt), returning in 1564 after nine months' stay. His ship, the *Barke Fox*, was of London, but he sailed in the Indies fleet with Don Pedro Melendes, and his business took him to Mexico City. On his return he offered his services to Sir Thomas Challoner, the English Ambassador to Spain, who made interest for him with the Count of Feria. Bodenham's kinswoman, Mrs. Damascene Stradling, was in the service of the Countess of Feria (a niece of Sir Henry Sidney), and since on 4 May 1565 the Countess gave him a letter of recommendation to Leicester, it may be inferred that he was then returning to England. Here he is next heard of in August

1566, when he has so impressed the Spanish Ambassador, de Silva, by his knowledge of the navigation to the Indies, and his professed Spanish and Catholic sympathies, that he is returning to Seville bearing the Ambassador's recommendations to His Majesty of Spain.

A reference made by the English Ambassador to Spain in February 1567 [1] shows that Bodenham was at that date making suggestions with regard to improving the Spanish metal working, and later in the same year, according to his fellow-merchants at Seville,[2] he was selected as one of five leaders of an official expedition to 'China', the term used for the Philippines, the sailing route from which had been discovered under the direction of Urdaneta in 1565. Since there is no further record of Bodenham until he dates his little tract on the improvement of English trade from London in 1571, it is not impossible that he actually made the voyage across the Pacific. Even if this were not so, it is quite clear that he had every opportunity to put valuable knowledge and experience at the disposal of the English group interested in overseas discovery.

Urdaneta, it will be recalled, was yne of the companions of Loaysa in 1526 who had remained for many years in the Moluccas, and had then entered a religious order in Mexico. Philip II was very anxious to make full use of his experience of navigation and of the East, and his correspondence with the friar and with the Governor Pedro Melendes between 1559 and 1566 turns often on the question of the North-West Passage.[3] Urdaneta believed it to run from about 70° N. on the Atlantic side, to 50° or less on the Pacific (cf. Fig. 8): he considered that it should be examined from the western end and occupied at some suitable strategic point by the Spaniards, in order to prevent foreign access through it to Mar del Sur.[4] In the same correspondence the story is also dis-

---

[1] Roger Bodenham's record is to be found in the Spanish Calendar for the years referred to.

[2] G. R. G. Conway: *An Englishman and the Mexican Inquisition.*

[3] Navarrete: *Noticia Histórica de las expediciones hechas por los españoles en brisca del paso del norveste de la America.*

[4] Urdaneta's views were probably well known in New Spain, and this would account for the exaggerated story told by Salvaterra (newly from that country) to Sir Henry Sidney, in Humfrey Gilbert's hearing,

cussed of the voyage of a French ship in 1554, which (with a man from New Spain aboard) discovered and partly explored a narrow channel in middle latitudes running across America. This channel appears on Michael Lok's map, and on Dee's of 1583, while there was a rumour that Drake returned that way in 1580. Roger Bodenham, who had the full confidence of the Spanish authorities, must have been familiar with all these matters.

After his visit to England in 1571, he returned to Spain in June 1574, writing to Burghley on that occasion from his native Bristol. In January 1575 he was preparing for another visit to England, and promised to bring a copy of a book by a learned physician, Dr. Monardes, in which he had read of many things likely to do Burghley's gout good. This was the volume presently translated by John Frampton under the title *Joyful News out of the New Found Worlde*, and dedicated to Bodenham's friend, Edward Dyer.[1]

Henry Hawks' voyage from Seville to New Spain was begun in 1567, and on his arrival he resided in Mexico City, where he was when the first news came of the discovery of Solomon's Islands, for Mendaña's company landed at Puerto de Navidad, Mexico, in December 1568, on their way back to Peru.[2] Hawks was accused of heresy in 1570, and after escaping from the Inquisition in 1571, was back in London by 1572. He is undoubtedly the 'Henry Hawk' whose name appears as a witness in John Frampton's suit in the Court of Admiralty in that year. Like Bodenham, Hawks had valuable information, especially about the recent Spanish discoveries and trade routes to the Pacific, to place before the English cosmographers, and the coincidence of dates suggests that the lawsuit afforded the occasion for the lawyer Hakluyt to obtain that information.

---

that the friar himself had actually passed through the Strait from west to east. Salvaterra stated that Urdaneta showed him a map of the Passage in 1560.

[1] Roger Bodenham's letter to Michael Lok of 28 May 1582, intended for Burghley's ears, hints at a scheme (involving a breach with Spain) which the writer as a far travelled man can carry into execution, presumably a Pacific venture. State Papers, Spain, I, 97a.

[2] The fact that the Spaniards at first believed them to be ' Lutherans ' suggests an awareness of English projects for a north-west passage venture at that period.

It is clear that Henry Hawks' written account of New Spain has been carefully edited—it says nothing, for example, of his sufferings at the hands of the Inquisitors—nevertheless, he mentions his especial intimacy with the famous pilot and cosmographer, the younger Diego Gutierrez, who had been with Urdaneta on the historic voyage to and from the Philippines of 1564–5, and from whom therefore he could learn details of the trans-Pacific trade immediately instituted. Hawks mentions also a recent voyage of two ships from Culiacan, sent to seek the western end of the passage between Newfoundland and Greenland [1] (i.e. the straits of Anian), ' which they call the Englishman's strait ', perhaps because of Cabot's and Rut's voyages. He speaks, too, of the return from the Islands of Solomon, a name equivalent in its implications to Islands of Gold.

All this was information which may be linked up with the interest shown in the '70's in the possibilities of an English entry into the Pacific Ocean (e.g. in the Grenville Plan already cited), but the specific objective on which some men at least fixed their eyes was that mysterious land of gold of which Mendaña had seen the margin. This land, if Ortelius' map was to be believed, was continuous with that which Marco Polo had described under the name of Locach (or Beach), also rich in gold, and opinions differed as to how best to reach it.

There is now documentary evidence [2] that the promoters of Drake's voyage included the Earl of Leicester, Walsingham, and Hatton, with all of whom Dee was on terms of close acquaintance (Edward Dyer acting as a go-between when necessary). Hence it is relevant to see first what light on the subject of the voyage Dee's actions at this period afford. It was to Christopher Hatton that he dedicated the opening volume of his great work on the ' British Impire ' to which reference has been made. This volume is catalogued in the British Museum (in accordance with the title-page) as follows : *Genera and Rare Memorials pertayning to the perfect Arte of Navigation.*

---

[1] This voyage is not chronicled by Navarrete (*loc. cit.*). It must have been sent out as a result of the discussions already noted.

[2] E. G. R. Taylor : *The Missing Draft Plan of Drake's Voyage.* Geographical Journal, January 1930.

Annexed to the Paradoxal Cumpas, in Playne : *now first published* : *24 years, after the first Invention thereof.* J. Daye : London 1577. This, however, is the general title of the work as a whole, and the running title of the first volume is the *Pety Navy Royall,* while Dee also refers to it as ' The British Monarchy ', ' The Hexameron Brytannicum ', ' The Imperium Brytannicum ', and in one of the Prefaces to the book itself as ' The Hexameron Plat Politicall of the British Monarchie '. Although published under a thin veil of anonymity, this book contains much autobiographical detail. In particular we learn that Dee's intimate friend, Edward Dyer, the poet and courtier, acted as the constant link between the author and Christopher Hatton ; also that the MS. was completed in great haste in six days, early in August 1576, and that a printed edition, deliberately limited to one hundred copies, was not issued until August 1577. We are further told that the second volume, namely, *Queen Elizabeth her Arithmetical Tables Gubernatick : for Navigation by the Paradoxall Compass and Navigation in Great Circles* (unfortunately lost), was finished in the autumn of 1576, that a third volume (presumably politically dangerous) was finished and burnt, and that a fourth volume, *The Great Volume of Famous and Rich Discoveries,* was written (also in haste) in the spring and early summer of 1577. Of this fourth volume, the greater part (from chapter 7 onwards) is preserved at the British Museum,[1] although badly mutilated by fire. The first six chapters (70 leaves) came into the possession of Purchas through Hakluyt, and we can glean their contents from this source,[2] but unfortunately Purchas considered them too long to print, and they are now lost.

The general purpose of *Famous and Rich Discoveries* was to show how the English might bring back the riches of the East, not spices merely, nor even the fabled riches of Cathay, but the wealth of Ophir besides. In his opening chapters Dee reaches the conclusion that Solomon's navy made a round trip through Further India and the East Indies (*vide* Purchas), and in the surviving MS. (fol. 26*b*) he says :

[1] Vitellius, C. vii. Cotton MSS.
[2] *Purchas his Pilgrimes,* Vol. I, pp. 105 *et seqq.*

' Upon the Premisses about the Ophirian voyage I have bestowed some days to make evident how, every three years once, that most noble Ophirian provision might be got to Jerusalem. But upon the rest of these Collections (speedily ruffled together) it will become evident how this Incomparable Islandish Impire may every two years once : or (by good order devised and continued) every year . . .'

The last two words are struck out, and the following lines burnt, but it is clear that his theme is a British voyage to Ophir. Towards the end of the MS. (fol. 248) we read :

' In sundry places afore hath mention been made of Iles in the Scythian Ocean : but ever with this respect, as to note the records thereof to some evidence of proving the Asian Periplus and the Navigation from Cape Comfort, or this most comfortable Brytish Kingdom, to the lands of BEACH etc. to be open and commodiously enough possible to be made.'

Now Beach is Marco Polo's Locach, the ' land rich in gold ', and was clearly the most desirable objective for English discoverers in Dee's view. He refers to it as such in guarded terms on fol. 205, and on fol. 68b in discussing a new estimation of longitude writes :

' till we be sure that we are in due place to turn our course southerly to the New and Oriental Guinea : and so not only to have accomplished and made expert the Periplus Scythian and Asiaticall, but to enter and proceed upon the further discovery of that part which is least known to Christian men, and lies in the eye of Envy of other great Conquerors Christian ; and, most apt for the Brytish wisdom, manhood, and travail to be bestowed upon henceforwards.'

Beyond New Guinea, according to the maps which Dee himself tells us lay under his hand (Ortelius of 1564, Mercator of 1569), was Locach or Beach, while between it and Magellan's Strait, according to the information of the Seville merchants, were the Islands of Solomon.

Now it was of course of cardinal importance, in relation to this Periplus of Asia, which Dee considered the best approach to the Far East, to settle the controverted existence of the Straits of Anian, separating Asia and Atlantis (as he preferred to term North America). To this point, then, Dee devotes several chapters, including Chapter 20 (fol. 168b) which is dated 15 May 1577, and Chapter 21 (fol. 174) which is undated, but was apparently written on the same day, since fol. 191 is dated 16 May. (The first and last dates on this MS. are 30 March and 8 June 1577.) The sub-titles of Chapter 21 include : ' of Ania and Toloman, and of the Straits of Anian often mentioned of late years.' On folios 174–7 the evidence of Marco Polo is discussed, and Ortelius' interpretation of the region ; the argument is then carried forward (fol. 177*b*) by reference to ' The King of Spain his subjects ' . . . who ' have attempted to make this very N.W. corner of Atlantis known to them, as you may perceive of the unlucky attempts specified in the letter of Don Antonio de Mendozza, Vice Re della nove Spagna '. Ramusio's version of this letter is then quoted as to the Spanish search by sea, and the same writer's account ' of the search by land '. Then follows a passage which it is hardly possible to interpret other than as a direct reference to *Drake's intention of solving the problem.* Frobisher was within a week of starting on a voyage of which the objective was perfectly well known, Gilbert was not to obtain his letters patent for more than a year, while Drake's voyage alone was in active preparation.

The critical passage is as follows—interpolations where the MS. is burnt being put in square brackets :

' Of how great importance th[en to] you is that attempt which is by a Britis[h Sub]ject presently intended to God's glory the ben[efit of] all Christendom, and the honour and profit of this [realm] chiefly, and contentment of many a noble mind [which] delighteth to understand how, *Domini est Terra* [*et*] *Plenitudo ejus, orbis Terrarum et universi qui habi* [*tant*] *in eo* ; who (God sparing life and health) hath se[cret]ly offered up to God and his natural Soverayne and Country the employing of all his skill [and] talent, and the patient enduring of the great toyle of his body, to that place being the very ends of the world from us to be reckoned, to accomplish that discovery which of so many and so valient captains By Land and Sea hath been so oft attempted in vain. The consequence of which exploit is greater than is yet to any Christian State credible.

The marginal heading to this paragraph is ' A worthy attempt at Discovery, faithfully intended by a true Brytish Subject '. It is to be emphasized that it is the setting of this paragraph, interpolated as it is in the midst of the discussion as to the Straits of Anian, coupled with its date, 15 May 1577, that warrants its interpretation in the sense suggested. A visit by

Drake to latitudes 40°–50° N. would settle whether those maps
were correct that joined the continents in about that latitude,
or whether, as other maps indicated, the mouth of the Anian
Strait was there to be found. 'They say', wrote Henry
Hawks in 1572, 'that straight lieth not farre from the maine
land of China, which the Spanyards account to be marvellous
rich.' This, too, was the view expressed in the Grenville
Document.

The evidence that Dee was in the counsels of those responsible
for Drake's venture is cumulative, if the various hints be considered together and not separately. Thus in the *Pety Navy
Royall*, he writes (p. 62) :

'There remayne also to be declared the reasons why my Instructor
[Dee himself] doth wish and advise part of the publik threasory to be
bestowed upon some two or three honest men who should be skilful
in Far-Forreyn languages : As, in the Sclavonian or Moscovite, the
Arabik vulgar, the Turkish, the Tartarian, the Chiny language, the
Canadian, and the Islandish, etc. For that (within these next few years
following) with men of all these Cuntries, *and farder*, Great Affayres are
by some of our Cuntrymen to be handled : if God continue his Gracious
Direction and Ayde thereto, as he hath very Cumfortably begonne ;
and that, *by means not yet published*.

The earliest entries in Dee's *Private Diary* [1] refer to visits
from Drake's friends : '1577 Jan. 16th, The Erle of Lecester,
Mr. Phillip Sydney, Mr. Dyer etc. came to my house.' 'Jan.
22nd, The Erle of Bedford [Drake's godfather] came to my
howse.' From the Diary also we learn that a few days after
Drake had sailed, Dee spent a week at court. 'Nov. 22, I rod
to Windsor to the Q. Majestie . . . Dec. 1st, I spake with
Sir Christopher Hatton. He was made knight that day. I
went from the Cowrte at Wyndsore.'

Nowhere, however, does Dee make a suggestion as to a
voyage through Magellan's Strait, probably because in his
mind the North-East Passage was to be preferred as leading
the ships past Cathay and Cipangu *en route*, a point made also
by Richard Willes relative to the North-West Passage. For
the moment, then, the point to be emphasized is the shifting
of the focus of interest to 'Lands beyond the Equinoctial',

[1] *The Private Diary of Dr. J. D.* (from 1554 to 1601). Edited by
J. O. Halliwell, 1842.

or more specifically to Terra Australis, which alike from its extension in latitude, and from the reports of Mendaña and Marco Polo, should prove as rich a prize as either Mexico or Peru.

The newly discovered Draft Plan [1] of Drake's Voyage shows that the initial scheme was a reconnaissance of the shore of the southern continent from Magellan's Strait to 30° S., i.e. a section which could not on any grounds be claimed by the Spaniards. Actually, however, when final plans were made, the statements of John Winter [2] show that a voyage from the Strait's mouth in high southern latitudes was intended, with the Moluccas as its term, this allowing of a complete examination of the coast of Terra Australis *en route*, since the maps (and Gallego's report) suggested that it ran roughly north-west from latitude 52° to the Oriental Guinea just south of the Moluccas. It is easy to understand that when it came to financing Drake's voyage, men of a practical character, like the Winters and John Hawkins, would demand a known objective, rather than one the importance of which was a matter of inference, however probable. The scheme did not exclude the attempt to solve the Anian problem, for there were strong reasons for believing, as so experienced a pilot as Pedro Sarmiento did, that the North-West Passage would form the most ready and practicable exit from the Pacific. As far as the evidence went (e.g. Sebastian Cabot's), it was only its extreme eastern end that lay in high latitudes, since it trended rapidly southwards after 100 leagues or so. The south-westerly winds across the Pacific would carry the ships to its western extremity (the Strait of Anian), and on through the passage itself, while if the voyage were carefully timed to reach the most northerly section, that between the New Found Land and Greenland, in late summer, no danger from ice was to be anticipated.

Such were the views of Drake and his contemporaries. They did not anticipate the violent head winds and storms of the belt of the Brave West Winds which they encountered in issuing from Magellan's Strait. These winds precluded the

---

[1] E. G. R. Taylor: *loc. cit.*

[2] E. G. R. Taylor: *More Light on Drake*, 1577–80. Mariners' Mirror, Vol. XVI, No. 2.

passage to the Moluccas along the shore of Terra Australis, while Terra Australis itself, so far as the section immediately to the south and west of the Straits was concerned, had proved to be a figment of the imagination. Drake had ample excuse for formulating a new plan nearer to his own desire, but he did not neglect to seek, if only somewhat cursorily, for light on the Anian problem when that desire had been fulfilled. His visit to New Albion proved that there was no reason to suppose the approaches from the north to be blocked by a land bridge, while the land he claimed in the Queen's name was that already pointed out by Gilbert as suited to serve as a half-way house to the East, supposing the north-west or north-east passages to be opened.

III

Meanwhile Dee himself had thoughts of taking a journey which would lead to the unveiling of north-eastern Asia. This, of course, was scarcely feasible, although he had taken minute particulars of the overland route from Alexander Simon, the 'man born in Mosul', whom, as he declared, Providence sent to him at Mortlake in the very moment of writing. Four years later, in 1581, he found a man who professed himself willing to undertake the task. This man, John Leonard Haller, of Hallerstein, was in point of fact a Government spy, and although he listened to Dee's manifold instructions, he never took even a single step towards the actual journey.[1]

Dee's 'secret' hopes as to the outcome of establishing communication with Cathay are hinted at in the *Pety Navy Royall* [2] in terms which Dyer, himself a student of the occult, could readily interpret to a Royal Reader.

Meanwhile, between the writing of the first and last volume of the *Memorials* by Dee, Frobisher had been home with his sworn account of finding an authentic Strait, and his fragment of ore. Dee, no doubt, like Willes and Lok, found Frobisher's statements, backed by his charts, and the 'Pycknean' or 'strange man of Cathay',[3] sufficiently convincing.

[1] Document 14, No. iv.   [2] See Document 14, No. ii. *b*.
[3] Document 13, No. iv. *b*.

Michael Lok's unpublished account of this first voyage [1] shows plainly enough the importance that was attached to the Mongoloid characteristics of the kidnapped Eskimo.

' And so (they) came to London with their ship Gabriel the ixth day of October : and they were joyfully received with the great Admiration of the people, bringing with them their strange man and his Bote, which was such a wonder unto the whole city, and to the rest of the Realm that heard of it, as seemed never to have happened the like great matter to any men's knowledge.'

He thereupon goes on to describe the man, who had a

' very brode face, and very fat and full in his body.   But his legs shorter and smaller than the proportion of his body required . . . his heare cole black and long hanging, and tyed above his forehead.   His eyes lyttle, and a little black Beard.   His cullor of skyn all over his Bodye . . . of a dark Sallow, much like to the tawny Mores : rather to the Tartar nation whereof I think he was : Countenance sullen or churlish and sharp withall.'

The inference that the captive was an Asiatic was a very natural one, and in January 1579 (after further prisoners had been brought home), a formal protest came from Moscow to the effect that Frobisher was unlawfully carrying off Russian subjects.   The news of what had been accomplished spread quickly over the Continent, not only through private letters, such as those of Philip Sidney to Languet, and Languet to his master, but by the issue of a French edition of Settle's *Discourse* in 1578 at Geneva, and of a Latin translation of this French version in 1580.

With Dyer, Jenkinson, Lok and others, Dee was on the commission to investigate the truth as to the gold ore, and his conviction of its genuineness is sufficiently clear from the fact that he was an investor in the second and third voyages. That there was deliberate fraud on the part of Dr. Burchet in respect of this gold ore, seems almost certain : to discuss such a point here, however, is irrelevant.   All that need be noticed is that Dee was on the committee which watched the trials on a larger scale made at Sir William Winter's house in the winter of 1577–8, and that he was also among those commissioned in 1578, 1579, and 1580 to deal with the financial difficulties that arose when the third voyage had still nothing

[1] Otho E. viii.

to show but quantities of ore now realized to be spurious. Details as to the use made of his services in these respects are to be found in the Lansdown MSS., Codex 100.

In passing, the work of Humfrey Cole in connexion with the Frobisher voyages may be noticed. Employed by Wm. Humfrey, paymaster and assaymaster at the Mint since 1565, he yet found time to take charge of the ' New Art ' enterprise, already mentioned, between 1572 and 1575, and to make dials, compasses, astrolabes and other instruments, of which a few examples, bearing dates from 1568 to 1575, have survived. He made, or supervised the making of, the instruments which Frobisher took with him, and was engaged as an expert in connexion with the Dartford Works erected for dealing with the ore. There is some evidence that he also made the instruments described in Digges' *Tectonicon* and *Pantometria*, while William Bourne mentioned in 1578 his device for measuring the way of a ship (modelled on one of Besson's inventions). It is a reasonable assumption, too, that he made certain instruments (e.g. the astrolabe now in Mr. Gabb's possession,[1] bearing Queen Elizabeth's emblems) to Dee's specification, and when in 1578 he supplicated Cecil for a certain appointment at the Mint, for which he claims to have been waiting twenty years, it was Dee's friend, Edward Dyer, who used his influence on Cole's behalf.

Dee's *Pety Navy Royall*, the first volume of the *General and Rare Memorials pertayning to the Perfect Art of Navigation*, was, as has already been mentioned, only ' put to printing ' in August 1577, although it was written and dedicated to Hatton in the first six days of August 1576. Hatton was to bring it to the notice of the Privy Council, while Dyer, who appears to have borne the printing charges, was to bring it to that of the Queen. The work does not bear directly on discovery, but its object was to set forth the advantages of having a Navy of vessels in permanent commission, and to suggest means whereby such a scheme could be financed : such a fleet was, of course, a pre-requisite of the policy of expansion which Dee was advocating, namely, that of establishing a

[1] Exhibited at the International Geographical Congress, London, 1928.

British maritime Empire in high latitudes. The speeches of
Pericles, and an exordium upon Pompey, are among the
arguments and examples brought to bear upon the vital
question of 'command of the seas'.

The question of the limits of sea-jurisdiction is carefully
discussed, the view held being that it extends 100 miles from
the shore, or in the case of narrow seas (less than 200 miles
across) to a point mid-way between the home and foreign
coasts. By laying claim for England to the shores and islands
(including the Orkneys) conquered by the ancient British
kings, Arthur and Malgo, and hence to a stretch of sea for a
hundred miles around each of these, Dee was able to establish
fairly well a rightful jurisdiction across the North Atlantic and
Arctic Oceans, the discoveries of Stephen Borough having
extended British rights towards the north-east. This matter
was elaborated and made more explicit in ' the treatise which
I compiled speedily, at her Majesty's Commandment Anno
1578, whose title is Brytannici Imperii Limites', and in 'Her
Majesty's Title Royal to many foreign countries, kingdoms
and provinces' which was 'set down in writing with Hydrographical and Geographical description', also in 1578. Dee
says that he refused £100 (then a very large sum) for a copy of
the latter, and, although neither of these MSS. is known to
have survived, a summary statement of 'Her Majesty's
Title', etc., is to be found on the back of the map of Atlantis
(*Atlantidis emendiator descriptio quem adhuc est divulgata*),
drawn on vellum expressly for the Queen, which is among the
Cotton MSS. and is dated 1580.

Among the areas included in the title was the coast of
Atlantis from Florida northwards, first discovered by Owen
Madoc in the twelfth century (according to the Welsh tradition)
and later by Thorne (under date 1494),[1] and Cabot (1597 *sic*),
and this priority was the justification for Gilbert's colonizing
scheme, for which he obtained a patent in June 1578. Gilbert
had been to Mortlake to seek Dee's advice in the previous
autumn (3 November 1577), about three weeks before the
latter's visit to Court. At Windsor Dee explained her title

[1] This date is discussed by J. A. Williamson, *The Voyages of the
Cabots*, London, 1929.

to the Queen by word of mouth, and he had an interview with
Secretary Walsingham on the same day as he spoke of this
matter to the Queen: Walsingham was behind Drake's
voyage, as well as Gilbert's, and he and Dee had a mutual
friend in Walsingham's brother-in-law Beale, the clerk to the
Privy Council. It will be recalled that the Thorne documents,
with reference to the elder Thorne's discovery, were brought
to Dee by Cyprian Lucar in 1577, when he was at work on his
Great and Rich Discoveries volume.

The colonizing venture of Gilbert was one which had the
elder Hakluyt's firm support, because of the opportunity that
it afforded for improving English trade, and in the same month
that Gilbert obtained his patent, Dee has the entry in his diary,
' June 30th I told M. Daniel Rogers, M. Hakluyt of the Middle
Temple being by, that King Arthur and King Malgo both of
them, did conquer Gelindia, lately called Friseland '. The
reference is, of course, to the Friseland of the pseudo-Zeni
document, which Dee, like most of his contemporaries, held to
be an authentic narrative of discovery, although actually the
Friseland of the Zeni map is a duplication of Iceland.
Frobisher imagined that he touched it on his first voyage,
although the coast he skirted was actually that of Cape Farewell, Greenland. That Dee was keeping in touch with Gilbert
is further suggested by another diary entry of 1578 : ' Aug. 5,
Mr. Reynolds of Bridewell took his leave of me as he passed
toward Dartmouth to go with Sir Umfrey Gilbert toward
Hochelega.' The actual start was made on 23 September
1578, and was celebrated in verse by Thomas Churchyard, but
early in November before home waters had been left behind,
Gilbert was writing to complain to Walsingham that his companions were deserting him, and the expedition was abandoned.
It may be noticed that young Walter Raleigh, always Dee's
friend, sailed on this occasion with his half-brother.

It is difficult to believe that the autumn would have been
chosen had Hochelaga (i.e. the New York and New England
area) been Gilbert's immediate destination : on the other hand,
it would have been a suitable date for wintering at a point
nearer to Florida, or for following Drake to Magellan ; but
according to Sir John Gilbert the fleet was provisioned only for

a year.   The solution of the problem is, however, immaterial to the present study, although Gilbert's statement that he had 500 fighting men with him is significant.[1]

John Dee had been again summoned to the Court (then temporarily at Norwich), in August 1578, where he had conferences with the Queen, and with his friend Daniel Rogers, and he had a copy of the *Pety Navy Royall* with him.   Later in the year he was sent abroad to Frankfurt on a mission connected with the Queen's health.   This was the year of Dee's third marriage to Jane Fromond, who was in the retinue of Lady Howard, wife of the man who was later Lord Admiral. The Howard family were patrons of the younger Hakluyts, Edmund Hakluyt being for four years tutor to one of Lord Charles' sons, while Richard Hakluyt was a favourite with Lady Sheffield, Lord Charles' sister, who after bearing a son (Lord Robert Dudley) to Leicester, became Lady Strafford, wife of Hakluyt's employer of 1583.

Before passing on to Dee's work in 1579 and 1580, some further reference may be made to his *Pety Navy Royall*.   It contains an approving reference to a plan for England's betterment that has already been noted in an earlier chapter, namely, that of Robert Hitchcock for the development of the home fisheries and fishing fleet.   This ' plat ' was not printed until 1580, but its author had brought it before a number of prominent burgesses at a dinner-party in 1575, among whom was Dee's friend, Thomas Digges, who thought so well of it as to speak on the subject in Parliament, just before the House rose at the end of the Session.   Dee did not make Robert Hitchcock's acquaintance until 1579, but he already knew his sailor brother, Thomas Hitchcock, who made the translation of the *Travels of Cæsar Frederick*.   Thomas was, in fact, the recipient of one of the hundred printed copies of the *Pety Navy Royall*, the British Museum copy being endorsed by himself ' Saylor Hickock, the gift of Doktor Dee 1577 ', with an eulogium of the scheme which the book contains.   Records such as this, trifling in themselves, serve to illustrate the way in which Dee kept in touch with such men of action as were likely to be of use in his schemes.

[1] Otho E. viii, Cotton MSS.

CHAPTER VII

JOHN DEE AND THE SEARCH FOR CATHAY: 1580–1583

I

BY 1579, the Frobisher voyages had come to a close, while Sir Humfrey Gilbert was faced with the necessity of commencing the work for his planting scheme all over again, although Simon Fernando, ' Mr. Secretary Walsingham's man ', who was subsequently pilot in succession of Fenton's ship (1582) and of the Virginia fleet (1586 *et seq.*), made a quick trip to Norumbega and back. Fernando, like so many excellent pilots, came from Terceira in the Azores, and was not a man to be overlooked by Dee as a source of authoritative information. He called on the great mathematician at Mortlake in November 1580, and showed him a chart of the North Atlantic, of which one of Dee's band of student-assistants made a copy. This chart still survives among the Cotton MSS.

In 1579, as his Diary records, Dee was already in touch with Adrian Gilbert and John Davis, the two men associated with the North-West Passage attempts of 1585–7 : we learn that after a quarrel they reconciled themselves with him on 18 October. There is no reason to suppose, however, that this quarrel had anything to do with voyages of discovery. Adrian Gilbert was an amateur of alchemy and of the occult (in which he was associated with Mary Sidney, Countess of Pembroke), and this must have formed a link with Dee, of whom, besides, the whole Sidney family, including Mary, thought very highly. Young Philip Sidney and Edward Dyer were at this time constantly together, and Dyer showed his affection for Dee by becoming godfather to his eldest son, Arthur, on 13 July 1579. The same year, it will be remembered, was that in which Dyer encouraged John Frampton to make the third and fourth of his series of translations from the Spanish : it was also the year in which the elder Hakluyt made careful notes for a dyer going on one of the last Persian voyages, and that in which Thomas Digges had begun a *Treatise on the Art of Navigation*, which, however, he never actually published. Dee wrote at this time yet another tract on Empire—' *De imperatoris nomine, authoritate et potentia*, dedicated to Her Majesty in English ', but looked at as a whole, the year 1579 was one in which, while schemes for discovery and expansion were being actively resolved, no real advance was made.

The disappointments of the Muscovy Company, alike in Russia and Persia, the return of John Winter with news of the violent storms of the ' Pacific ' Ocean, and the disgrace of Michael Lok (on whom as Treasurer fell the burden of the financial collapse of the Frobisher quest), were probably among the factors that led the Company to look favourably on the suggestion of a renewed search for the North-East Passage. William Borough had not forgotten his own success of over twenty years since, or his careful, but wasted, preparations for the Bassendine voyage in 1568 : he was, moreover, receiving increasing recognition as a man of note in sea causes. During August 1579, he had been consulted by the Dover Harbour Commissioners, and his long and valuable discussion of coast erosion and coast accretion in Kent is extant.[1] In this work at Dover Arthur Pet had been joined with Borough, and when the details of the proposed 1580 voyage were settled, William Borough was appointed director, and placed Arthur Pet in command. Pet was an experienced Muscovy Captain, and had commanded the *Jesus* in 1560. With him was joined, as Vice-Admiral, Charles Jackman, who had made a reputation in the Frobisher voyages, at first as mate under Hall, and then as master under Fenton. Borough was perhaps hardly satisfied to have his instructions supplemented by his own former teacher Dee, who according to precedent, was summoned to Muscovy House before the start was made : the now middle-aged seaman had already, in 1578, expressed his opinion of learned men who were without practical experience afloat.

In the case of this new voyage, however, Dee did more than

---

[1] Lansdown MSS. 22, Nos. 10–14.

instruct the two masters in the use of instruments and tables, and in the mathematics of navigating practice : his *Volume of Great and Rich Discoveries* had been largely directed to collecting evidence upon this very question of a north-east passage to Cathay, and his conclusions were not those generally accepted. Hence, in addition to the charts and sailing directions supplied by Borough, the Masters had each a chart and sailing directions supplied by Dee. These were formally presented to them at a Court held at the Muscovy House on 17 May 1580, and the fact that in the MS. title to the document [1] Charles Jackman is placed before Arthur Pet (the senior commander) suggests that whereas Pet was Borough's man, Jackman (one of those instructed for the Frobisher voyages) was Dee's. The instructions were drawn up on 15 May.

As he had done on previous occasions, the elder Hakluyt drew up the notes on the trade relations it was hoped to establish by the voyage, either with Cathay or with intermediate countries, and to make certain that this important aspect of the voyage would be capably managed, Nicholas Chancellor, now himself a merchant of standing, and with his experience of the north-west behind him, was made a member of the expedition. It would be interesting to know whether he carried all the trade samples, the atlas and the maps, advised by the Company's economic expert.

The younger Hakluyt was privy to all the plans and preparations, and, as will presently be shown, there is reason to think that Dee had allowed him to read the *Volume of Great and Rich Discoveries*. Alarmed at views which were so novel, he wrote post-haste to Mercator, whose son Rumold was his friend, and put to him a number of queries, besides begging for general advice upon the proposed voyage. This he did, asking for a pledge of secrecy, as Mercator revealed in a letter to Ortelius the same year, but unfortunately delays in the post caused his letter to reach Duisburg only by 19 June, when Pet and Jackman had already reached Norway. Nor did Mercator even then reply until nearly the end of July, and it may be surmised that although he was courteously ready to impart his views to a learned young contemporary, the Flemish cosmographer was

[1] A contemporary transcript, Lansdown 122.

not ready to promote a foreign discovery venture. Among the facts that Mercator learned was that the expedition was provisioned for a full two years and a half, and as he believed (with Dee) that Cathay could be reached the first summer, he surmised that there was some further business afoot in the China Seas, possibly a rendezvous with Drake, of whose start he had heard from Rumold.[1]

Drake was, of course, still away in the spring of 1580, a fact which was beginning to cause grave anxiety, but news of him had come to hand, in the shape of the evidence given by San Juan de Anton, master of the looted treasure ship, before the Court in Panama on 26 March 1578. The fact that an English version of this evidence, apparently forming part of a news letter, accompanies the original Pet and Jackman documents in Otho E. viii, and that a transcript of it in the same hand and on the same paper as the Instructions for the Masters is found in Lansdown 122 (the two together being endorsed ' Mr. Dee's Boke '), is strong evidence that the planning of the Pet and Jackman voyage was not unconnected with Drake's failure to return, at least so far as Dee's share was concerned. Did the coast of Asia run as Dee supposed, it would be an easy matter to lead Drake back that way supposing him to be still in the Pacific.

The instructions and plans for the Pet-Jackman voyage, thanks to Hakluyt, are very completely documented. In the first edition of the *Principal Navigations* he printed the Company's Commission, William Borough's Instructions, John Dee's Instructions, Mercator's letter, and the narratives of Nicholas Chancellor and Hugh Smith, who were both in the *George* with Pet. The Chancellor narrative was dropped in the second edition of the Navigations. Dee, as we should expect, had the original manuscript of the narrative written by the son of his old friend, and it bears his marginal notes,[2] but he made further inquiries as to the voyage of Hugh Smith, who drew for him, as he relates in the Diary, a little sketch-map of the position of the two vessels when they were beset by ice in the Kara Sea.[3] This Hugh Smith had been with Captain

[1] Document 9, No. x.   [2] Otho E. viii.
[3] Document 15, No. ii.

Winter in 1577–8, and so had passed and repassed Magellan's Strait.

According to the Muscovy Company's Commission, the Masters were to receive each a 'plat of spirall lines made by master William Burrough . . . one other sailing carde, and a blank plat'. The other sailing card must have been Dee's,[1] and it is to be remarked that Borough had here attempted a chart with the true rhumbs, although he was content with the conventional (and erroneous) straight rhumbs (arranged on the pattern laid down in Cortes' *Arte de Naveguar*) in the chart he prepared for Frobisher. If Cathay was reached the first season, then a further exploration was suggested : if it was not reached until after wintering *en route*, then the return could be delayed until 1582. Should Cape Tabin stretch beyond 80°, then the river Ob was to be explored.

William Borough's instructions are all directed towards the accurate charting of the voyage. Soundings are to be taken at regular intervals, and the ship's position estimated by dead reckoning. Frequent observations of latitude and of the variation of the compass are to be made, preferably on land, no doubt because a much greater accuracy was ensured. The coast was to be charted by the method of intersecting rays, directions being taken by the sailing compass, and the base-line measured by time of sailing ('1, 2, 3, or 4 glasses at most'). Sketches of landmarks were to be added to the plat, after the fashion of the early rutters, e.g., that of Pierre Garcie. Tides and currents were to be noted, and when a landing was made for observing latitude and compass-variation, the opportunity was to be seized for making a topographical map. For this, instead of the sailing compass, an 'instrument for trying of distances' was to be employed. This instrument may have been a plane-table, or the 'topographical instrument' of Digges' *Panto-metria*. The latter is the more likely, since Borough mentions the Topographical Instrument in the list of instruments useful to a Mariner given in his tract on the Variation of the Compass, which was published in 1581. It will be remembered that Robert Norman had been making instruments to Borough's specification during this period, and hence the stress on

[1] Document 15, No. i.

compass observations in the instructions. 'These orders ',
Borough concludes, ' if you diligently observe, you may thereby
perfectly set down in the plats that I have given you, your
whole travell, and description of your discovery, which is a
thing that will be chiefly expected at your hands.'

Dee's Instructions are brief, and deal in the first instance
with his view of the trend of the coast, and the distances to
be covered. The map he made, which he mentions in his
catalogue of MSS., is lost, but a sketch of the Asian coast is
included in the map prepared for Gilbert in 1583, which has
been preserved, although it has unfortunately passed to an
American collector. A study of this map (reproduced for the
Geographical Society's *Journal* in 1928), side by side with the
Instructions, and the *Volume of Great and Rich Discoveries*,
makes Dee's ideas perfectly clear.

His main point was that the passage to Cathay nowhere
lay as far north as North Cape in 72°. Tabin Promontory
stretched only to 70°, and could be reached from Wardhouse
in thirty-six days, i.e. before the end of July. Once past
Tabin, the coast ran south-easterly, so that the great river
Orchardes, supposed to flow past Cambalu northwards, had
its mouth in latitude 50° or 52°. They might be able to sail
up this river three or four hundred miles to Cambalu in latitude
45°, or sail round Ania Province to the famous harbour of
Quinsay, which Dee placed in 46° N.

Before examining the method by which Dee reached these
carefully considered conclusions, the opinions of Mercator,
drawn from him by Hakluyt's interrogations, will be put
down for comparison. In the first place he agrees with Dee :
' the voyage to Cathaia by the East is doubtless very easy and
short, and I have oftentimes marvelled, that being so happily
begun, it hath been left off, and the course changed into the
West, after that more than half of your voyage was discovered '.
He goes on to say that beyond Vaigatz is a great bay, enclosed
to the east by the mighty promontory of Tabin (C. Chelyuskin,
77° 36'), into which fall great rivers navigable by sea-going
vessels into the heart of the continent. These form the high-
way to Serica. It can be hardly doubted that the great
Siberian rivers, already known to the Russians who traded

beyond the Urals, formed a factual basis for this view. This is confirmed by Mercator's remark that the great gulf enclosed by Tabin (actually the Kara Sea) is ' *as they say* ', frozen hard every year, which again is actually the case.

Mercator is strongly against any attempt to round Tabin, not only because of the ice difficulty but because such a course would carry the navigators towards the magnetic pole. The great cosmographer had as early as 1552 formulated his conclusion that the compass oriented itself in respect to a pair of points situated on the earth (the magnetic poles) and not a point in the heavens. Assuming that the magnetic meridians were great circles, the intersection of two of these gave him the position of these poles ; the north magnetic pole stood in 73° 2' N., and 180° east of a prime meridian through the Azores. Tabin was only 30° away, while navigators through the north-west passage to the Strait of Anian would come even closer to the danger zone. The danger lay, of course, in the extremely rapid variation of the compass from point to point, which was likely to result in a sailor wandering up and down, quite off his course. Dee did not consider the point, since he was convinced that the passage did not lie in such high latitudes, and the Masters had besides a compass of variation.

The *Volume of Great and Rich Discoveries* gives the grounds of his conclusions. In the first instance, he re-examined minutely the old story of the Indians storm-driven to Germania, proving by reference to Johannes Magnus that Pliny's Germania would include Scandinavia. ' The Indians voyage into the King of Sweden his jurisdiction is a principal point to make reckoning upon, for a Scythian and an Orientall wishful voyage ; for all Asia the Great of us to be traded withall, *and farder.* '

Turning, then, to a detailed analysis of the Arctic Coast, he compares ' my friend Mr. Stephen Borough, his plot ' with Mercator's world map of 1569, and his Europe of 1572, incidentally giving some sensible advice about the determination of longitude, and the choice of a prime meridian, so as to facilitate such comparisons. Next he reviews what in his mind was the most important evidence of all, that contained in the writings of Abulfeda Ismaël. When this Arabic author's Cosmography was brought back from Constantinople by the

French linguist Postellus, the writer was hailed as a new
Ptolemy, who could at last supply an authoritative interpretation of Asia.   Dee retells the story of the pawning of the
book in 1549 with the Duke of Bavaria, and says that before
parting with it, Postellus had given a *Compendium* of the
Geography to Ramusio, who used it in his commentaries on the
journey to Marco Polo (*Viaggi* 1559).   Thus it is from Ramusio
that Dee quotes the Arab authority.   Abulfeda distinctly says
(according to Ramusio), that to the north of China, the Asian
coast trends uniformly north-westward to the confines of
Russia, and it is this statement that Dee endorses ' A record
worthy to be printed in gold ', and adds :

> ' Oh, of what estimation ought this record to be [held which] con-
> teyneth all that remayned either unknown [or in] controversey in respect
> of this perfect Periplus int[ended].   And here you may perceive that
> it is evident that none of our Tripartite mayn land is more to the North
> than the Cape (by our countrymen) named the North Cape, in the Coast
> of Norway, to which, from the Russie coast confines, he noteth the course
> to lie nere north west.'

A capital reason for putting the geography of Abulfeda on a
level with that of Ptolemy was that the Arabic writer accepted
the canons of his Greek predecessor, and based his description
on determination (or calculation) of latitude and longitude :
thus Ramusio (quoted by Dee) could seriously speak of his book
as ' coming divinely to light in our time ', and Abulfeda's
positions for Cambalu and Quinsay are substantially those
which Dee adopts, after conference with Ptolemy's Tables.
As proof of his accuracy, Dee quotes his latitude of 39° 30' for
Bokhara, which he is able to confirm from his personal knowledge of Jenkinson's observations, and similarly Samarkand is
correctly set in 40° 8' : ' and yet by our best Christian Geographers supposed to be far more to the north than it is '.

Dee also confirms Abulfeda by comparing him with the
' collection made by the wise, discrete, and expert Roger
Bachon ' (i.e. the *Opus Majus*), dwelling particularly on the
narratives of Rubruck and Planocarpini.   He is emphatic that
both Ortelius and Mercator are in error, and of the latter says :

> ' According to the Information of the Premisses, the expert and grave
> Cosmographer, Gerardus Mercator, hath published the description

thereof [Margin : In his universall chart made for navigation A? 1569]
which if you will confer with these notes, you will take great pleasure
therein.   But for all the rest of the Scythian tract to the Orientall
Ocean, I am very sorry his labour took a wrong bihas : as he himself
now . . . may infer and infallibly conclude.'

The Englishman was at the time of writing in correspondence
with Mercator on the subject, and quotes a letter from his
friend beginning, ' Habes, mi Domini Dee, omniae x quibus
meam septentrionis descriptam concinnare. Illud preterea
addenda mihi est, non ita dudum mihi a Dnõ Joh. Metello
Colonia scriptum esse . . .', and going on to tell the story of
one who travelled from Mexico to the Oriental India, crossing
only a river in between.   The material as to the far north
which Mercator here refers to, is contained in another long
letter from him which concludes the Volume of Dee's manuscript, and begins, 'Clarissimo viro, D. Joanni Dee ', and closes,
' Bene vale, vir doctissime, mihique amantissime collende,
1577 '.   Practically the entire letter is a transcript of the
Itinerarium of Jacobus Cnoyen van Tsertoghenbosch, partly
in the exact words of the Dutch original, partly in a free Latin
translation.   This was the work (briefly summarized on the
map of 1569) on which Mercator relied for his delineation of the
Polar Regions.   The author quotes the *Gestae Arthuri*, and
ascribes to King Arthur conquests of islands as far north as
78° ; the story is then told that in 1364, when only eight men
of the stock of those that had been with King Arthur survived,
a priest ' who had an astrolabe ' told the king of Norway of the
English friar from Oxford, a good astronomer, who in 1360
visited those northern islands, and wrote a book for the King
of England called *Inventio Fortunatae*, which book begins at
the seventh climate and continues to the Pole.   Then follows
the narrative, derived from this old book, which Mercator used
as his authority for this map.

This section of Dee's MS. is the source of the note on Nicholas
of Lynn later printed by Hakluyt, and the MS. has marginal
notes throughout, written in another hand than Dee's, one
having the reference ' this 1580 '.   Now, according to Mercator's
letter, Hakluyt in 1580 asked him particularly about the source
of the Jacobus Cnoyen material, and about the William of

Rubruck and Planocarpini narratives. He told him also that the Epitome of Abilfada (i.e. Abulfeda) was translated, and Mercator replied that he wished to have sight of it. It can hardly be a coincidence that the three rarest and most notable sources used by Dee were mentioned by Hakluyt in writing on the same matter to Mercator ; rather it points to the young Cosmographer having just turned from Dee's manuscript, which had failed to convince him, and seeking a confirmation of his opinion from his great contemporary. Only two years were to elapse before the appearance of the *Divers Voyages*, and indeed, at the very time of this correspondence, the younger Hakluyt was procuring the translation of Cartier's Voyages from his own copy of Ramusio. The term of Dee's influence was approaching.

II

While, however, the rising generation might be doubtful of Dee's authority, he was still the chosen adviser of older men. In June of 1580 he was once more in touch with Adrian Gilbert and John Davis, who were on a visit to London from Devonshire ; in August he was obtaining from Sir Humfrey Gilbert a grant of a part of his privileges, and eventually had assigned to him ' the royalties of discovery all to the North above the parallel of the 50th degree of latitude ', itself an evidence of Dee's faith in more northern lands. Three days later Michael Lok, who declared that in the last two years he had seen the inside of every prison in London except Newgate, brought his son Benjamin, one of fifteen children, to be apprenticed to Dee, with whom the youth stayed two years. It is clear, therefore, that Dee, who had been one of the auditors of the Frobisher accounts, did not believe in the charges of fraud that had been launched against Lok : nor had Lok at all abandoned his hopes of Cathay, as his transactions with the younger Hakluyt prove.

Queen Elizabeth, in this same September, graciously commanded Dee to be more at her Court, and to let her know through her ladies when he was there. He was not slow to avail himself of the invitation, and on 3 October took her another proof of her *Titles to Foreign Lands*, written on two parchment rolls, of which one (already referred to) survives. A week later the Queen called at his house and told him that the Lord Treasurer had greatly commended his doings for her title, but when Dee had speech with Burghley on the subject, the results were not encouraging, although the gift of a haunch of venison came presently to Mortlake to show that there was no ill-will. Drake had just returned with his news of New Albion, so that Dee's discourse on a ' British Impire ' must, to the Queen, have been peculiarly apposite.[1]

Christmas Day saw Arthur Pet with his ship in the Thames, while there was no news of Charles Jackman : the Cathay voyage was again a failure. Yet Dee never lost hope, and during 1581 and 1582 was trying to set John Leonard Haller of Hallerstein on his way overland, as already described. Young William Hawkins, who had been with Drake, came to see him early in the year 1581, so that he was able to learn first-hand particulars of what had transpired on that voyage. His thoughts now centred on America, and he wrote a great volume in Latin upon the Propagation of the Christian Faith among the Infidels of Atlantis. This was in four books, of which the first was addressed to the Queen, the second to the Privy Council, the third to the King of Spain, and the fourth to the Pope.

Meanwhile Gilbert had once more secured influential support, including that of Sir George Peckham, a man with Catholic leanings, who came to Dee in July 1582 to be resolved of his doubts as to the title for Norumbega, in view of the Pope's partition of all the world's discoveries between Spain and Portugal. He also promised Dee further privileges in respect of the expected gains from ' this new conquest ' as Dee terms it.

In the autumn, an entirely new plan for reaching Cathay, or rather China, was formulated by what may be termed the ' geographical group ', there being direct evidence for the connexions of Dee, and Hakluyt of Oxford, with the scheme. The year 1580 had witnessed the chartering of the New Turkey Company (later the Levant Company) for trade with the Near East, through Constantinople and Aleppo, and the elder

---

[1] The Spanish Ambassador's official complaint of Drake's piracies had, however, been delivered in this same month, and the situation was a delicate one.

Hakluyt had been commissioned to write one of his carefully thought-out economic tracts for the guidance of one of the Company's first factors, who went out in 1582. At about the same time (10 September) the Governor of the new Company, Alderman Osborn, came to confer with Dee. Two months later Dee received another visitor, Mr. Newbery, ' who had been in Cambaia in India '. This was the man selected to open up Ormuz and India for the Company's agents, and to carry from the Queen a letter to the Emperor of China. He was peculiarly fitted for the task, for not only was he familiar with the Ormuz trade, but he had command of Arabic, which would carry him practically anywhere through Asia. He had, moreover, great courage and business ability, and had already secured the friendship of the Governor of Ormuz. All these facts can be gleaned from the later narratives of the journey he was presently to undertake.

As to Newbery's discussions during this winter with the younger Hakluyt, there is the evidence of his own letter, despatched from Aleppo, beginning, ' Right wellbeloved and my assured good friend '. From it we learn that Hakluyt had given him a note from the writings of Fernando Fernandez, a Portuguese, probably a pilot, and had lent him the original of Thomas Stevens' Letter from Goa (November 1579) to take a copy from. This letter was written to Thomas Stevens, Senr., and if the latter is the gentleman of that name who was the elder Hakluyt's friend in the Middle Temple, it is easy to understand how Hakluyt of Oxford came by the letter, which contains very important information as to the Portuguese sailing route by the Cape. The younger Thomas Stevens was a Jesuit, and John Newbery's introduction to him later proved very valuable, for had it not been for his good offices, writes Newbery, ' we might have rotted in prison '.

Besides receiving geographical notes from Hakluyt, Newbery was charged by him with a very important commission : to search for a second copy of the Geography of Abulfeda. No copy could be heard of in Syria, when Newbery wrote, but he was hopeful of more success at Baghdad or in Persia. That Hakluyt did eventually get hold of a copy is certain, for Ortelius, writing to Camden in November 1588, says that he has heard from Emanuel Demetrius that Hakluyt is bringing out an edition of Abulfeda, which he has every hope will be published that year.   John Newbery, however, was last heard of bound for Lahore, and thence ostensibly for Persia, but perhaps to make trial of the overland route to Cathay.

There is no evidence that Dee had any connection with the Fenton voyage of 1582, but the gossiping diary (preserved in MS.) of Richard Madox,[1] the young Oxford Chaplain to the expedition, appointed by Leicester, gives some sidelights on the geography of the day.   With young Mr. Torporley (the mathematician) Madox went down to Ratcliff to see Norman, the compass-maker,[2] who showed them his lodestones and instruments, and with Cyprian Lucar he went to see a neighbour who was making trifles for Humfrey Gilbert to sell in Norumbega. This man (Mr. Ashley) declared that there was a sailable passage across America between 43° and 46° (i.e. the channel supposed to have been discovered in 1554) and that it was by this route that Drake had returned from the Moluccas.   He looked to see the day when a letter posted in London on 1 May would reach China the midsummer following a twelvemonth.   At dinner too, at Sheriff Martin's, with his new son-in-law Julius Cæsar (Lok's stepson, and a Judge of the Admiralty), the talk fell on Drake, and the Sheriff spoke of a rumour that his lost ship (the *Marigold*) was returned.

A friend made Madox the appropriate gift of a pair of globes, but he promptly gave them away.   He equipped himself, however, with a *mappa mundi*, a set of ephemerides, and some dials, although he required these, not for geographical purposes, but to cast a horoscope !   During his stay at the Lucars', he heard about their cousin Emanuel, who had been with Drake, and was presented with a rosary of beads by Cyprian's mother : this an indignant Protestant fellow-traveller threw overboard.

To return, however, to John Dee.   The new year of 1583 saw the definite formulation of Adrian Gilbert's plans, based on technical advice given by Dee, who is officially named in the request that year for a Patent as one of the chief men associated with the enterprise.   The first meeting took place at Dee's

[1] Document 14, No. iv.
[2] His *New Attractive* had not long been published.

house on 23 January, and as Secretary Walsingham chanced to call that day, he was invited to join the conference. On the following day, the Diary entry runs : ' I, Mr. Audrian Gilbert, and John Davies went by appointment to Mr. Secretary to Mr. Beale his house, where only we four were secret, and we made Mr. Secretary privie of the North-West Passage, and all charts and matters were agreed upon in general.'

On 18 February, Sir Francis called again with Edward Dyer, and on 6 March the three promoters went before the officials of the Muscovy Company, George Barn, Wm. Towerson, Mr. Young and Mr. Hudson. The negotiations, however, did not prove successful, and it was not until two years later that Adrian Gilbert secured his patent. Long before that date, Dee had abandoned his geographical activities for others that he believed would bring him more quickly to his goal, the Philosopher's Stone.

In the previous year, Dee had made the acquaintance of a young man, Edward Kelly, who had marked mediumistic powers. Daily crystal-gazing séances were begun, and Dee believed himself to be conversing with angelic spirits. In May 1583, Leicester invited him to meet the Polish Prince Lasky, then on a visit to England. Lasky, like Leicester, was a secret disciple of the Occult, and visited Dee at his house before going on to Oxford. From Oxford Philip Sidney brought Lasky back down the Thames by barge to Mortlake to do Dee honour, and the distinguished visitor remained all night learning of hidden mysteries from the English Philosopher. It is clear that Dee now came to the belief that he and Kelly would find more active support on the Continent, and early in the autumn the two men betook themselves with their wives and families to Trebona. Directly Dee had gone, the mob, who had learned of the nightly conversations with spirits, broke into the house at Mortlake, and wrecked his library and laboratory. Friends saved many of the books, manuscripts and instruments, but the losses were such as could never be made good, and John Davis was the last pilot to be instructed at Dee's hands, that instruction bearing fruit in his *Seaman's Secreates*, published after he had gained the experience of his Arctic Voyages.

One other contribution to geography remains to be recorded.

Walter Raleigh, Gilbert's half-brother, had contrived during this year more than one kindly service to Dee, notably in seeing that the Queen did not forget him.   Raleigh was to have sailed with Gilbert in June, and so he, too, must be accounted among those ' Englishmen beginning a navigation to the shores of Atlantis ' to whom Dee made a gift of a beautifully executed map.

If the actual attainment of the goal is a measure of success, then Dee was a failure, as Hugh Willoughby was a failure, and Humfrey Gilbert.   Nevertheless it was such failures as Gilbert's on the practical side, and such mistakes as Dee's on the theoretical side, that paved the way for the successes and the clearer knowledge of the following decades.   Dee's vehement declaration that, had England been able to furnish a Christian Alexander, she had not lacked a Christian Aristotle, showed a passionate belief in his own powers which we cannot share ; yet his English Euclid and his efforts for the Reformation of the Calendar have won him an honoured place in the History of Mathematics.   So, too, his unceasing efforts for the instruction of mariners, and for the unveiling of the hidden corners of the earth, entitle John Dee to an honoured place in the History of Geography.[1]

[1] Dee's Geographical and Related Works are catalogued separately in Appendix IA.

CHAPTER VIII

PRACTICAL SURVEYING AND NAVIGATION IN THE SIXTEENTH CENTURY

I

THE history of the adaptation of astronomical theories and observations to the practical needs of navigation has been fairly thoroughly explored, and it has been shown by Bensaude [1] and others that the Portuguese seamen of the fifteenth century owed little in this direction to the German humanists, but much to the Jews of the Western Mediterranean. The adaptation, or perhaps more truly the re-adaptation, of geometry to the practice of geodesy and cartography has attracted less attention, but in this case the debt of the surveyor and the cartographer is certainly to Central Europe. In Nuremberg during the last half of the fourteenth century Regiomontanus and his disciples taught, not only the use of the astrolabe and cross-staff for astronomical purposes, but also the use of the cross-staff and the geometrical square for everyday practical measurements ; while during the same period the Nuremberg city craftsmen, famed all over Europe for their beautifully made instruments, excelled themselves in the construction of compasses, designed not for mariners but for travellers by land, who carried road maps. A compass was commonly known, in fact, as *organum viatorum ;* it was combined with a tiny sun-dial, the instrument thus forming a portable timepiece, or *horologium.*

Just at the time when the intellectual and practical activities of Nuremberg were making cartographical survey a possibility, the stimulus to its actual undertaking was supplied by the recovery of Ptolemy's Geography, and by the multiplication of MS. copies of this work between 1409 and 1474. In Book I

[1] Joachim Bensaude, *L'Astronomie Nautique de Portugal.*

the great Alexandrine geographer lays down the fundamental principle of geography, namely, the accurate fixing of position : if possible by latitude and longitude astronomically determined. This new concept of what a map should be made a profound impression, and certainly not later than 1475 the maps accompanying some of the MS. copies of Ptolemy included Tabulæ Novæ drawn on the new principle.

In Italy the method of obtaining detail for such maps was naturally by an adaptation of the mariner's compass, individual positions being fixed by compass-bearing and distance. This is made clear by Niccolo Tartaglia, the Brescian *savant*, in his *Quesiti et Inventioni* (Venice, 1546), a book containing material gathered much earlier than the date of publication. The dedication of this work is to King Henry VIII, and the author says that he recalls how, in discourse with his ' compeer ' Richard Wentworth, he had learned of the English King's interest in military affairs, and since the book was largely concerned with gunnery, addressed it to His Majesty. This Richard Wentworth was a gentleman of Suffolk, who was at the Field of the Cloth of Gold ; he probably died about 1529, since he then no longer appears as a Commissioner of the Peace, and the date of his meeting with Tartaglia is not recorded. In the *Quesiti*, which is cast in dialogue form, he is represented as saying : ' Compare carrissimo, Haria molto accaro che me dechiaristi, come se poteria messere in disegno rettamente un sito ouer un particolar paese, et simelmente la pianta di una citta, la cui practica da Ptolomeo come sapeti nella sua Geographia, è detta Chorographia ? ' Niccolo replies that a compass is employed, and that there are two instruments, one the more convenient, the other more commonly employed. The instruments are reproduced in the accompanying figures (Fig. 9), that with the small inset compass being the usual pattern.[1] The ' more convenient ' type with the large, centrally placed mariner's compass must have been more difficult to construct, as the sight rule and T-square had to be attached to a

---

[1] Actually, as Tartaglia's detailed instructions for making the instrument reveal, the inset is of one of the ' little clocks that are made in Germany', described above, suggesting that a small compass as a separate instrument was not available at this date.

collar which turned about the compass.   The scale graduation
was in divisions of 5°, with in addition the eight points of
the compass.   The method of utilizing the instrument was to
sight on to each landmark and then measure its distance.

It is necessary now to return to events in Nuremberg.   Here,
towards the close of the fifteenth century, a new type of map
had appeared, showing roads marked off in miles, and designed
for use with the compass clock, or *organum viatorum*.   The
earliest extant example is the *Rom-Weg* of Erhard Etzlaub,
himself a compass-maker, which was published in 1492.
Waldseemüller's *Carta Itineraria* of 1511, published at Strassburg, is of the same type.   Both have on the bottom margin
a compass-rose on which the deviation or variation of the
needle is plainly marked, and in the pamphlet printed to
accompany Waldseemüller's map, the traveller is instructed
how to orient it by placing his *horologium* above the printed
rose, and then turning the map until the north-south line upon
it coincided with that indicated by the gnomon of the compass-
clock.   The map then served to give the true direction, as
well as the distance, to any particular city.

To Waldseemüller are also due the famous maps of Lorraine
and the Rhine valley, printed as ' Tabulae Chorographiae '
in the 1513 Strassburg Ptolemy, the accuracy of which [1]
indicates that some method of instrumental survey of distance
and direction was in use.   An instrument which would serve
the purpose is depicted in a woodcut accompanying a tract,
written by Waldseemüller, and painted in the 1512 (Strassburg)
edition of Reisch's *Margarita Philosophica*.   This instrument
was named *Polimetrum*, and as the figure (Fig. 10) shows, was
capable of giving a combined altitude and azimuth.   It was, in
fact, a very early prototype of the theodolite.   It should be recalled, however, that every contemporary academic treatise on
the astrolabe, or on mathematical instruments in general, contained a supplement showing the application of the properties
of a right-angled triangle to the measurement of lengths, heights
and depths, an application familiar also to medieval astronomers.   Such measurements were probably practised by archi-

[1] E. G. R. Taylor, *A Regional Map of the Early Sixteenth Century*.
G.J. May, 1928.

ouer trafguardo, fara girabile, cioe che la fe potra girare per ogni uerfo a torno à torno, & per quelli dui bufettini che faranno in quelle due lamette quadrā gole in alto elleuate, fe potra trafguardar con uno occhio li fegni, & termini che fi uora uedere, come per lauenire p effempio fe moftrara, uero è che in luos co de quelli dui bufettini à mi me piace, et me pare anchora piu fpediête, due

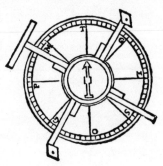

la iftremita del brazzo.c.d.ui fe potra incaffar, & incollar el brozzetto. e f. a fquadro come nella fopra fcritta figura appare. Et dapoi quefto nel Cento di tal dioptra bifogna fa: ui un bu,ettino & con un pironcino di ferro, ouer di ot tone piantare tal dioptra nel centro di tal iftromento, laqualcofa facendo fal iftrometo ftara precife come di fotto appar in figura, et di ouefto uene potreti

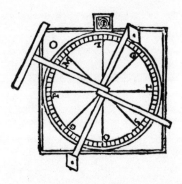

FIG. 9.—SURVEYING INSTRUMENTS, c. 1530
Tartaglia

tects and their usefulness in military operation soon became apparent. It is their employment in cartography that gradually takes shape in the early sixteenth century. The greatest advance was made when Gemma Phrysius, the Flemish mathematician and cosmographer, published the first account of the method of triangulation.

Gemma Phrysius (b. Dec. 1508) issued in 1529 (as already mentioned) the first of the several Antwerp editions of the *Cosmographia* of Petrus Apianus, making his own corrections and additions to this work. In the following year he issued his own *De principio astronomiæ et cosmographiæ*, notable for the description (quoted by Richard Eden) of a method of finding longitudes by carrying a true timepiece from place to place. Bound up with the second, or 1533, Flemish edition of Peter Apian, we find the first edition of a *Libellus*, thus described on the title-page: *Item ejusdem Gemmae Phrysii Libellus de Locorum describendorum ratione, et de eorum distantiis inveniendo, nunquam ante hac visus.* It is in this work that Gemma Phrysius gives details of what he claims to be an entirely new method of surveying a large area, a province, or even a kingdom, without having recourse to a single direct measurement. That it was a novelty is confirmed by the description of a makeshift piece of apparatus to be employed in the survey, while we know that Gemma's nephew, Gualterius Arsenius, was among the first instrument-makers to construct astrolabes with compass inset,[1] specially adapted for plane-table survey. Gemma Phrysius, who was in the first instance a mathematician, always showed a very keen interest in the practical side of geometry, and later devised what was in effect an improved and elaborately graduated cross-staff, to be used for horizontal as well as vertical measurements. This is described in *De Radio Astronomico et Geometrico Liber*, published in 1545. In a later work, *De Astrolabo Catholico Liber*, 1556, completed after his death by his son Cornelius, Gemma's priority of invention of triangulation is referred to, and also the name *epipedometron* which he gave to the apparatus as later improved upon.

The passage in the *Libellus* relative to triangulation is of

[1] R. T. Gunter, *Scottish Geog. Magazine*, Vol. XLIII, p. 135.

sufficient interest to be transcribed in full. The reference is to folios 58 and 59 of the 1533 edition of Peter Apian. ' Primum in assere plano confice instrumentum tale, fiat circulus, qui in quatuor quadrantes dissecetur, quadrante quolibet rursus diviso (ut solet) in 90 gradus, postea affigatur per centrum index cum perspicillis aut pinnulis quemadmodum in dorso astrolabii.' This description of the makeshift instrument— a graduated circle drawn on a flat piece of wood, with a pointer carrying sights or pins, like that on an astrolabe, fixed in the centre—suggests immediately that the author is dealing with something quite new to his readers. He next describes the method of orienting the instrument :

> ' Hoc instrumento facto opus erit etiam instrumento nautico (quod Compassum appellamus) nam ab illo fere tota res pendet, quibus habitis ita procedito. Pone instrumentum planimetrum primum in plano, et super ipsum Compassum, ita ut latus Compassi quadrangularis adjacet lineae meridinae instrumenti inferioris. Deinde verte instrumentum cum compasso eo usque quo index compassi correspondeat sibi sub-scripto indici, et post haec instrumento ita manente, compassum tanquam perfunctum suo officio remove.'

Gemma rightly remarks that it is on this part of the operation that the whole success of the method depends. The plani-metrum is to be placed flat, and the ' nautical instrument which we call a compass ' placed upon it so that the edge of the compass-box lies along the zero, or north-south, line of the graduated circle. Instrument and compass must then be turned together until the compass-needle lies in the *magnetic* north as engraved upon the compass-rose. The last point is not made clear in the passage quoted, but is dealt with in the *Cosmographia* of Peter Apian to which the *Libellus* is attached : the relevant section is that describing how to fix a meridian line. The woodcut accompanying the text, which appeared in the first (1524) and each subsequent edition, shows the compass-needle lying about 8° east of north, roughly the variation at Ingolstadt in the early sixteenth century. A mariner's compass is not depicted, but an ' organum viatorum ' or ' travellers' companion, commonly called a compass ', that is to say the instrument already described. The researches of A. Wolkenhauer and L. Bauer have shown that such

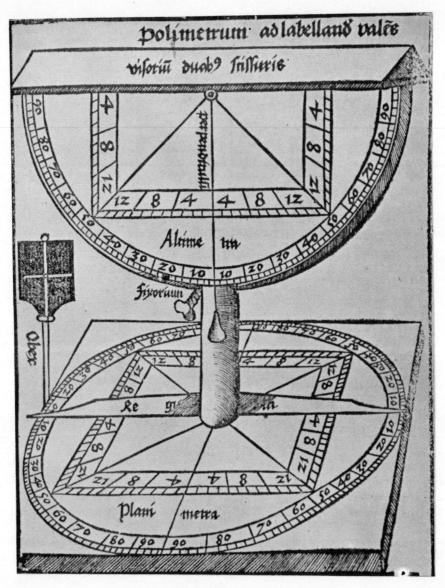

FIG. 10.—WALDSEEMÜLLER'S POLIMETRUM

' compass-clocks ' must date back at least to the first half of the fifteenth century, for an elaborate example is extant, with the declination engraved on the metal compass-dial, which is dated 1451.

Once the planimetrum is oriented, Gemma Phrysius tells us, it must be kept in the same position, when the compass can be dispensed with. The name ' planimetrum ' which he coins for his new piece of apparatus is replaced by the Greek form ' epipedometron ' in later editions of the *Libellus*. The next passage shows how the angle of position of any point with relation to the north-south line can be found by means of the movable pointer :

' Si nunc angulum positionis alterius loci a tuo scire velis, manente instrumento immoto, volve indicem donec per perspicilla ejus videas locum alium, videbis mox angulum positionis a meridie vel Septentrione secundum ipsius indicis remotionem ab eis. Sed quorsum haec ? roget aliquis, etiam si habeam ab uno loco positiones vel situs omnium locorum, si non adsit distantia nota, nihil profuerit. Verum dicis ab uno loco, nam nisi a duobus locis habeas angulos positionum, non poteris describere tertium.'

What is the use, here says an imaginary critic, of a bearing without a distance ? True, there must be bearings from two points, before the position of a third can be fixed.

The practical application of the method to the mapping of a whole province is next described : a beginning can be made at any selected town, and the bearings found must be plotted on a sheet of paper. Any point on this paper is selected to represent the place of observation, and with this point as centre a circle must be drawn, graduated like that on the planimetrum. The correct name must be assigned to each ray when drawn :

' Igitur si nunc provinciam totam depingere placet, investiga primum ab uno oppido, a quo placet incipere, omnium circumjacentium locorum situs : eosque trahe in plano descripto primum circulo ex uno puncto posito ad libitum, eoque diviso in 360 gradus ut est ipsum instrumentum planimetrum, et cuique lineae positionis adsigna suum nomen.'

The surveyor is advised that he can save himself much journeying if he chooses the highest tower in the town for making his observations ; then he must go elsewhere and repeat the process : ' Ut autem evites multam peregrinationes, ascende turrim oppidi altissimam, atque inde quasi e specula circumspice. Post haec proficiscere ad aliud oppidum, atque ibi similiter agito cum angulis positionum omnium circumjacentium locorum.' The directions that follow are important, and may be rendered as follows :

' When you have found them (i.e. the second set of bearings) make a dot for this (second) town at any distance you please from the first, provided it is on the right ray, and with this point as centre draw a faint circle, and through it a meridian parallel to the first (i.e. to the meridian passing through the first town). Next draw from this point lines representing the bearings just found, and wherever a pair of rays drawn to the same place intersect, a little dot must be placed, which represents its position.'

The same directions must be followed until all required places are on the map. The original passage runs :

' Quos ubi habueris, pone punctum istius oppidi a priori puncto in quacunque velis distantia, super tamen sua linea positionis, atque ex hoc puncto trahe circulum obscurum et meridianum distantem a priori meridiano undique aequaliter. Demum trahe ex hoc puncto lineas positionum locorum jam inventas, et ubi tunc sit intersectio lineæ alicujus cum priorbus ejusdem loci, ibi notula ponenda est pro tali loco. Haud dissimili ratione ages cum omnibus locis alicujus regni, proficiscendo eo usque donec omnia quae describere decrevisti, bis in tuum conspectum venerint, atque omnium duas lineas habeas positionum.'

An actual detailed example is then given, accompanied by the woodcut which was reproduced by de Rojas in his work of 1550 and 1551.

' Exempli causa, describamus aliquot loca Brabantiae, atque id quo facilius fiat, ascendo turrim Antverpiae cum instrumentis, pono instrumentum secundum plagas mundi, et video circumquaque quaecunque possum loca. Reperio autem Gandavum tendere ab Arctis 40 gradibus quasi in occidens, Liram ab ortu 30 gradibus in austrum declinare, Mechliniam 8 quasi gradibus ab austro in occasum, Lovanium 4 ab austro ad ortum, Bruxellas 25 ab austro in occasum, Mittelburgum 30 ab occasu ad Arctos, Bergas 20 ab Arctis in occasum. Sintque haec loca satis pro exemplo, his habitis pono punctum in medio plani alicujus quod locum Antverpiae significet, hinc duco circulum, quem divido in 4, adscriptis 4 plagis mundi, Oriens, Occidens, Meridies, Septentrio. Quadrantem deinde quemlibet divido in 90 partes, aut saltem semicirculum in 180 gradus, post haec ex puncto duco cuique locorum praedictorum lineam per suos gradus, et relinquo ita cartam imperfectam cum lineis tantum. Et mecum instrumentis confero Bruxellas, ubi iterum omnium quem visu adsequi possum locorum lineas positionis quero. Invenio Lovanium etc. . . . Necque volo quod quisque putet me hic veras lineas positionum assignare esed tantum pro declaration, comminisci. Inventis igitur hoc modo lineis positionum quero in carta incepta lineam Bruxellae, in qua pono punctum distans ab Antverpia quantum mihi placet, ex hoc iterum puncto duco circulum, quem seco primum per meridianum distantem a Meridiano Antverpiensi ut solent parallelae lineae, simili modo divido eum in 360 gradus, adscriptis quattuor plagis mundi ut jam ante cum Antverpia egi. Demum ex centro quod jam Bruxellam significat duco lineas positionum locorum prescriptorum adjuciendo regulam centro et gradibus inventis. Ubi igitur nunc fit intersectio lineae Lovanii cum priori quae ex Antverpiae ducitur, ibi est locus Lovanii. Atque haud aliter invenies omnium locorum punta.'

The difficulty that two rays may meet in a straight line is anticipated ; it must be solved by taking a third bearing. Physical features, details of rivers and coasts, and so forth, can be mapped in the same way :

' Si vero contingat (ut nonnunquam usu venit) quod utraque locus quispiam venerit in medio inter duo loca principalia sive primum nota, tunc necesse est tertia vice hunc locum ex transverso aspicere. Atque hoc modo non opus erit omnia provinciae describendae loca peragrare, sed tantum videre : [fluviorum] vero et [littorum] facile descriptis oppidis [et vicis] secundum suas hinc distantias, ortus et exitus habentur.' [1]

Gemma Phrysius goes on to point out that the value of his method lies in its elimination of measurements of distances. These, he notes, were very inaccurate, owing to the turns and windings of the roads along which they were measured, and also to the unequal spacing of the milestones. He promises, however, to describe later a method of distance measurement.

' Haec igitur descriptio et facilis est et altero modo qui per distantias operatur, certior ; nam illae distantiae fere incertae sunt, cum ob viarum atque itinerum flexionem et ambitum, tum ob miliariorum inaequalitatem : quem tamen modum paulo post describemus et facilem etiam reddemus.'

Meanwhile, since it may be necessary to ascertain distances from the map made by triangulation, a scale can be added by the following means : the actual distance between any one

[1] The words in brackets are not found in the first edition.

pair of towns (Antwerp and Mechlin in the example given) is ascertained ; then the distance in miles between these towns is equated to the distance as measured on the map, and a scale drawn out.

'Nunc autem si post descriptam hac ratione cartam placet incertas dimetiri distantiis (quod tamen mirum videri possit quum hic nulla distantiae habita sit ratio) inquire aliquorum duorum locorum distantiam, aut per profectionem, aut certius per modum quem postea docebimus. Ut verbi gratia video inter Antverpiam et Mechliniam 4 esse milliaria parva. Quare spacium inter Antverpiam et Mechliniam in carta divido per 4. Et per has divisiones potes dimetiri omnia loca in carta descripta.'

The promised simple method of determining the distance between two places is by similar triangles. A large open space must be chosen, where two rods, a and b, are set up, about 200 feet apart, so as to be in a straight line with the distant spot, c. A third rod, d, is set up, distant about 50 feet from b, and such that bd is perpendicular to ab. Then a fourth point, e, is found behind d, such that e, d, and c are in a straight line, and ea is at right angles to ab. The difference in measurement between ea and cb is in the same proportion to ab as the distance between e and a is to the distance between a and d. Gemma says that since the proof of the method requires mathematics (and so will not be followed by the reader) he will not give it.

Subsequently to the publication of this *Libellus* of Gemma Phrysius, triangulation must have come into rapid and general use, for during the latter half of the sixteenth century instruments for the purpose were numerous and elaborate. An account of the most important of these is to be found in Laussedat's *Recherches sur les Instruments, les Méthodes et le Dessin Topographiques*. Particular mention may be made of the *Geographical Hemisphere* of Orontius Finaeus, which is pictured in Gallucci's *Della fabrica et uso de diverse stromenti*, published in 1597.

II

The grave difficulty remained that the average surveyor had not at command even the simple knowledge of mathematics that was demanded for the use of these various geometrical instruments. It was to meet the needs of those who could only work by rule of thumb that the plane-table and sight-rule came into use, and the first stage in their development is represented by the Holometer of Abel Foullon, which therefore deserves examination. Foullon published an account of his instrument in Paris in 1551,[1] and since he added the name and address of the instrument maker from whom it could be obtained, it is clear that it did not exist merely on paper.[2]

Foullon's book enjoyed a wide circulation, being translated into Italian and Latin. From the Royal Privilege attached to it, and from the preface, something can be gathered as to the author himself. He was ' varlet de chambre ' to the French King Henri II, and had devised certain improvements in printing, while he had begun the translation of Vitruvius' *De Architectura* into the vernacular, taking great pains to render the technical terms into those used by builders and masons. Of the fruits of this labour he had, however, been robbed by one in whom he had placed too great confidence.[3]

The monumental work of Vitruvius, written in the last quarter of the first century B.C., was first printed in Venice in 1511, and was, as the numerous references to it prove, accepted as the standard work on the subject during the sixteenth century. It dealt with the theory and also the practice of architecture, and the clumsiness of the ancient Roman levelling and other instruments depicted in the printed illustrations (including the *dioptra*) is doubtless due to the poor draughtsmanship of the Renaissance blockmaker, and not to defects in the instruments of the classical period themselves.

In addition to his study of Vitruvius, Foullon acknowledged a debt to his mathematical teacher, and to another patron, M. de Saint-Gelays, who devised a suitable name (*L'Holometre*) for the instrument of his invention. The various parts of this

[1] Abel Foullon, *L'Holometre.* Paris, 1551.

[2] It should be noticed that Foullon's work appeared in the year following the publication of *de Rojas'* popular treatise *De Astrolabio*, which sets out Gemma Phrysius' method in full, with his example of a triangulation in Flanders, but the original tract had been published in the French version of Apian of 1544.

[3] Philander's French version of Vitruvius appeared in 1546.

Holometer, somewhat obscured in Fig. 11 by the bad perspective, are also set out separately by the author. The first part to be prepared is the table, which has a small compass inset in the centre, and the four quarters of the horizon marked upon it. Along one edge of the table is a ruler divided into 1,000 equal parts, which may be used to represent 1,000 paces, 1,000 toises, or whatever unit the surveyor is working upon. Pivoted on this fixed ruler at either end are the right- and left-hand rulers (*verges*), similarly divided, of which the right is fixed, while the left is made to slide along the base rule to any desired point on the scale. Each of these side rules is furnished with a semicircle mounted on a vertical rod, the semicircle carrying sights, and a plumb-line (*recteur*). These attachments can be used for horizontal sighting, or for reading heights or depths, since the semicircles are pivoted on the supports. The table is mounted on a pedestal by means of a ball and socket device, which allows it to be turned horizontally, and then clamped with a screw.

The instrument, as its name implies, was adapted for every type of measurement, but it is with its use in surveying that the present article is concerned. The relevant section will therefore be quoted in full : [1]

' Estant le mesurer au mylieu d'une compaigne, environne de clochers, ou de plusiers autres choses, desquelles il veut sçavoir promptement la distance : c'est a sçavoir, depuis le lieu ou il est, jusques a chacune desdittes choses : il doibt besogner en ceste maniere.

' Premieurement, il couvira la Table de son Holometre d'un feuillet de pappier : le quel feuillet, il attachera avecques cire ou autremet, et le mettra entre laditte Table et les Verges, pour manier aisément les dittes Verges par dessus. Et sera ledit feullit, percé a l'endroit de l'aiguille, pour s'en aider quant il sera besoing.

' Puis apres avoir recongnu quelque marque, pour servir de seconde Veüe, et addressé la Base vers icelle, le meseurer retira la Verge qui luy aura servy a dresser la Base, et par le Recteur d'icel le (*sic*) Verge verra l'une des choses, qui sont autour de luy ; puis fera dessus le feuillet, un petit traict avecques une pointe desplinge le long de laditte Verge, pour remarquer par le traict, la ligne directe qui tire devers laditte chose. Apres sans remuer, ny aucunement varier l'instrument, il dressera la mesme Verge par le moyen du Recteur, vers un autre clocher ou chose

---

[1] The transcription follows the original exactly without correction of what appear to be errors.

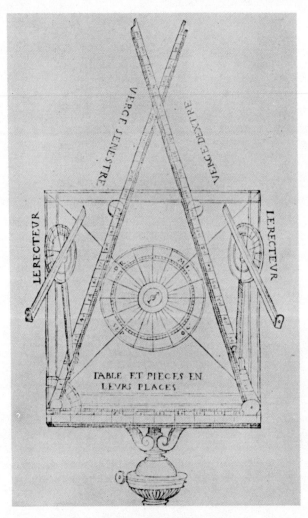

Fig. 11.—ABEL FOULLON'S HOLOMETRE

éloignée, et remarquera laditte chose, d'un autre traict dessus le feuillet mesme, et continuera, de ceste façon, regardant d'ordre toutes les choses qu'il veut mesurer l'une, apres l'autre, et remarquent sus ledit feuillet chacune d'icelles, avec un petit traict.

' Reste maintenant a transporter l'Holometre, sus la marque de seconde Veüe, et remettre par le jugemêt de l'aiguille, ainsi qu'il estoit auparavât. Puis d'approcher le neu de le Verge qui n'a point servy, si pres de l'autre, qu'il n'y ait nom plus de degrez entre les Verges, qu'il y a de pas, ou de piedz, entre les dittes Veües.

' Cela fait, il faut revoir d'ordre par le Recteur de laditte Verge qui n'a point servy, toutes les choses qui ont esté remarquées par traictz, dessus le feillit : car remettant l'ordre la premiere Verge sus chacun traict, et revoiant les choses eloignees, l'une apres l'autre, par le Recteur de la derniere Verge (j'appelle derniere, celle qui n'a point serve) l'endroit ou la premiere Verge est coupée par la derniere, môstre de traict en traict, la distance, qui est entre le premiere Veüe, et chacune desdittes choses.'

An actual example follows, of which it is sufficient to give the illustration of the measured base and sighting points shown in Fig. 12.

Now it is clear that fitting a sheet of paper to a table encumbered with fixed rules and inset compass was a clumsy and difficult business, and the substitution of a ' plain ' table (for such seems to have been the original name) and a movable sight-rule would suggest itself to a practical man : Foullon's great step in advance was to adopt direct drawing on the table in the field. That the obvious improvement of his method was soon made can be gathered from the reminiscences of the famous English surveyor Ralph Agas. Writing in 1596,[1] he says that at the beginning of his career, thirty years earlier, i.e. in 1566, he used the ' plain ' table, ' sometimes directed by needles, sometimes by the former station (i.e. a back sight) as is now used ', so that it was then clearly no novelty. Five years later, i.e. in 1571, having considered the defects of the plane-table, Agas abandoned it completely for the ' Theodelite ': the coincidence may be noted that 1571 was the year of publication of Digges' *Pantometria*, containing the descriptions of the instrument called ' Theodelitus ', and the ' Topographical Instrument ', the latter of which (derived from Waldseemüller's

[1] R. Agas, *A Preparative to the Platting of Lands.* London, 1596.

Polimetrum) [1] was the instrument used by Agas under the name Theodelite.

For the use of Foullon's combined 'Verge' and 'Recteur' as the earliest sight-rule the evidence is not very direct, but seems quite conclusive. Thomas Digges published a new edition of the *Pantometria* in 1591, and in it referred to the use of the plane-table (which he deprecated) by such as had no knowledge of arithmetic. In this connection he writes: 'Some take the semicircle of my Topographical Instrument, setting the perpendicular thereof upon a straight long Ruler divided into a thousand or more equal parts '—a sufficiently clear description of Foullon's sight-rule detached from the table.

Well before the end of the century a sight-rule approximating to the modern pattern had already been devised, of which Cyprian Lucar writes in 1590 as follows: [2]

'Although you may set on every of the said rulers two clipping sights perpendicularly reared, yet I think it better in the place of the said sights to make in every of the said rulers from one of their ends to the other, a right, narrow and shallow groove or channel covered over with a thin piece of wood, so as you may look through it at any mark within a convenient distance.'

A normal surveyor's outfit, as depicted in *Lucar Solace*, is seen in Fig. 13. The substitution of a drum for a plane-table is a reminder that it was the usefulness of rapid surveying for military purposes that led to the comparatively rapid advances in cartography in the sixteenth century. The pronged foot by which the plane-table was supported was an improvement on the clumsy pedestal of the holometer, but the much more practical tripod appeared before the end of the century, being described by Philip Danfrie, the well-known French instrument maker, in 1597. This, however, is much later than the period under review and we may turn back again to the date associated with the appearance of the 'Theodelite' (as it was then spelled).

[1] E. G. R. Taylor, *A Regional Map*, etc. G.J., Vol. LXXI, 1928.
[2] Cyprian Lucar, *Lucar Solace*. London, 1590. Cf. also the MS. book of Political Surveying by the noted teacher John Godwyn, who was working towards the end of the century. Sloane MSS., No. 838.

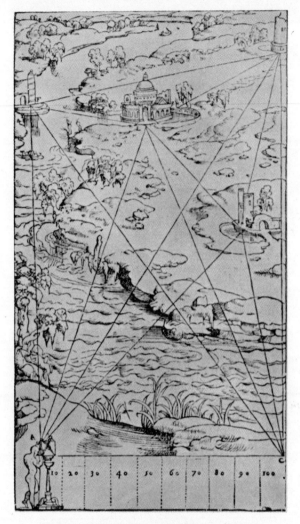

FIG. 12.—TRIANGULATION BY THE HOLOMETRE
From the original woodcut

III

Four years before the publication of the *Pantometria*, William Bourne had just issued his first attempt at Popular Science, for such seems the most just description of all his writings. This singular man, who was about the same age as John Dee and the younger Digges, was a native of Gravesend, where he spent his whole life. He was at one time an inn-keeper ; he also served as a gunner (probably on the bulwarks at Tilbury), and as port-reeve he was a man of some note among the townsfolk of Gravesend. Beyond all this, he was a keen reader (a student of the Mathematics, as he describes himself) and an intensely practical man ; whatever he read, he wished to see translated into terms of use, and this translation was the task he undertook. All his books show clearly their derivation from contemporary writings by continental authors, but Bourne was in no sense a plagiarist. His situation at Gravesend (when as a young man he must have seen, for example, the send-off of the *Searchthrift* in 1556) determined that he should address his writings especially to seamen and explorers, while his experience as a gunner led him also to undertake the discussion of military problems. His self-appointed task was to bridge the very patent gap between the theoretical treatise and the actual shipmaster, pilot, shipwright or master-gunner with whom he was in daily contact.

Copies of William Bourne's first printed work are no longer in existence, and indeed, according to his own reference to it, it was no longer to be had in 1578. The title, *An Almanack and Prognostication for iii yeres, with serten Rules of Navigation*, 1567, suggests the influence alike of Leonard Digges' ' Prognostications ' and of Eden's Translation of Cortes made in 1561, and that the booklet found a ready sale is suggested by the issue of a second edition carrying the Almanack and Prognostications through the years 1571–2–3, when the original Almanack was out of date. Of much greater importance, however, was a work that Bourne had prepared in manuscript apparently in the same year. The first part was a treatise on gunnery and range-finding, based obviously on the first section of Tartaglia's *Quesiti et Inventioni* : the second part dealt

with the measurements of heights and breadths by the ' backside of the astrolabe ' and by the cross-staff, and with survey
by triangulation almost exactly as set forth by Gemma Phrysius, together with further instruction on maps based on
Apian's *Cosmographia* : the third part dealt with the measurement of solid bodies, and here the author refers to ' Mr. Digs '
treatise on the same subject, called *Tectonicon*, noting that his
own work includes matter not found in the earlier publication. This manuscript was dedicated and presented to Lord
Burghley, who was sufficiently interested in it to have some
speech with the author, and to question him especially on his
practical rules for mensuration relevant to shipbuilding.

The surveying instrument (Fig. 14) proposed by Bourne in
the section on triangulation is an improvement on those of
Gemma Phrysius and Tartaglia, and is less clumsy than the
astrolabe with inset compass, held in a horizontal position,
which it probably superseded. It is not an original invention,
having already been described by Cuningham (also without
claim to originality) in his *Cosmographical Glasse* (1559), and
a similarity of phraseology suggests that Bourne had either
used Cuningham, or that their descriptions had a common
source. The essential feature was a circular brass plate,
graduated round the edge in degrees, and having the 32 points
of the compass-rose radiating from the centre. An excentric-
ally inset compass-needle (like that on a dial or compass-clock)
and an ' athelidey ' (alidade) like that of an astrolabe, completed the instrument. There is no mention in the MS. of a
plane-table, or of any tripod or other support for the instrument, which Bourne placed (according to his MS.) on the stump
of a tree or any convenient flat object.

Confusion has been introduced into the history of surveying
instruments by the nomenclature adopted by Thomas Digges
in his posthumous edition of his father's *Pantometria*. The
instrument to which he gives the name ' theodelitus ' is simply
a variant of that described by Cuningham and Bourne (the
latter suggests the name ' horizontall sphere ' for it) : on the
other hand, Digges gives the name ' topographicall instrument '
to what surveyors already knew as the ' theodelite '. This is
quite clear from Rathborne's volume *The Surveyor* of 1616,

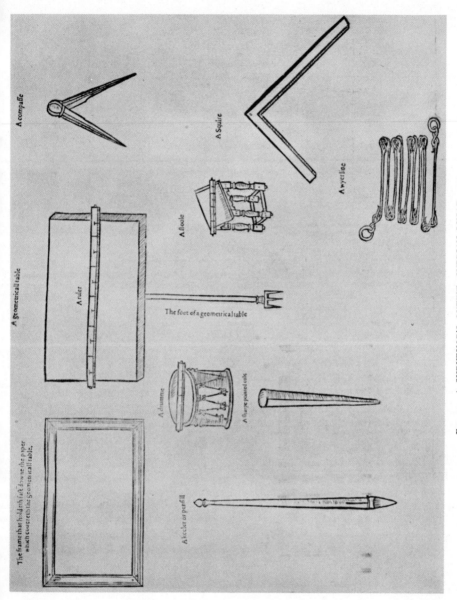

A compasse

A Squire

A wyerline

A floole

A geometricall table

A ruler

The foot of a geometrical table

A lumme

A large poined rule

The frame that holdeth fast downe the paper
whan it coucreth the geometricall table.

A ticker or penfill

Fig. 13.—A SURVEYOR'S OUTFIT, CYPRIAN LUCAR, 1590

where the author, after giving a brief account of the latter instrument, says that it is described in detail in *Pantometria*. The vignettes in the engraved frontispiece of Rathborne's work (*see* Frontispiece) show the theodelite (as it was still spelled) and the plane-table in use, substantially as they had been for some sixty years.

The importance of Bourne's Manuscript of 1571 lies in the fact that it gives an actual example of a triangulation carried out by means of his simply designed instrument, with the result shown in Fig. 15. The scale of the original is 1/52,800, and the degree of accuracy shows that it was an actual piece of work, and not a mere diagram. Bourne goes on to explain how to add topographical detail, such as rivers and hills, and again gives an actual example : a survey map of the Thames from Northfleet to the Nore, including the Medway up to Rochester. In this case the surveyor took a boat down mid-stream, having as his sole instrument a mariner's compass. With the compass he took the direction of each reach of the river, and fixed his position at the end of the reach by taking the bearings of two objects already fixed by the triangulation of the area. While Bourne was content to pace his base line, in order to fix his scale, it would seem that the surveyor's chain, the ' wyer line ' described and pictured by Cyprian Lucar in 1590, was already in use among professional cartographical sur-veyors. The evidence is found in a MS. map of Ireland by Lawrence Nowell, Dean of Lichfield, dated either 1563 or 1565 (the date is not easily legible), for the artist who fair-copied the map has shown the Dean with a bundled-up chain at his feet. It will be recalled that it was Lawrence Nowell who in 1563 first proposed to Burghley making maps of the English counties,[1] a work later executed by Christopher Saxton, but financed by Thomas Seckford, the friend of Lawrence Nowell and of his brother Robert, the lawyer.

Robert Lythe's great map of Ireland, completed in 1570–1, measured 8½ feet by 5½ feet, and in writing to Burghley on the subject [2] the surveyor states that he first made a perambula-tion of the coast (although he was obliged to omit the north-

[1] Lansdown MSS., Vol. 6, Art. 54.
[2] Lansdown MSS., Vol. 22, Art. 72.

west) and then filled in detail of the interior. Like Saxton he
made use of local guides to show him boundaries and view-
points, while he was at great expense for the hire of horses (he
wore out several), and of boats from which to view the coast.
Unfortunately he says nothing as to the instruments that he
employed, but the evidence of William Bourne and Ralph
Agas is sufficient to show that instrumental methods would be
used. Bourne has also some notes on the addition of lines of
latitude and longitude to a survey. The latitude could be
directly observed by a quadrant or astrolabe as at sea, but he
considered that in the absence of any simple astronomical
method of fixing longitude, it was necessary to consult tables
of positions already computed by astronomers. It appears
from Bourne's description (borrowed directly from Apianus)
that it was considered sufficient to have a single point on the
map of which the latitude and longitude was known, and to
mark the rest of the network by calculation, assuming a degree
of 60 miles. Both meridians and parallels were assumed to be
straight lines (the former converging) although they were not
necessarily drawn across the map. Such a method of procedure
helps, perhaps, to explain why it was so long before the grave
error in the measurement of the degree remained unrectified.

Bourne, in his prefaces to the various sections of his MS.,
declares himself neither learned nor receiving any help from
the learned, and complains that many have shown displeasure
at his boldness in publishing the *Rules of Navigation*. Nevertheless, within three years of the presentation to Burghley of
the MS. work described, there appeared a much more comprehensive work on Navigation from Bourne's pen entitled *A
Regiment for the Sea*. It was published in 1573, when the second
edition of the ' Almanack ' had become out of date. By this
time Bourne had read and, as he himself makes plain, been
influenced by, not only the *Arte of Navigation*, but the
Tectonicon, Pantometria, and above all John Dee's famous
Mathematicall Preface to the English translation of Euclid's
Elements, published in 1570.

The full title of Bourne's work is *A Regiment for the Sea* ;
*Conteyning most profitable Rules, Mathematical experiences, and
perfect knowledge of Navigation, for all Coastes and Countreys* ;

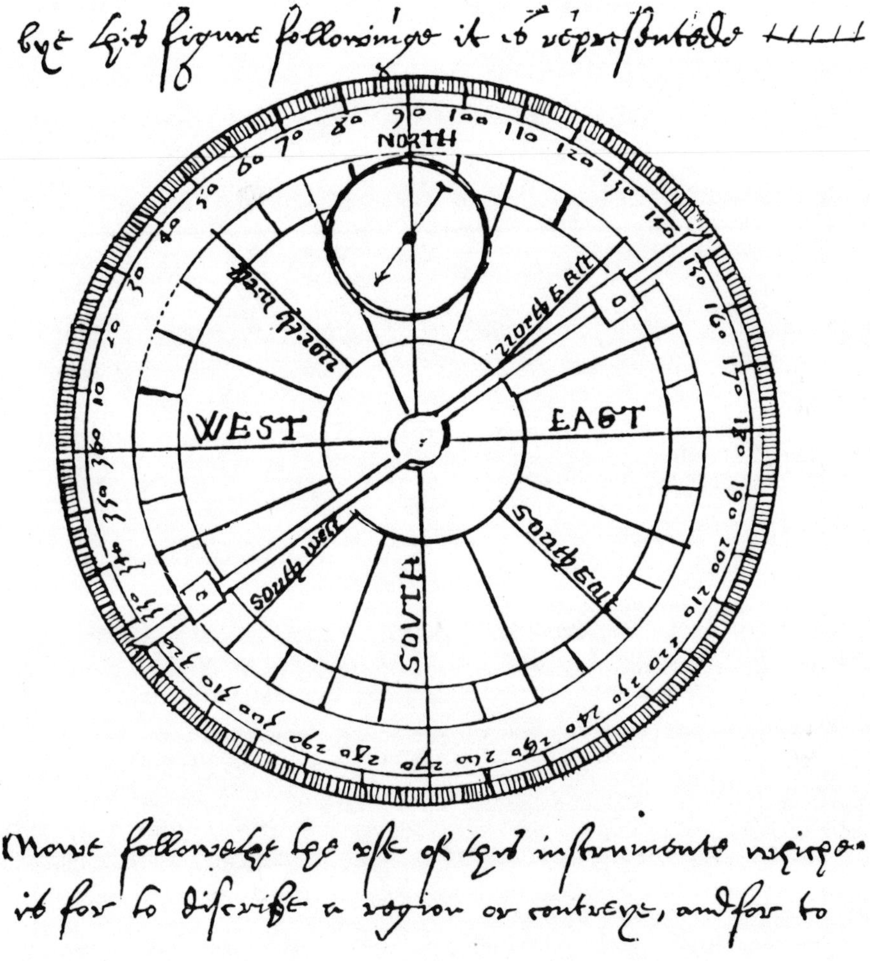

byt ƈʒtʒ ſigure followingꝰ it ꝭ repꝛſentede ┼┼┼┼

FIG. 14.—WILLIAM BOURNE'S SURVEYING INSTRUMENT
MS. Brit. Mus.

most needful and necessary for all seafaryng Men and Travellers,
as Pilots, Mariners, Merchants, etc., exactly derived and made by
William Bourne. The Dedication is to the Earl of Lincoln,
Captain-General of the Royal Navy, and in it the author says :
' It came into my remembrance how necessary a thyng it was
for seafaring men to have some good instructions : whereof I
have written this base and simple Regiment for the Sea, and
Rules of Navigation.' The Preface to the Reader is again
marked by the diffidence of a writer who knows that he is
encroaching on the field of ' learned men ', but according to one
of the versifiers, whose weak but commendatory rhymes
addressed to the author prefix the text,

> ' Thou hast beside all this the Truth
> By *practice* truly tride,'

and that Bourne is giving the fruits of experience is borne out
incidentally in the text over and over again. According to the
same Preface, the book contains ' necessary things meete to be
known in Navigation, and not mentioned in the booke of
Martin Curtise (*sic*), called the Art of Navigation '. There is,
for example, a simple table of the Declination of the Sun,
with directions for its use in finding the latitude, whereas
Cortes gives the successive positions of the Sun in the Signs
of the Zodiac, with a second table of declinations of the Signs,
which demands much more complicated calculations. Bourne
is especially careful in dealing with the taking of position in the
southern hemisphere, since he has known sailors who, having
lost their familiar stars and marks, have beaten up and down
by ' Ginnie and Bynney ' unable to proceed.

His discussion of the variation of the compass is of the
greatest interest. He repeats Cortes' warning ' not to meddle
with the mending of the compass, or whettynge of the side of
the needle to make it stand due north ', and then goes on to the
vexed question of proportional variation and its relation to
longitude. Here he very sensibly says :

> ' No Maister or Pilot of a shippe doth keepe so simple account of
> the shippes way, but that he may know what distance he hath into any
> place, better than he shal know by the varying of the compass ; also
> whether it be or not, that the compass doth keepe any such proportion

in the variation, I do refer that unto them that have tried the experience thereof : for I for my part can say nothing in that matter.'

He inclines to the opinion that the variation of the compass depends in part upon the meridian upon which it was ' touched ' by the lodestone, but admits that he has inquired of those who had been to America (i.e. with Hawkins or Drake) as to how needles stand that are made over there, and none can inform him.

In repeating Cortes' directions for making an Equinoctial Dial (a sun-dial which could be adjusted for any latitude), he remarks that he knows only one master who possesses such an instrument, and that even he has obtained it merely to brag of it, and not for use. Indeed, he says, masters commonly possess instruments which they are incapable of using. An instrument similar to that which Bourne describes was the *Horologium Universale* made by H. Cole for Frobisher's expedition of 1576, together with a *Holometrum Geometricum*, which suggests Foullon's Holometer, a *Compassum Meridianum* for determining the variation, a *Balestilha*, an Astronomer's Ring, and an Astrolabe.

The success of the *Regiment* (there were, in all, three authorized editions, and one unauthorized) probably encouraged Bourne to put his further ideas into print, for in 1578 he issued his three remaining books, *A Treasure for Travellers*, *Inventions & Devices*, and *The Arte of Shootyng in Great Ordnance*, the substance of which was in MS. before 1571.

The first and the third of these are simply taken, with some additional matter, from the three sections of the MS. of 1571 : thus it was in the *Treasure for Travellers* that the account of triangulation, with a wood-cut of the instruments and of the specimen map, first appeared in print ; unfortunately the section of the MS. on mapping a river (as an example of incidental topographical detail) was omitted. The fourth section of the ' Treasure ' deals with the origin of certain land forms—cliffs, islands, marshes and so on—and Bourne expresses the view that off-shore islands originally formed part of the main-land from which they have been separated by erosion.[1]

---

[1] It was this view, quite correct in principle, which led cosmographers to the conclusion that the discovery of, e.g., the Solomon Islands pointed to the neighbourhood of a continent—Terra Australis.

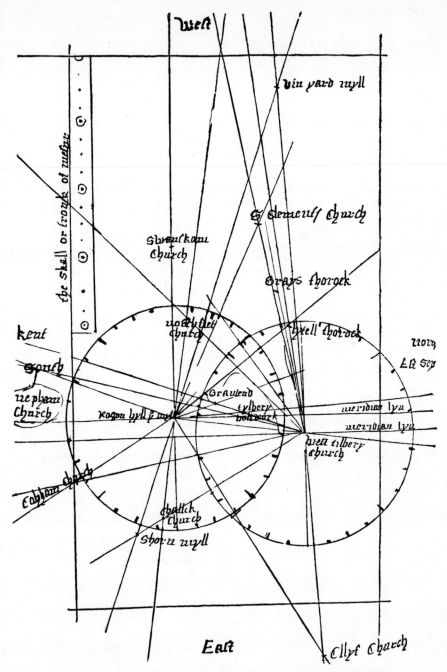

FIG. 15.—BOURNE'S TRIANGULATION ROUND GRAVESEND AND TILBURY
MS. Brit. Mus.

At some time in 1578, Lord Burghley addressed some further queries to Bourne, who prepared for him a manuscript pamphlet on *Glasses for Optical Purposes*,[1] in which he again shows his familiarity with the work of Dee and of Digges, who had both apparently made experiments with lenses and looking-glasses for viewing clearly effects at a distance.

One of the most important of the ' Inventions and Devices ' described by Bourne in the work bearing that title is the apparatus for measuring the ' way or going of a ship ', which is said to have been made by Humphrey Cole, best known and most versatile of contemporary English scientific instrument makers. Cole, however, was not the originator of this device ; it is one of the many depicted by the inventor, Jacques Besson, ' Master of the Engines to the French King ', in his *Théâtre des Instruments*. Attention was drawn to it by Richard Eden,[2] who had met Besson while he was on the Continent (1563–72). The French inventor confessed that he left to practical men, familiar with the sea the task of working out the details of the cogs and dials described, which were to make the instrument register in miles the distance covered.

It is worth noting that another book of Besson's, *Le Cosmolabe* (1567), dealing with the construction of a ' universal ' measuring instrument, throws some light on the practical details of contemporary map-survey. He gives, as the essential equipment of the Cosmographer, a compass, a large jointed ruler called a ' sauterelle ' for measuring the turns of the road, and a device for registering distance. For the latter he recommends a mule litter, with a single large wheel, geared by cogwheels to a dial, so that the surveyor, sitting within it, reads off the distances, and transfers them to his parchment as he travels.

It is from the second (authorized) edition of William Bourne's *Regiment of the Sea* that we learn that he came into personal contact with John Dee, visiting the ' great learned man ', at his house at Mortlake. The talk was on a favourite theme of both—the voyage to Cathay—and to confirm his arguments Dee showed his visitor this and that written in a book, a book which, as the context reveals, was none other than the *Travels*

[1] Printed by Halliwell in his *Rara Mathematica*.
[2] In the Preface to his translation of Taisnier.

of Marco Polo. It was for this same edition of the *Regiment* that Bourne wrote his *Hydrographical Discourse of the Five Ways to Cathay*,[1] the date of which is probably 1579 or 1580, i.e. before Drake's return from his World Voyage. Much new material is also embodied in the text of the *Regiment* itself (besides a revision of the declinations), and one new passage runs: ' There is devised by one Norman a compasse-maker, a very necessary device in the compasse, that you may set the north point, upon what degree you list, according to the true variation of the compasse.' This instrument is described by Robert Norman in his book *The Newe Attractive*, published in 1581, which has already been mentioned.

That Bourne's work was taken seriously by his contemporaries, we learn from the reference to his method of topographical survey, side by side with that of Digges, in Blagrave's *Familiar Staff* (1590), in Blundeville's *Exercises*, a compendium of information for ' young gentlemen ' published in 1594, and in Rathborne's *Surveyor*. Much more interesting is the apparent direct influence of the relevant section of *A Treasure for Travellers* on the instructions issued by William Borough, on behalf of the Muscovy Company, for the later voyages in search of the North-East Passage—a point touched upon already in dealing with the preparations made for the Pet and Jackman voyage.

Both William Borough and William Bourne deserve more detailed study and appreciation than they have hitherto received, for in working for the advance of Navigation, Charting and Surveying they had tough material to deal with. As Bourne himself wrote :

' I have known within this 20 yeres that them that wer auncient masters of shippes hath derided and mocked them that have occupied their Cardes and Plattes, and also the observation of the Altitude of the Pole, saying : that they care not for their sheepes skinnes, for hee could keepe a beter account upon a boord. And when they dyd take the Latitude they would call them starre shooters and sun shooters, and would aske if they had striken it.'

The years following Bourne's death, which took place near

---

[1] A Castilian translation of this tract was appended to his *Hidro-grafia* of 1584, by Andres de Poza (Navarrete).

the closing date of the period of Dee's work and influence, were years in which practical mathematics, especially in its relation to cosmography and kindred subjects, found many English exponents, and original treatises began to be multiplied. William Bourne afforded an example to his contemporaries of learning outside the lettered world of the Universities, and he and his like were given their due by Sir Philip Sydney's friend, Gabriel Harvey, who wrote in 1593 :

' He that remembereth Humphrey Cole a Mathematicall Mechanician, Matthew Baker, a shipwright, John Shute an architect, Robert Norman a Navigator, William Bourne, a gunner, John Hester, a Chymist or any like cunning and subtile empirique, is a prowd man, if he contemn expert artisans, or any sensible industrious practitioners, howsoever unlectured in Schooles or unlettered in bookes.'

NOTE ON BIBLIOGRAPHIES

The two accompanying Bibliographies of contemporary Geographical Literature are included as being the main source from which conclusions can be drawn as to the geographical thought of the Tudor Period.

The Catalogue of English works, of which a large proportion are translations, is indicative of what was actually read by the general public demanding a vernacular literature. The Catalogue of the Libraries of Dee and Lord Lumley indicates what was being read by English scholars : the proportion of works in the vernacular is very small. Much critical work on early maps and documents is vitiated by the assumption that the early author had access to all the material in existence when he wrote. Such was not the case : libraries even so complete as the two catalogued were very rare indeed, and many books, and still more manuscripts, were practically unprocurable.

As regards the compiling of the Catalogues, that of English works was based on Bale (1558), Dee (1583), Lumley (1610), Pollard (1926), and Arber's ' Transcript ' as regards printed books, while the MSS. are those noted during a general search for material, the list in this respect not being exhaustive.

Dee's Catalogue, written in the hand of one of his assistants, is difficult to decipher, but contains bibliographical notes, while Lumley's Catalogue, taken from a modern transcript, contains titles only.

Notes have been added as and where they appeared useful.

APPENDIX I

CATALOGUE OF ENGLISH GEOGRAPHICAL OR KINDRED
WORKS (PRINTED BOOKS AND MSS.) TO 1583; WITH
NOTES

Works before 1480

BEDA (Venerable Bede). 8th century.
1. *Historia gentis anglorum ecclesiastica.*
2. *De Natura Rerum* and *De Temporum ratione.*
3. *Cronica.*
4. *De Imagine Mundi* (Bale).

> The *Historia* was printed at Strassburg in 1475.
> The *De Natura*, etc., printed at Basel, 1529.
> Roger Bacon quotes from *De temporum ratione*. The MS. cited
> by Bale cannot be identified, but may be the *De mundi coelestis
> terraeque constituone*, wrongly attributed to Bede.

ALFRED THE GREAT (translations into Anglo-Saxon). 9th century.
1. *Pauli Orosii Historia, Saxonicé.*

> (In hoc codice prima Ohtheri Periplus, fol. 7 *b*. secunda autem
> fol. 11. Wulfstanii etiam fol. 11 *b*. habentur. Tiberius B. 1.)

2. *Gesta Anglorum, Bedae, Saxonicé* (Bale).

FITZSTEPHANUS, WILLIAM. 12th century.
Libellus de situ et nobilitate Londini.

> Printed by Stowe in his Survey of London, and written towards
> the end of the 12th century in the reign of Henry II.

GALFRIDUS MONUMETENSIS. 12th century.
Historia Britonum.

> Robert Record prepared a new edition of Geoffrey of Monmouth
> before his death. A printed edition (quoted by Hakluyt)
> appeared at Heidelberg in 1587.

GIRALDUS CAMBRENSIS. 12th century.
Topographica Hibernica.
Topographica (or Descriptio) *Cambriae.*
Itinerarium Walliae (or Cambriae).

> Written in the last decades of the 12th century.

GERVASE OF TILBURY.　13th century.
De Mundi Descriptione.

> Part of a larger work, written about 1210.

MALMESBURIENSIS, GULIEMUS.　12th century.
De gestus regum Anglorum.

> Quoted by Hakluyt on the early importance of London and Bristol.
>
> Obit 1142, says Bale.

SYLVESTER, BERNARDUS.　12th century.
Cosmographia.

> This Latin work is written partly in verse and partly in prose, and is a Cosmogony rather than a Cosmography.　The MS. was well known in the 16th century.

BACON, ROGER.　13th century.

> Bale lists the following MSS. of geographical interest :

1. *De fluxu et refluxu maris* (Anglicé).
2. *De Descriptione locorum or Descriptiones locorum mundi.*
3. *De mirabile potestate artis et naturae.*
4. *De philosophorum lapide.*

> No. 3 was printed in Paris in 1542, and was therefore well known.　The *Opus Majus*, containing the geography of the world, was very scarce.　Dee had several of the seven books (including Bk. IV) as separate MSS., and Leonard Digges had Bk. V on Optics.　Ortelius, writing to Camden in 1588, speaks of the latter having promised to let J. Cole make a copy of his example of *Bacon's Geography* for him.

SACROBOSCO, JOANNES.　13th century.
De Sphera Mundi.

> Written about 1233, it was to be found in numerous continental printed editions before 1500, and was everywhere accepted as the standard elementary text-book.

MATTHEW PARIS.　13th century.

1. *Chronicon* and *Chronica Majora*.　(With Map of Britain.)
> Bale lists a *Descriptio Mundi*, actually part of the above.

2. *Angli historia major.*
> Edited by Archbishop Parker, printed by Reyner Wolf 1571.

GROSSETESTE, ROBERT, Bishop of Lincoln.　13th century.
Compendium sphaerae Mundi.

> Printed Venice, 1508.

De Astrolabio (Bale).
De impressione aeris.

Hugo de Hibernia, Minorite. 14th century.
Itinerarium quoddam (Bale). Cl. 1360.

Matthew of Westminster. 14th century.
Flores Historiarum.
> Printed by R. Jugge, 1567.

Chaucer, Geoffrey. 14th century.
De Astrolabio.
> First printed 1929.

De Sphaera (Bale).

Lynn, Nicholas of. 14th century.
De usu astrolabii (Bale). Cl. 1370.
Inventio Fortunatae. (Ascribed to Nicholas.)

Mandeville, Sir John. 14th century.
The boke of John Mandeville, Knight, of ways to Jerusalem and marveyles of ynde. G. 6713.
> Printed by Pynson, 1496 ?

Higden, Ranulph. Monk of Chester. 14th century.
Polychronicon. G. 6011. Wm. Caxton, 1480.
> Contains ' The descrypcion of . . . Britayne and also Ireland ' and a ' Mappa Mundi '.

Anonymous (Copy dated 1408).
Rutter of the English Coasts.

Anonymous.
Libel of English Policy, or *De Politia Conservativa Maris. Circ.* 1436.
> The earliest treatise on economic and political geography in English. First printed by Hakluyt, who had access to more than one MS. copy.

Frea, John.
De Cosmographiae Mundi (Latin excerpts from Pliny).
Diodorus Siculus (Latin version).
> The above according to Bale, who adds of the author ' clericus Anglus, de Bristollia natus, obit Romae 1465 '.

Skelton, John, poet laureate.
Diodorus Siculus (English version). *Circ.* 1475.
> From the Latin version of Poggio Bracciolini, to whom the translation is dedicated. C.C.C. Camb. viii, 5.

NORTON, THOMAS, of Bristol. Cl. 1477.
De Transmutatione Metallorum. Circ. 1477.
> In Dr. Record's Library, says Bale.

1480

CAXTON, WILLIAM.
The Ymage or Mirrour of the Worlde, translated from the French
by W. C.   W. Caxton, 1480.
> Another edition, C. 11, b. 13.   1527.   From a 13th century
> French original.

MORGAN, DAVID (David of Llandaff). Cl. 1480.
Antiquitates Cambriae.
Geographia (Bale, who adds ' ex Cambria oriundus ').

1482

KENT, JOHN (for Thomas). Cl. 1482.
Tabulae Astronomiae (Bale).

1497

WYNKYN DE WORDE.
Descrypcyon of Englonde etc. Added to the *Chronicle of
England or Fruit of Times.* C. 11, b. 1. Wynkyn de Worde,
1497.
> From Higden's Polychronicon : as in Caxton's Chronicles 1480.

1498

ANONYMOUS.
Informacōn for pylgrymes unto the holy londe. Advocates'
Library, Edinburgh. W. de Worde, 1498.

1499

LINACRE, THOMAS.
Proclus, De Sphaera (Latin trans.). Venice, 1499.

1503

ARNOLD, RICHARD.
*The Copy of a Carete Cumposynge the Circuit of the Worlde and the
Compace of every Yland,* contained in Arnold's Chronicle.
John of Doesborowe, 1503.
> This section was reprinted by R. Wyer 1535 (717, a. 49) under
> the title of ' Mappa Mundi ', and by the same publisher at about

the same date entitled ' The Rutter of the Distances from one Porte or Countree to another ', as an addendum to the 'Compost of Ptholomaeus '.

1507

GUYLFORDE, SIR RICHARD.
The Pylgrymage of Sir Richard Guylforde to the Holy Land.
A.D. 1506. R. Pynson, 1507 (?).

1510

CLAYMUND, JOHN. Cl. 1510.
Pliny, Omnia Opera, lib. 37.
Ad Simonem Grynaeum Epistolae, (Bale).
The author was of Magdalen College, Oxford.

1511

ANONYMOUS.
Of the new lādes and of ye people founde by the messengers of the kynge or portygale. Antwerp, John of Doesborowe, 1511 (?).

1517

TORKINGTON, SIR RICHARD.
The Journal of Sir Richard Torkington's Pilgrimage to the Holy Land, in the year 1517. MS.

1519

RASTELL, JOHN.
A new interlude and a merry of the nature of the iiij elements.
643, b. 45. Rastell, 1519 (?).

1522

LANGTON, ROBERT.
The Pylgrymage of M. R. Langton, clerke, to Saynt James in Compostell. R. Copland, 1522.

1523

FITZHERBERT, MASTER (JOHN).
Here begynneth a ryght frutefull mater : and hath to name the boke of surveying. R. Pynson, 1523.
And again published in 1526, 1539 (1381, a.), 1567.

1526

BOETHIUS, HECTOR.
Scotorum Historiae a prima gentis origine. Paris, 1526.
Revised and enlarged by Joannes Ferrerius. Paris, 1574.

1527

THORNE, ROBERT.
Letter to Dr. Lee on Routes to the Spice Is. 1527.

1528

COPLAND, ROBERT.
The Rutter of the Sea, with the laws of the Isle of Auleron, (1266
A.D.), trs. by R. Copland. R. Bankes, 1528.
From the French of Pierre Garcie, with omission of the woodcuts
of land marks in the original, and with the addition of a preface.
Several times reprinted.

1530

ANONYMOUS.
Cosmographia. MS. transcribed 1530. Written *circ.* 1510 ?
Royal MSS. 13. E. VII.

THORNE, ROBERT (and BARLOW, ROGER ?).
Address to King Henry VIII on routes to Spice Is. 1530 ?

1533

GOES, DAMIANUS À.
The legacye or embassate of prester John unto Emanuell, Kynge of
Portingale (trs. by J. More). W. Rastell, 1533.
From the 'Legatio magni imperatoris Indorum Presbyteri
Joannis', first published Dordrecht, 1518, and subsequently em-
bodied in a Letter to Joannes Magnus by Damian, published
1531. More used the latter version.

VERGIL, POLYDORE.
Anglicae Historiae, Libri 27. Simon Grynaeus. Basle, 1533.

1534

ANONYMOUS.
Map of British Isles. 1534 ? Cotton MSS. I. i. 9.
Bears some resemblance to Lily's Map, but with more detail.

1536

BELLENDEN, JOHN.
*The history and croniklis of Scotlande, with the cosmography and
description thairof.*   Edinburgh, 1536.
   From the Latin of Hector Boethius.

1537

BENESE, SIR RICHARD DE.
The Boke of Measurying of Land.   Preface by Thos. Paynell.
C. 40, e. 36.   London, 1537.
   Many times reprinted.   Author was Surveyor of Works to
Henry VIII.

1540

LINDESAY, ALEXANDER.
*The Rutter of the Sea, with havens, roades, soundes, etc., from
Humber northward, round about Scotland.*
   Scots original, accompanied by a chart, prepared 1540.

1541

BARLOW, ROGER.
A briefe summe of Geographie.   MS.   1541.
   Based on the *Suma* of M. Fernam de Enciso.   Seville, 1519.

PROUDE, RICHARD.
The New Rutter of the Sea for the North Parts.
   Based on the MS. Rutter of 1408 (above).   The date 1541 ascribed
to the New Rutter occurs in the printed version of 1550 (?) below.

1542

ROTZ, JEAN.
*Traicte des differences du compas aymante, et de certains poinetz
notables ducelluy, etc.*   MS.   Dieppe, 1542.
   Dedicated to Henry VIII.
The Boke of Ydrography.   MS.   1542.

RECORD, ROBERT.
The Ground of Arts.   London, 1542 (?).

1545

MAILLARD, JEAN.
Le premier livre de cosmographie en rethorique francoise. 1545 (?).
MS. Dedicated to Henry VIII.

MARSHALL, JOHN.
Small treatise contayning the times of full seas etc. of the havens about the coasts of France, Flanders, Britane, Wales, Ireland and Spain. Circ. 1545.
A booklet containing tables and maps dedicated to the Earl of Arundel.

Rutter for the Sea about Scotlande, the Islands of Orkney and Schetland. Circ. 1545.
Dedicated to the Earl of Arundel.

PETIT, THOMAS.
Harbour Plans of Calais, etc. MSS. *Circ.* 1545.
The author was one of Henry VIII's Surveyors.

1546

JOVIUS, PAULUS.
A short treatise upon the Turkes Chronicles. Trs. by Peter Ashton. 280. b. 36. Ed. Whitchurch. 1546.
From ' Commentarj della cose de Turchia '. Venice, 1541.

VERGIL, POLYDORE.
An abridgement of the notable works of P. Vergil by Thos. Langley. R. Grafton, 1546.
Taken from the ' De Inventoribus Rerum '. Venice, 1499.

LILY, GEORGE.
Mappa Britanniae. Rome, 1546.
The author was a son of the famous grammarian Wm. Lily, and was under the patronage of Reginald Pole, with whom he returned from Italy, 1556.

1548

LILY, GEORGE.
Nova et antiqua locorum nomina in Anglia et in Scotia.
Used by P. Jovius. 1548.

1549

ADAMS, CLEMENT.
World Map of Sebastian Cabot. 1549 (?).
'Cut by Clement Adams', *vide* Hakluyt.

LELANDUS, JOANNES.
The laborious Journey and serch for Englandes Antiquities : with declaracyons enlarged by J. Bale. (291. a. 48.) J. Bale. 1549.
Bale catalogues also 'Descriptiones Angliae'.

1550

DEE, JOHN.
Prolegomena et dictata Parisiensa in Euclidis Elementorum Geometricorum librum, primum et secundum in Collegio Rhemensi. 1550.
Dee's famous public lectures on Euclid delivered in Paris.

De usu globi cœlestisis, ad Regum Edoardum sextum. 1550.
Probably presented through John Cheke, the King's tutor, and Dee's friend.

COPLAND, ROBERT.
The Rutter of the Sea, etc.   The New Rutter of the Sea for the North Parts, A.D. 1541, by Richard Proude. (C. 21, a. 48.) Wm. Copland. 1550 (?).
Also in 1553 and 1587.   The Rutter of 1528, with the addendum of R. Proude.

SALYSBURYE, WILLIAM.
The Description of the Sphere or Frame of the World.
Proclus' Sphaera. 717. a. 20. 1550.

1551

DEE, JOHN.
De Planetarum, in errantium stellarum, nubiumque à centro terrae distantiis : et stellarum omnium veris inveniendis magnitudinibus. 1551.
'Liber apodeiktikòs ad Edoardum VI. Angliae Regem.' Afterwards enlarged to Lib. 2.

RECORD, ROBERT.
The Pathway to Knowledge. 530 g. 1. R. Wolfe. 1551.

THOMAS, WILLIAM.

Travels of Josafa Barbaro. 1551 ?

> From the Italian edn. of 1545. In MS. only.

Sacrobosco, De Sphaera. Trs. into English. 1551 ?

> Egerton MSS. 837.

1552

WADE, ARMIGELL.

His Travels.

> Collected and published by another hand, 1552. 4to, says Tanner. Bibl. Brit. 744. Wade went to Newfoundland in 1536 with Master Hore. This work has not been traced.

1553

EDEN, RICHARD.

A Treatise of the newe India . . . after the description of Sebastian Munster in his Universal Cosmographie. 793. a. 27. Ed. Sutton. 1553.

> Dedicated to the Earl of Northumberland.

DEE, JOHN.

The True Account (not vulgar) of Floods and Ebbs.

> Written at the request of the Right Honourable Lady, Lady Jane, Dutchesse of Northumberland. MS. 1553.

An Astronomical Treatise. 1553.

> At the Request of the same. MS.

The Astronomicall and Logisticall rules and Canons to calculate the Ephemerides by, and the other necessary accounts of heavenly motions, written at the request and for the use of that excellent Mechanician, Master Richard Chancellor, at his last voyage into Moschovia. MS. 1553.

CHANCELLOR, RICHARD.

Inventio geometricae. 1553 (?).

> A MS. in Dee's library, presumably dealing with Chancellor's inventions during their astronomical work together.

Astronomical Tracts. 1553 (?).

> ' In astrologia pleraque scripsisse dicitur ' (Bale).

DIGGES, LEONARD.

A Prognostication of right good effect. T. Gemini. 1553.

> Dedicated to Sir Ed. Fines, afterwards Earl of Lincoln and Lord High Admiral. New editions in 1555, 1556 and at intervals to 1635. Edited after 1570 by Thos. Digges.

STEVENS, WALTER.
  The conclusions of the Astrolabie by Geoffrey Chaucer, amended by
  Walter Stevens, with an epistle dedicatory to Edward, Earl of
  Devonshire, a preface to the Reader and a table of contents.
  1553-4. Sloane MS. 261.

1554

PRAT, WYLLYAM.
  The Description of the Country of Affrique. W. Powell. 1554.
    Dedicated to Ed. Courtenay Earl of Devonshire, as a New Year's
    Gift. From the French version of 'Omnium gentium Mores'
    with additional matter.

CHANCELLOR, RICHARD.
  *Voiage into Moscovia, with the description of the names of the
  people there.* 1554.
    MS. in Lumley's Library.

  *The booke of the great and mighty Emperor of Russia, and Duke of
  Moscovia, and of the dominions, orders, and commodities thereto
  belonging :* drawn by Richard Chancellor. 1554.
    Printed by Hakluyt. 1589.

ADAMS, CLEMENT.
  Anglorum navigationes ad Moscoviam. 1554.
    Printed in Latin and English by Hakluyt, but Eden's reference
    in the Decades suggests that the original Latin was available for
    the general reader, i.e. was in print. Adams 'received it at the
    mouth of the said Richard Chancellor' on his return in the summer
    of 1554.

1555

BOEMUS, JOANNES.
  The Fardle of Facions, trs. by Wm. Watreman. C. 22. a. 17.
  John Kingston, 1555.
    Dedicated to the Earl of Arundel, Lord Steward of the House-
    hold. From 'Omnium gentium Mores', 1536.

EDEN, RICHARD.
  *The Decades of the newe worlde or west India . . . written in the
  Latine tounge by Peter Martyr of Angleria.* C. 13. a. 8. London.
  W. Powell. 1555.

GEMINI, THOMAS.
  Hispaniae Tabula, excusum per T. G. London. 1555.
    Dedicated to Philip and Mary.

HOMEM, DIEGO.
  Portolan Atlas.
    Dedicated to Philip and Mary, 1555 (?)

1556

CANDISH, RICHARD.
  Geometria Euclidis Megarensis, Lib. 15.
    Translated into English (Bale) 1556 ?

DEE, JOHN.
  1. *Brevis epistola, qua vulgares isto Ephemeridum fictores merito reprehendit.* 3 July 1556. T. Marshe. 1556.
    Printed as an introduction to John Field's ' Ephemeris 1557, supputata et examinata ad meridianum Londinensam '.

  2. *Inventum mechanicum paradoxum* de nova ratione delineandi circumferentiam circularem ; unde (valdè rara) alia dependent inventa. Lib. 1. 1556.

DIGGES, LEONARD.
  A Book named Tectonicon. T. Gemini. 1556.
    New editions appeared in 1562, 1570, 1585, 1592 and up to 1637.

RECORD, ROBERT.
  The Castle of Knowledge, containing the explication of the Sphere. 526. 1. 6. Reginald (Reyner) Wolf. 1556.
    Dedicated to Queen Mary, and with a letter to Cardinal Pole. Probably the ' Introductio in Geometriam atque Cosmographiam ' listed by Bale.

1557

TESTA ROSSA, BATTISTA, Pilot of the Ocean Sea.
  Art of Navigation (in Italian). MS. London. 1557.
    Dedicated to Marco Baldu. The Neapolitan author had arrived in London in 1556. John and Sebastian Cabot are named with Columbus and Magellan in a brief note on the great Discoveries.

DEE, JOHN.
  Speculum unitatis, sive apologia pro frattre Rogero Bachone, Anglo. 1557.
    Of this work, Dee writes to Mercator : ' It demonstrates that he did nothing by the help of Demons, but was a very great Philosopher, and did naturally, and by methods lawful for Christian men, those very great things which the vulgar teach that he

accomplished by the aid of Demons.' (Translation from Latin original.) Dee's defence of Bacon is also a defence of himself, as he was already accused in a like manner.

1. *De Annuli Astronomici multiplici usu.* Lib. 2. 1557.
2. *De Nova Navigatione Ratione.* Lib. 2. 1557 (?).

RECORD, ROBERT.
The Whetstone of Witte. John Kyngstone. 1557. 530. g. 37.
> Dedicated to the Moscovy Governors. ' I will . . . shortly set forth a book of Navigation,' says the author. . . . ' In that book I also will show certain means how without great difficulty you may sail to the north-east Indies, and so to Camul, Chinchital, and Balor.'

1558

JOVIUS, PAULUS.
Scotiae Descriptio.
> Trs. by J. Bale, included in ' Scriptorum illustrium . . . catalogus '. Basle, 1558.

VERGIL, POLYDORE.
Hiberniae Descriptio ex libro XIII Anglorum Historiae.
> Trs. by J. Bale, in ' Scriptorum illustrium . . . catalogus '. Basle, 1558.

PERLIN, ESTIENNE.
Description des royaulmes d'Angleterre et d'Ecosse. C. 32. c. 1. Paris. 1558.
> Dedicated to the Duchess of Berry.

1559

CUNINGHAM, WILLIAM.
The Cosmographical Glass. 59. i. 28. J. Day. 1559.
> Dedicated to Robert Dudley. Preface dated from Norwich, 18 July, Royal Privilege, 28 October, licence to print, 6 November 1559.

1560

DEE, JOHN.
De Itinere subterraneo. Lib. 2. 1560.
> Method of survey of underground mining tunnels.

BOROUGH, WILLIAM. 18 D. iii. 124.
Chart of Northern Navigation. 1560 (?).
> ' The entire sayling plat that we use for those parts.

1561

DEE, JOHN.
Record's Ground of Arts, edited by J. D. R. Wolf. 1561.

EDEN, RICHARD.
The Art of Navigation, trs. from Martin Cortes. G. 7310.
R. Jugge. 1561.

> The original was published in Seville 1551 and 1556 under the
> title : *Breve Compendio de la Sphera y de la Arte de navegar* . . .

NORTH, GEORGE.
Description of Swedeland, Estland and Finland, chiefly out of
Sebastian Munster. 154. d. 31. J. Awdley. 1561.

> Dedicated to Thos. Stuckley.

APIANUS, PETRUS.
The unyversall Coosemographe Apyane in Englesshe. Licensed to
Thos. Hackett. 1561–2.

> Probably translated but never printed. A fresh licence to print
> was obtained by T. Purfoote in 1567–8.

1562

ANONYMOUS.
1. *The Carde of London.* G. Godhed. 1562–3.

> Probably the Plan of London and Westminster 1563. B.M.
> 3480 (61).

2. *The Mappe of England and Skotlande.* G. Godhed. 1562–3.
Licence only extant.

JENKINSON, ANTHONY.
Russiae Tabula. London. 1562.

> Dedicated to Sir Henry Sidney.
> According to W. Borough, he himself drew a map of
> Jenkinson's Journey to Boghar and Persia, which was used by
> Mercator in preparing his map of 1569. It was therefore a map
> in circulation, i.e. in print, and probably the above.

LEIGH, VALENTINE.
Treatise of Measuring all Kinds of Lands. T. Colwell. 1562.

> Later editions, 1577 *et sqq.*, are entitled The Science of Surveying
> of Lands. The licence to print, and the date of the dedication
> subsequently reprinted, are the evidence for the 1562 edn. which
> is not extant.

1563

RIBAULT, JEAN.
  The whole and true discovery of Terra Florida . . . never found out before the last year 1562. Trs. by T. Hackett. C. 33. c. 17. T. Hackett. 1563.
    Dedicated to Alderman Sir Martin Bowes.

NOWELL, LAWRENCE.
  Map of Ireland. 1563 ?
    Several of the MSS. maps of this author, bearing close resemblance to the Mercator Britain of 1564, are extant.

SEALE, ROBERT.
  A Commendation of the Adventurous voyage of Thomas Stukeley and others towards the land called Terra Florida. John Allde. 1563.
    Unique copy in the Henry Huntington Library, U.S.A.

ANONYMOUS.
  A ballad made by one being greatly impoverished by the viage prepared to Terra Floryday, etc. A. Lacye. 1563.
    Licence only extant.

1565

DEE, JOHN.
  Reipublicae Britannicae Synopsis, in English. 1565.
    A Tract on British expansion overseas written at the request of Edward Dyer. It belongs to the period of first advocacy of the search for a north-west passage, and its corollary of planting in N. America.

ANONYMOUS.
  The Wonders of Italy about Napolies and Rome. 1565 ?
    The licence only extant.

1566

SHALLEUX, NICHOLAS DE.
  A true and perfect description of the last voyage or navigation attempted by Captain John Rybaut 1565. 278. a. 44. N. Denham (for T. Hackett). 1566.

PLINIUS SECUNDUS, CAIUS.
  Summary of the Antiquities and wonders of the Worlde, out of the sixteen first bookes. Trs. by J. A. from the French of Pierre de Changy. 433. a. 4. 1566 (?).

1567

BAKER, ROBERT.
The briefe Dyscourse of Roberte Baker in Gynney, India, Portyngale and Ffraunce.   Fraunces Coldoke.   1567–8.
> Licence only extant.

BOURNE, WILLIAM.
An Almanacke and pronostication for iii yeres with serten Rules of navigation.   T. Purfoot.   1567.
> New Edition 1571; the ' Rules ' are the germ of the author's ' Regiment of the Sea '.

GOUGH, JOHN.
Map of Ireland (MS.).   1567.

1568

THEVET, ANDRÉ.
The Newfound World or Antarctic.   Trs. by T. Hackett.   798. C. 34.   T. Hackett for H. Bynneman.   1568.
> Dedicated to Sir Henry Sidney.   The original was published in 1558.

MANDEVILLE, SIR JOHN.
The Voyage and Travail of Sir John Mandeville.   1045. h. 2. Thos. East.   1568.

1569

HAWKINS, SIR JOHN.
A true declaration of the troublesome voyage to the parts of Guinea and the West Indies in 1567 and 1568.   C. 32. a.   L. Harrison for T. Purfoot.   1569.
> Licensed as ' The iii^{de} voyage of Master Hawkyns '.

1570

DEE, JOHN.
Preface to the English Euclid.   8532. g.   J. Day.   1570.
> The translation is ascribed to Henry Billingsly, but in addition to the Preface, Dee made many notes and additions to the text. ' His mathematical preface unto these Elements is a work of such singularity and necessity to all students of the Mathematicalls, that I wish them to make it a manual,' writes E. Worsop, Sept. 1581.

ROGERS, DANIEL.
De veterum Britannorum moribus et legibus Commentarium. MS.
1570.
> Mentioned by the author in a letter to Ortelius, Feb. 1570, and
> ' nondum edidit ', says Ortelius in 1571.

1571

LYTHE, ROBERT.
Survey Map of Ireland. MS. 1571.

BODENHAM, ROGER.
*Certein things to be considered of, for the special welth of the realme
of England,* by R. Bodnam. MS. 1571.
> A tract on economic geography by a man who had experience
> in Seville, Barbary and the W. Indies.

DIGGES, LEONARD.
A Geometricall Practise named Pantometria . . . lately finished by
Thos. Digges. 8532. b. H. Bynneman. 1571.
> Dedicated to Sir Nicholas Bacon, Leonard Digges' friend.

LHUYD, HUMFREY.
De Mona Druida Insula . . . epistola. 1571. H. Toy for H.
Bynneman. 1573.
> Printed by Ortelius in the Theatrum. English ed^{n}. attached
> to Sir J. Price's ' Defensio ', 598. d. 11(2).

Cambriae Typus. (Map.) 1571.
> As before.

ANONYMOUS.
Discourse of Floudes and Waters. J. Allde and W. Pikerynge.
1570–1.
> Licence only extant.

1572

ROGERS, DANIEL.
Description of Ireland in verse, dedicated to Thomas Phediger.
> Referred to by Ortelius. 1572. Not traced. The author
> visited Ireland in 1572, and brought back a ' very exact map ',
> possibly Lythe's. His *Antiquae Britanniae observationes* (N.D.)
> is in Titus. X. (Cotton MSS.)

LHUYD, HUMFREY.
Commentarioli Britannicae Descriptionis Fragmentum. Cologne.
Js. Birknammus. 1572.
> From the MS. sent to Ortelius by Lhuyd.

COLE, HUMFREY.
Map of Palestine. R. Jugge. 1572.
> Engraved on copperplate from the original of Tilleman Stella, 1557, printed by Ortelius in 1570.

DIONISE, ALEXANDRINE.
A Survey of the World, or Situation of the Earth as much as is Inhabited. H. Bynneman. 1572. Trs. by Thos. Twyne. 10003. aa.
> Dedicated to Wm. Lovelace, Sergeant at Law.

HAWKS, HENRY.
A relation of the Commodities of Nova Hispania, and the manners of the inhabitants. MS. 1572. Printed 1589 by Hakluyt the Preacher.
> The first evidence of the elder Hakluyt's work in gathering particulars of economic geography of N. America, directed towards planting a colony.

ROWLANDS, RICHARD.
The Post for divers parts of the World: to travelle from one notable citie unto another. T. East. 1572.
> Translated from the ' High Almaine ' ; 2nd edn. 1576.

MUNSTER, SEBASTIAN.
A briefe collection of strange things out of the cosmography of Sebastian Muenster. 793. a. 28. T. Marsh. 1572.
> Anonymous abridgement.

1573

TWYNE, THOMAS.
The Breviary of Britayn. R. Johnes. 1573.
> Trs. from the ' Britannicae . . . Fragmentum ' of H. Lhuyd.

LHUYD, HUMFREY.
Angliae Regni Tabula. Map. 1573.
> In Ortelius' list of Maps. Printed in the Additamentum, as also a map of Ireland, and a map of Scotland.

P(OWELL), D(AVID).
Certain Brief Rules of Geography for the understanding of Charts and Maps. 12331. a. 30 (2). H. Bynneman. 1573.

BOURNE, WILLIAM.
A Regiment of the Sea. 8805. bb. T. Dawson. 1573.
> A simplified Manual for Navigators.

1574

FORSTER, RICHARD.
Ephemerides meteorographia ad annum 1575.   J. Kingston.
1574 (?).

1575

TURLER, JEROME.
The Traveller, divided into two books, the first containing a
notable discourse of the manner and order of travelling oversea
into strange and foreign countries.   The second comprehending
a description of the most delicious Realm of Naples.   C. 21. a. 6.
A. Veale.   1575.
> Dedicated to Barons Lord George and Hugh Vitus.

VOWELL, JOHN.
The Description of the Cittie of Exeeter.   291 C. 40.   1575 (?).

1576

GILBERT, SIR HUMFREY.
A Discourse for a Discovery for a new Passage to Cataia.
1045. N. 26.   Jones for H. Middleton.   1576.

BOROUGH, WILLIAM.
Chart of the North Atlantic.   MS.   June 1st 1576.
> Prepared for the first Frobisher voyage.

LAMBARD, WILLIAM.
Perambulation of Kent.   578. f. 1.   H. Middleton.   1570.
> Written for the most part in 1570.

1577

DEE, JOHN.
The British Complement of the Perfect Art of Navigation.
Vol. I.   General and Rare Memorials Pertayning to the Perfect
Arte of Navigation : annexed to the Paradoxall Cumpass in
Playne.
Vol. II.   Queen Elizabeth her Tables Gubernatick : for naviga-
tion by the Paradoxall Compasse, and Navigation by Great
Circles : and for longitudes and latitudes, and the variation
of the Compasse, finding most easily and speedily : yea (if
need be) in one minute of time, and sometime, without sight

of Sun, Moone or Star : with many other new and nedeful inventions Gubernatick.

Vol. III.   Contents unknown.

Vol. IV.   The Great Volume of Famous and Rich Discoveries. (Wherein is also the History of King Solomon, every three years, his Ophirian voyage, with divers other rarities.)

Addendum : The Description of divers wonderfull Isles in the Northern, Scythian, Tartarian, and the other most Northern Seas, and neare under the Pole, by Record within about 1200 yeres ago.

The whole work was completed between Aug. 1st 1576 and July 1577.   Vol. I was printed.   48. b. 18.   J. Daye.   1577.   Vol. II is lost, Vol. III destroyed as soon as written, and Vol. IV, with the Addendum, survives in a mutilated form in the original MS.

EDEN, RICHARD.

The Navigation and Voyages of Lewes Wertomannus (Varthema), trs. out of the Latin of Madrignanus in Novus Orbis.   1576. R. Jugge.   1577.

Published in Willes' new edn. of the English Decades, the ' History of Travayle '.

WILLES, RICHARD.

The History of Travayle in the West and East Indies . . . newly . . . finished by R. Willes.   566. c. 10.   R. Jugge.   1577.

The new material prepared by Eden included the Travels of Varthema, and the English Voyages to Persia up to date.   Willes added : (1) ' An Abridgement of P. Martyr his 5, 6, 7, 8 Decades, and particularly of Ferd. Cortesius conquest of Mexico.'

(2) ' Of the Island Giapan and the other little Isles ', derived from ' De rebus Japonicis ' of P. Maffeius, and the ' Litera Annua Japonensis, Feb. 1565–6 ', of Luigi Frois, a Portuguese Jesuit.

(3) ' Concerning China ', from the Italian of Galeotto Perera. This is therefore the first comprehensive account of Asia to be published in English.   Willes also added :

(4) The Discussion of the North-west Passage.

FULLER.

Farewell to master ffourboisur and the other gentlemen adventurers who labour to discover the right way to Cathay.   John Jugge. 20 May 1577.

The licence only is extant.

HAKLUYT, RICHARD, of the Middle Temple.

Notes given to certain gentlemen that went with M. Frobisher in his Northwest discovery.   MS.   1577 (?).

Printed by Hakluyt.

FRAMPTON, JOHN.
Joyful Newes out of the Newfound World, trs. from Nicholas Monardes. 968. e. 19 (1). W. Norton. 1577.

> Dedicated to Edward Dyer. Perhaps from the copy brought from Seville by Roger Bodenham.

NICHOLAS, THOMAS.
Newes lately come from the great Kingdom of China, trs. out of the Castylin tongue by T. N. T. Gardyner and T. Dawson. 1577.

SETTLE, DIONYSE.
A True Report of the last voyage into the West and northwest regions . . . in 1577 . . . worthily achieved by Captain Frobisher. G. 6479. H. Middleton. 1577.

HARRISON, WILLIAM.
An historicall description of the Islands of Bretayne in Ralph Holinshed's Chronicles. T. Woodcock. 1577.

> The Topographical description of England is partly compiled from Saxton's unpublished maps. There is also included:
> (1) The description of Scotlande, written . . . by H (ector) B (oethius) in Latin, and . . . trans. . . . by. W (illiam) H (arrison).
> (2) The description of Ireland, begun by Edmund Campion and continued by Richard Stonyhurst. (Dedicated by Holinshed to Sir Henry Sidney.)

ANONYMOUS.
A thing touching Ffourboyser. A. Maunsell. 1st July 1577.

> The licence only is extant; possibly a Ballad in Farewell.

1578

ANONYMOUS.
A description of the purtrayture and shape of those strange kind of people which the worthie Maister Martin Ffourboiser brought into England Anno 1576 and 1577. John Alldee. 1578.

> Only the licence, dated Jan. 30, is extant.

CHURCHYARD, THOMAS.
A pamphlet in the praise of Master Captain Ffrobisher in forme of A Farewell at his third voiage in Maye 1578 by the northeest (sic) seas towards the Island of Cataea. R. Jones. 1578.

> Only the licence is extant, but Churchyard refers to having composed such a work.

BOROUGH, WILLIAM.
Plat of the Coasts and Inward Parts of Russia. 1578.
Given to Queen Elizabeth with an autobiographical address, the latter printed by Hakluyt.

BOURNE, WILLIAM.
1. *Inventions and Devices.* 1398 b. 1578.
Dedicated to Lord Howard of Effingham.
2. *The Art of Shooting in Great Ordnaunce.* H. Bynneman. 1578.
3. A Booke called *The Treasure for Travellers.* G. 2934. T. Dawson for T. Woodcock. 1578.
Dedicated to Sir William Winter.

BOURNE, WILLIAM.
A Treatise on the Properties and Qualities of Glasses for Optical Purposes. MS. 1578 (?).
Dedicated to Lord Burghley.

FRAMPTON, JOHN.
A Briefe Description of the Portes and Havens of the West India.
Trs. from the Spanish of Martin Fernam de Enciso. *Suma de Geographia.* H. Bynneman. 1578.

NICHOLAS, THOMAS.
The pleasant history of the Conquest of the West India, now called New Spain, achieved by Hernando Cortez. 1196. b. 28. H. Bynneman. 1578.
From the Spanish of Francisco Lopez de Gomara. Dedicated to Sir Francis Walsingham.

GUEVARA, ANTONIO DE.
The Invention of the Art of Navigation, trs. by. E. Hellowes. 8806. de. R. Newbury. 1578.
Dedicated to Lord Howard of Effingham, from the Spanish, ' Aguja de marear y de sus inventores '. 1539.

BUCK, PAUL.
Praier for Sir Humfrey Gilberte. H. Kirkham. 17 July 1578.
The licence only is extant : the occasion is the abortive start for Norumbega.

CHURCHYARD, THOMAS.
1. *A Commendation of Sir H. Gilbert's Venturous Journey.*
2. *A Welcome Home to Master Martin Frobisher from Meta Incognita.* G. 11238. H. Bynneman. 1578.
3. *A Praise and Report of Master Frobisher's Voyage to Meta Incognita.* A. Maunsell. 1578.

DEE, JOHN.
1. *Her Majesty's Title Royal to many foreign countries, kingdoms, and provinces.* MS. 1578.

'In 12 vellum skins of parchment, fair written for her Majesty's use, and by her Majesty's commandment set down in writing with Hydrographicall and Geographicall description.' The work for which Dee refused £100.

2. *Brytanici Imperii Limites.* MS. 1578.

'A treatise which I compiled specially at her Majesty's commandment.'

ELLIS, THOMAS.
A True Report of the Third and last voyage into Meta Incognita, achieved by Captain Martin Frobisher. T. Dawson. 1578.

BEST, GEORGE.
A True Discourse of the late Voyage of Discovery, for finding a passage to Cathaya. H. Bynneman. 1578.

Dedicated to Sir Christopher Hatton.

PARKHURST, ANTHONY.
Report of the true state and commodities of Newfoundland. MS. 13 Nov. 1578. Printed by Hakluyt.

Written for Richard Hakluyt of the Middle Temple, for Humfrey Gilbert's voyage. Master Butler (afterwards commanding Walter Raleigh's vessel in Gilbert's fleet) is at the writer's elbow, desiring him to write fully.

LESLIE, JOHN (Bishop of Ross).
De origine, moribus et rebus gestis Scotorum . . . accessit nova et accurata . . . Scotiae, cum vera ejusdem tabula topographia, descriptio. 288. d. 2 (1). Rome. 1578.

The map engraved by Nicholas Bonifacius.

1579

FRAMPTON, JOHN.
1. *The most famous travels of Marcus Paulus.* 979. f. 25. Ralph Newbury. 1579.

Dedicated to Edward Dyer: from the Castilian version of Santaella, 1503. Published in January.

2. *A Discourse of the Navigations which the Portugales do make.* Trs. from Bernardino de Escalante, 'Discorse de la navigacion', 1577. C. 32 f. T. Dawson. 1579.

Thomas Nicholas, addressing Walsingham in 1578, spoke of his intention of undertaking the translation ' of the East India, which is now enjoyed by the King of Portingal '. The above works may have anticipated and frustrated his purpose.

EDEN, RICHARD.
A Very Necessary and Profitable Book of Navigation. J. Jugge. 1579.

Translated from Taisner's *De Magnete,* 1576. Designed as an addendum to a new edition of Cortes, it was also issued as a separate volume, according to Dee's Catalogue, and to the publisher's announcement (Ames).

HAKLUYT, RICHARD, of the Middle Temple.
Direction given to Master Hubblethorne, Dyer, going into Persia. MS. 1579.

Printed by Hakluyt.

SAXTON, CHRISTOPHER.
Thirty-five coloured maps of England and Wales, i.e. the Atlas. C. 43. i 1 (1). 1579.

FOX, JOHN.
An excellent discourse of an exployt of Jhon Fox an inglishman, who had been prisoner 14 years under ye Turkes, and killing the goaler delivered 266 Christians. T. Dawson and S. Peale. 1579.

The licence only, dated 23 July, is extant. A version of the story was printed by Hakluyt, but does not appear to be the above.

ANONYMOUS.
A Ballad of Delivery of 266 persons from the Turkes. John Alldee. 1579.

Only the licence, dated 4 Sept., is extant, and the Ballad was probably written upon the publication of the above narrative.

DEE, JOHN.
De imperatoris nomine, authoritate, ac potentia.

In English, dedicated to Her Majesty. MS. 1579.

DIGGES, LEONARD.
An Arithmeticall Military Treatise called Stratioticos, begun by Leonard Digges and finished by Thomas Digges his son. 58. e. 21. H. Bynneman. 1579.

Dedicated to the Earl of Leicester.

In this volume Thomas Digges states that he is preparing ' A Treatise on the Arte of Navigation, bewraying the gross errors by our Masters and Mariners practised '.

1580

HITCHCOCK, CAPT. ROBERT.
A Politic Plat for the Honour of Princes etc., with a Map. c. 27. f. 3.
J. Kingston. 1 Jan. 1580.

TWYNE, THOMAS.
A short and pithy discourse, concerning earthquakes. R. Johnes.
1580.

HAKLUYT, RICHARD, of the Middle Temple.
Instructions given to M. Arthur Pet and M. Charles Jackman.
MS. May 1580.
> Printed by Hakluyt.

BOROUGH, WILLIAM.
*Instructions and notes . . . to be observed by Arthur Pet and
Charles Jackman.* MS. 1580.
> With a chart.

DEE, JOHN.
Instructions for the two Masters, Charles Jackman and Arthur Pet,
given and delyvered to them at the Courte Day, holden at the
Moscovy House, the 17th of May, 1580. With . . . a new
Charte. MS. 1580.
*Navigationis ad Cathayam per septentrionalia Scythiae et Tartariae
Littera delineatio Hydrographica* : Arthuro Pitt et Carolo
Jackmanno versus illas partas navigaturis in manus tradita.
1580.
> The chart referred to above.

CARTIER, JACQUES.
A short Narration of two Navigations to New France : trs. by
Giovanni Florio from Ramusio's version. C. 32, g. 20. H.
Bynneman. 1580.
> Dedicated to Edmund Bray, Esq., High Sheriff of Oxford, and
> to all Gentlemen, Merchants and Pilots. Licensed 7 June.

FRAMPTON, JOHN.
*A Discovery of the Countries of Tartaria, Scythia and Cataia by
the north-east,* collected and written by a certain learned man
called Francisco Thamara of Cadiz. T. Dawson. 1580.
> Dedicated to Sir Richard Hayward, Kt., and to Master George
> Barne, Alderman, Governors of the Muscovy Co. Licensed
> 15 July. The Spanish original is mainly compiled from J. Boemus.
> MS. given to Pet and Jackman.

ANONYMOUS.

The Voyage of Fferdinando Maganasses (Magellan) unto the Malucos. T. Purfoote. 1580.

The licence only is extant. It was taken out on the day of Drake's return from a successful emulation of Magellan's feat. Can this be merely a coincidence, or was the licence to cover an account of Drake's voyage?

DEE, JOHN.

Atlantides, vulgariter Indiae Occidentalis nominatae, emendiator descriptio, quam adhuc est divulgata. 1580.

The map, with summary of Title on the back, forming one of the two Rolls delivered to the Queen in October by Dee.

GOLDING, ARTHUR.

De terrae motu (i.e. Earthquakes). 1580.
In English.

1581

NICHOLAS, THOMAS.

The Discovery and Conquest of Peru, trs. by T. N. 1061. b. 23. R. Jones. 6 Feb. 1581.

Dedicated to Sec^y. Thos. Wilson, and including a panegyric on Francis Drake. Licensed on Jan. 13. The original is the ' Historia del describrimiento y Conquista del Peru ', Antwerp, 1555, by Augustin de Zarate, whom Nicholas claims to have met in Spain. A special section is added on the Potosi mines.

FRAMPTON, JOHN.

The Arte of Navigation, wherein is contained all the rules, declarations, secrets, and advises, which for good Navigation are necessarie and ought to be known and practised : made by Master Peter de Medina, directed to the right excellent and renowned Lord Don Philippo, prince of Spain and of both Sicilies. T. Dawson. 1581.

Dedicated to Edward Dyer.
The licence was taken out on 28 Feb., immediately on the appearance of Nicholas' Discovery of Peru, and before the translation was actually made, hence publication was not until August. From the 1563 (Seville) ed. of the *Regimento de Navegacion* which contains an abridgement of the *Arte de Navegar* of 1545.

NORMAN, ROBERT.

The New Attractive. C. 31. d. 2. (1. 2.). J. Kingston. 1581.

B(URROUGH), W(ILLIAM).
A Discourse on the Variation of the Compass. C. 31. d. 2. (1. 2.).
J. Kingston. 1581.

> The two works were issued in one volume. A second edition appeared in 1585.

ANONYMOUS.
The Carde or Rutter of the Sea lyenge betweene Holland and Fryse-land. Rich. Ballard. 1581.

> Only the licence is extant, dated 17 June.

ANONYMOUS.
Ye Image of Ireland, with the pictures. London. 1581.

> From Dee's Library Catalogue : unidentified.

DEE, JOHN.
De modo Evangelii Jesu Christi publicandi, propagandi, stabiliendi, inter infideles Atlanticos. Volumen magnum lib. 4 quorum primus spectat ad Reginam nostram potentissimam ; secundus ad sui Privati Concilli Senatores : tertius ad Regem Hispaniae : quartus ad Pontificem Romanum. MS. 1581.

1582

PARMENIUS, STEPHANUS, BUDAEUS.
De Navigatione Humfredi Gilberte Carmen. T. Purfoot. 1582.

> The author had been brought to London by Hakluyt of Oxford to meet the principal adventurers and friends of this voyage.

PHILIPS, MILES.
A Discourse of his whole Travel. MS. 1582.

> Presented in writing to her Majesty, and printed by Hakluyt 1589.

HAKLUYT, RICHARD, of Oxford.
Divers Voyages to America. T. Dawson. 1582.

HAKLUYT, RICHARD, of the Middle Temple.
A briefe Remembrance of things to be indevoured at Constantinople, and in other places in Turkey, touching our clothing and our Dying etc. MS. 1582.

> Given to his friend, Master S., going as a factor to Constantinople. Printed by Hakluyt.

LOPES, HERNANDO, DE CASTANHEDA.
The History of the Discovery and Conquest of the East Indias enterprised by the Portingales. Trs. by Nicholas Lichefield. 582. e. 4. T. East. 1582.

> Dedicated to Sir Francis Drake. This may be one of Thos. Nicholas' translations thinly disguised. From the Spanish version of the first book of the Portuguese original.

WORSOP, EDWARD.
A discovery of Sundry Errors committed by Landmeaters ignorant of Arithmetic and Geometry. 967. K. 23. H. Middleton. 1582.

> Inspired by Dee's Preface to the English Euclid.

1583

CARLILE, CHRISTOPHER.
A briefe and summary Discourse upon the intended voyage to the hithermost parts of America. April 1583.

> A Tract addressed to the Muscovy Co. relative to Sir H. Gilbert's Planting. Reprinted by Hakluyt.

DEE, JOHN.
Hemisphaeri Borealis Geographica atque Hydrographica Descriptio longè a vulgatis chartis diversa : Anglis quibus dum versus Atlantidis septentrionalia littora navigationum instituentibus, dono data. 1583.

> A gift to the Adventurers sailing with Gilbert, still preserved.

NICHOLAS, THOMAS.
A pleasant Description of the Fortunate Islands called the Islands of Canaria. G. 7074. T. East. 1583.

> Containing autobiographical details : Nicholas was a factor of Castelyn and Lok and a victim of the Inquisition.

LAS CASAS, BARTOLOMEO DE.
The Spanish Colony, or brief chronicle of the acts and gestes of the Spaniards in the West Indies called the New World, trs. by M. M. S. G. 7104. T. Dawson. 1583.

P(ECKHAM), G(EORGE).
A True Report of the late Discoveries of the New Found Land by Sir H. Gilbert. C. 32. c. John Charlewood. 1583.

> Reprinted by Hakluyt.

APPENDIX I_A

LIST OF JOHN DEE'S
GEOGRAPHICAL AND RELATED WORKS

1. Prologemena et dictata Parisiensa in Euclidis Elementorum Geometricum librum primum et secundum in Collegis Rhemensi. MS. A. 1550.
2. De usu Globi Coelestisis ad Regem Edwardum Sextum. MS. A. 1550.
3. De nubium solis, lunae, ac reliquorum planetarum, immo ipsius stelliferi coeli, ab infimo terrae centro, distantiis, mutuisque intervallis, et eorundem omnium magnitudine.
    Liber Apodeiktikos ad Edwardum VI Angliae Regem. MS. A. 1551.
4. The True Account (not vulgar) of Floods and Ebbs : written at the request of the Right Honourable Lady, Lady Jane, Dutchesse of Northumberland. MS. A. 1553.
5. An Astronomical Treatise, at the request of the Dutchesse of Northumberland. MS. A. 1553.
6. The Astronomical and Logisticall rules and canons to calculate the Ephemerides by, and other necessary accounts of heavenly motions written at the request, and for the use of, that Excellent Mechanician Master Richard Chancellor, at his last voyage into Moschovia. MS. A. 1553.
7. Inventum mechanicum paradoxum de novâ ratione circumferentiam circularem ; unde valdè rara alia dependent inventa. MS. A. 1556.
8. Speculum unitatis, sive apologia pro fratre Rogero Bachone, Anglo. MS. A. 1557.
9. De Annuli Astronomica multipliei usu. Lib. 2. MS. A. 1557.
10. De Nova Navigatione Ratione. Lib. 2. MS. (before 1558).
11. ' Joannes Dinus seu, Deus, astronomus peritissimus, in Italia ac Parisiis studens, pleraque edidit.' Has published many things, writes Bale. (Notebook made before 1558.)
12. De Itinere subterraneo. Lib. 2. MS. A. 1560.
13. Edition of Record's Ground of Arts. Reginald Wolf, 1561.
14. Reipublicae Britannicae Synopsis. In English MS. A. 1565.
15. Preface to English Euclid. 25 Feb. 1570.
16. The British Complement of the Perfect Art of Navigation. A great

book, in which are contained our Queen Elizabeth her tables gubernatick for longitudes and latitudes finding most easily and speedily, yea, if need be, without sight of sun, moon, or star ; with many other new and needful inventions gubernatick. MS. A. 1576.

Alternative Title quoted by Casaubon.

A great volume, in which are contained our Queen Elizabeth her Arithmeticall Tables Gubernatick : for Navigation by the Paradoxall Compasse (by me invented anno 1557) and Navigation by Great circles and for longitudes and latitudes : and the variation of the Compasse, finding most easily and speedily : yea, (if need be) in one minute of time, and sometime, without sight of Sun, Moone or Star : with many other new and needful inventions Gubernatick. MS. A. 1576.

17. The Great Volume of famous and rich discoveries (wherein is also the History of King Solomon, every three years, his Ophirian voyage, with divers other rarities), written A. 1576.

The Description of divers wonderful Isles in the Northern, Scythian, Tartarian, and the other most Northern Seas, and neare under the Pole, by Record written about 1200 yeres ago. A. 1576.

18. General and rare Memorials Pertayning to the Perfecte Arte of Navigation : annexed to the Paradoxall Cumpass in playne : J. Day, Sept. 1577.

19. Britannici Imperii Limites. MS. A. 1578.

20. Her Majesty's Title Royal to many foreign countreys, kingdoms and provinces.

In 12 Vellum skins of parchment, fair written for her Majesties' use, and by her Majesties' commandment. A. 1578.

21. De imperatoris nomine, authoritate, et potentia. MS. A. 1579.

22. Atlantidis, vulgariter Indiae Occidentalis nominatae, emendiator descriptio, quam adhuc est divulgata. MS. A. 1580.

23. Navigationis ad Cathayam per septentrionalia Scythiae et Tartariae littora deliniatis Hydrographa. Arthuro Pitt et Carolo Jackmanno versus illas partes navigaturis in manus tradita. MS. A. 1580.

24. De modo Evangelii Jesu Christi publicandi, propagandi, stabilindi inter *Infideles Atlanticos*. Volumen magnum lib. 4. quorum primus spectat ad Reginam nostram potentissimam ; secundus ad sui Privati Concilii Senatores : tertius ad Regem Hispaniae : quartus ad Pontificem Romanum. MS. A. 1581.

25. Hemisphaerii Borealis Geographica atque Hydrographica Descriptio : longè a vulgato chartis diversa. Anglis quibusdam versus Atlantidis septentrionalia littora navigationum instituentibus, dono data. MS. A. 1583.

APPENDIX II

CATALOGUE AND BIBLIOGRAPHY
OF
CONTEMPORARY LIBRARIES

Cosmographical Works from John Dee's Library Catalogue dated 6th September 1583 : marked D.

Cosmographical Works from Arundel-Lumley Catalogue dated 1610 c. : marked L.

Cosmographical Works from Sir Thomas Smith's Library Catalogue dated 1566 : marked S.

Cosmographical Works quoted by Purchas in 1614 : marked P.

Dee added the mark △ to certain important books.

Index letters prefixed to each entry indicate the class of work to which each book belongs, viz. :—

A. Astronomy.
B. Cosmography.
C. Chronicles and Historical Geography.
D. Togography.
E. Voyages and Travels.
F. Mathematical Geography, Navigation and Survey.
G. Physical Geography and Natural Philosophy.

B. ABULFEDA ISMAEL. Geography.

> Dee uses him in Ramusio's version.
> MS. brought from Constantinople by G. Postellus. Referred to by N. de Nicolai, Mercator, Ortelius, Hakluyt. First printed edition in Latin 1650.
> ' Ex Emanuelis nostri (i.e. Demetrius) literis ad me intelligo, D. Haclutum Geographiae Abyfildae Ismaelis editionis spem firmam ostendere. Putat enim eam ante annum in publicum venturam.' Ortelius to Camden, 25th November 1588.

E. ACOSTA, EMANUEL, De Rebus a societate Jesu in orienti gestis.

> L.P.   Translated from Portuguese by P. Maffeius, friend of R. Willes.

C. AELFREDUS REX. Res gestae. fo. London. N.D. [John Day. 1574.]

> D.   Printed from the first fount of Anglo-Saxon type.

B. AETHICUS. Cosmographia. In aliis, 16°. Basel. 1575.

D(2). With Antonine's Itinerary, of which it probably formed
P. an original part. Fourth Century A.D.

B. AETHICUS HISTER. *Cosmographia*, ex versione Latine D. Hieronymi. (i.e. from S. Jerome).

D. MS. A gift of Master Beddar, Dean of Winchester, 21st February 1565.

This is probably another work by the author of the *Cosmographia* printed at Basel (see d'Avezac).

Dee quotes also :

Ethicus Astronomicus, Antiquitatis Historia, a work dealing with the Northern Regions, also quoted by Roger Bacon.

G. AGRICOLA, GEORGIUS. De Re Metallica. fo. Frob. 1556.

D. First Edition. Basel, 1546. The author was George Landmann (1494–1555) of Chemnitz, Saxony, a famous metallurgist, carrying on practical study at Joachimstal, Bohemia.

Quoted by Eden. Recommended to Philip Sydney by Hugh Languet.

F. AGRICOLA, GEORGIUS. De mensuris et praeteribus. Basel. 1550.

D. △

G. AGRICOLA, GEORGIUS. De ortu et causis subterraneorum, etc. Basel. 1558.

D. △

E. ALARCHON, FERNANDO. Navigatione con l'armata di A. de Mendozza, quale andò per mare à scopire il Regno delle sette Città. 1540. Ramusio, Viaggi. 1556.

D.P. (Familiar to Eden, Gilbert, Hakluyt.)

A. ALBATEGINUS. Liber de Scientia Stellarum.

D. Al-Battânî, an Arab Astronomer, fl. 929.

' Unto which book Joannes de Regio Monte made additions, and Copernicus by this book had good aid in observations astronomical.' (Dee.)

' Wrote sundry books mathematical, and among others a Geography, imitating the methods of Ptolemaus.' (Dee.)

D. ALBERTUS, F. LEANDRUS. Descrittione di tutta l'Italia. Bologna. 1550.

L. By a Dominican monk of Bologna (1479–1552).

A. ALBUMASAR. De magnis conjunctionibus, etc. Venice. 1515.

D.   Albumasar or Japhar, of Balkh, Khorasan, fl. 776 A.D., a famous Arab Astronomer.
This work treats of astronomy and astrology with many woodcuts. Quoted by Dee on the *Climata*.

E. ALEXANDER MAGNUS. Epistola de mirabilibus Indiae. Paris. 1537.

D.

A. ALFRAGAN (Al-fergânï).

D.   Numerous works.
Wrote on sundials, astronomy, etc., and translated the *Almagest* into Arabic. A retranslation into Latin was published, Ferrara, 1493. Nürnberg, 1537. The latter is probably that quoted by Dee.

F. ALHAZEN ET VITELLIONI. Perspectiva. fo. Basel. 1573.

D.   Al-Haitam of Basra (*c.* 965–1039).
The above work is probably :
Optice Thesaurus Alhazani Arabis, libri septem, nunc primum editi, ejusdem liber de Crepusculis ; item Vitellionis Thuringopoloni, Libri X, a F. Risnero (illustrati et instaurati). Basle, E. Episcopius, 1572.
This is the *editio princeps* of Alhazen, and includes matter on optical lenses said to be the source of Roger Bacon's knowledge.

B. ALIACO, PETRO DE. De Imagine Mundi. fo. Venice.

D.   The famous work of Pedro d'Ailly, used by Christopher Columbus, is a compilation *c.* 1350–1410, including matter from the *Opus Majus* of Roger Bacon.

E. ALIARIS, PETRUS. Navigationis et mercatorum quorundam epistolarum opusculum. Novus Orbis.

D.L.P.   The same pieces as in the *Paesi* of 1507 and the *Itinerarium* of 1508, including two letters of Petro Pasqualigo, of which one gives the Corte Real story.

E. ALONSUS, PETRUS. Navigatio (Madrignano interprete). Novus Orbis.

D.L.P.

A. ALPHONSUS. Tabulae Astronomicae. Paris, 1545.

D.   The Alfonsine Tables were in general use among sixteenth-century mathematicians. They derive from Alfonso X, King of Castile (1223–84), called the Wise, who ordered their compilation. First printed, Venice, 1483.

C.   ALTHAMERIUS, ANDREAS. In Taciti Germaniam. August. vindelic. 1580.
> D.   The author (ob. 1540) was a Lutheran pastor of Nuremberg and Anspach. First Edition Nürnberg, 1529.

E.   D'ALVARADO, PIETRO. Lettere due à F. Cortese. Ramusio, Viaggi, 1556.
> D.P.

E.   ALVAREZ, FRANCESCO. Viaggio fatto nell' Ethiopia, 1520. Ramusio, Viaggi, 1550.
> D.P.   A French edition *Historiale description de l'Ethiopie, par Andrea Corsali et Francisco Alvarez*, was published at Antwerp by J. Bellere in 1558.

E.   ALVAREZ, PEDRO. Navigatione da Lisbona in Calicut. Ramusio, Viaggi, 1550.
> D.P.

C.   ANGIOLELLO, G. M. Della vita e fatti d'Ussuncassan, Re di Persia . . . 1462–1524. Ramusio, Viaggi, 1559.
> D.P.   Angiolello of Vicentia was the close friend of Montalboddo Francan, the compiler of the *Paesi*; he served in the Turks' Wars. Quoted by Dee in his *Great and Rich Discoveries*.

D.   ARETIUS, CL. MARIUS, SIRACUSANI. Siciliae Chorographia.
> L.(2).

G.   AUGUSTUS, SAXONIAE ELECTOR. Bergwerk Ordnung, constitutio mineral, etc., Germanicé. Breselae, 1577.
> D.

F.   AUTHORI VARIORUM. Annuli astronomici usus. 8° Paris, 1557.
> D.   The authors include Gemma Phrysius and Orontius Finaeus. [Edited by P. Beausardus.] C. 74. a. 16.

D.   ANTONINUS AUGUSTUS. Itinerarium Provinciarum. 16° Paris. N.D. and Lugd.
> D.(2).
> L.(2).

B.   APIANUS, PETRUS. Cosmographia. 4° Antwerp, 1545.
> D.
> D.   *Also* Cosmographie en françois, 4° Antwerp, 1581.
> L.(2).   Cosmographia, aucta per Gemmam Frisium.
> S.P.

Quoted by (*inter alia*) Eden, Gilbert, Rotz, Lhuyd, Cuningham, Ortelius, Harvey, i.e. most widely known work on subject. First Edition, 1524. Peter Bienewitz (1495–1552) was Professor of Astronomy and Mathematics at Ingolstadt in 1528. He gave instruction and wrote in the vernacular. His first world-map, based on Waldseemüller, was drawn to illustrate Camers' Solinus, Vienna, 1520, and Vadian's Pomponius Mela, Basel, 1522.

Two English licences to print were taken out, but apparently no English edition was printed. The Phrysius-Apian appeared in Castilian and in French.

B. APIANUS, PETRUS. Introductio Geographica, etc. Ingolstadt, 1530.

 D.

 L.   Do. Do. (In Annotationes Verneri).

F. APIANUS, PETRUS. Sphaera cum commentariis. fo. Venice. N.D.

 D.   The basis of many other editions.

A. APIANUS, PETRUS. Horoscopion Generalis. fo. Ingolstadt, 1532.

 D.

A. APIANUS, PETRUS. Primum Mobile. fol. Norimb., 1534.

 D.

A. APIANUS, PETRUS. Instrumentum Sinuum seu primi mobilis, etc. Norimb., 1541.

 D.

F. APIANUS, PETRUS. Arithmetica germanicé. 8° Frankfurt, 1537.

   Probably an edition of ' Eyn Newe ennd wolgegründte underweysung aller Kauffmanss Rechnung '. Ingol. 1527.

F. APIANUS, PETRUS. Quadrans Astronomicus, et alia instrumenta ab eodem inventa. 1532 and 1533.

 L.   This collection of Mathematical Tracts includes use of Astronomer's Staff for taking a Lunar Distance (illustrated in the Frontispiece) from a Fixed Star, and is the source of this method for e.g. Rotz. It contains Werner's translation of Ptolemy, Bk. I, with the translator's ' single heart ' projection. Also Apian's Improved Torquetum, Quadrant, Geometrical Square and Horoscopion. Gives stock methods of geometrical measurements of length depth, and height, with illustrations of towers and wells. Source book for Digges and others.

E. APOLLONIUS, LEVINIUS. De Rebus Peruvinis. 8° Antwerp, 1567.

D.P.   On Dee's list of Books important for Navigation. Author born in Flanders, died in Canary Is. on his way from Peru. English translation licensed 1596. Apollonius wrote also : De Navigatione Gallorum in Terram Floridam, 1568.

G. ARISTOTELES. Opera. 2 vols. Basel, 1538.

D.

A. ARNALDUS DE VILLA NOVA. Opera. Ven., 1527.

D.   Author a famous alchemist and teacher of Ramon Lully, fl. 1290. Dee has many other of his works, both printed and MSS.

C. ARNOLD, RICHARD. Arnold's Chronicle. fo. N.D.

D.   See Catalogue of English works.

E. ARRIANO. Lettera, della sua Navigatione d'intorno al Mar Maggiore. Ramusio, Viaggi, 1559.

D.P.   The Periplus of Arrian.

E. ARRIANUS. Periplus ponti euximé et maris Erythraei. fo. Geneva, 1557.

D.(2).P.   4° Frob., 1533.

E. ARRIANO. Navigatione del Mar Rosso, fino all' Indie Orientali, tradotta per il Ramusio.

D.P.   Ramusio, Viaggi. 1550. The Periplus of the Erythraean Sea.

E. AVISI diversi et nuovi del' Indie de Port igallo, riceunto dall' anno 1551 sino al 1558 e 1560, dalle reverendi patri della Compagnia di Gieusu. Italicé. 2 vols. N.D.

L.   A series of volumes of these letters from various parts of the Portuguese dominions was published by Michele Tramezzino, at Venice. The work catalogued here includes Series I–IV.

E. AVISI dall' Indie Orientali, Italicé. 3 vols. Venice, 1560.

D.   On Dee's list of Books important for Navigation.

B.G. BACHON, ROGER. Opus Majus. Pars quarta, Pars sexta (*bis*) pars septima.

> D. Dee has many other MSS. of Bacon, and quotes the geographical section of *Opus Majus* at length in the *Great and Rich Discoveries.*

G. BACHON, ROGER. De mirabili potestate artis et naturae. Paris, 1542.

> D. Quoted also by Eden and used by L. Digges.

F. BAYFIUS, LAZARUS. De re navali. 4° Frob. (Basle), 1537.

> D.L. Quoted also by Eden and by Dee. The author was French Ambassador to Venice and Germany. He died in 1547.

A. BAKER, HUMPHREY. Rules touching the use of Almanacks etc. London, 1557.

> L. (*Under title* Rules for the Ephemerides.)
> The author wrote also *The Well Spring of Sciences*, 1568, and a commercial *Arithmetic.*

C. BALEUS, JOHN. De Scriptoribus Brytannicis et Anglicis. fo. Oporin. N.D.

> D.L. See English catalogue.

C BALEUS, JOHN. De Scriptoribus Britanniae. Wes., 1549.

> D.

F. BARBARO, DANIELE. Perspectiva. fo. Venice, 1568.

> D. The Venetian author also edited Vitruvius' Architecture. He was Ambassador to England in the reign of Henry VIII.

E. BARBARO, JOSAFA. Viaggio della Tana, e nella Persia. 1436. Ramusio, Viaggi, 1559.

> D.P.

E. BARBARO, ODOARDO. Libro di, dell' Indie Orientali, 1516. Ramusio, Viaggi, 1550.

> D.P.

B. BARROS, GIOVAN DI. Delle Historia, con alcuni capitoli estratti appartementi alla Cosmographia. Ramusio, Viaggi, 1550.

> D.

D. BARROS, GIOVANNI DI. Asia. 4°. Venice, 1562.

> D.L.S.P. Lumley has Decades 1 and 2 del Asia, tradotto en volgare Italiano.
> The original title runs : *Asia de Joam de Barros, dos*

fectos que os Portugueses fizeram no descobrimento e con-
quista dos mares et terras do Oriente. 1552. The Second
Decade was published 1553, and the Third in 1563. The
Portuguese author lived 1496–1570 ; the Fourth Decade
was not published until 1615.

C.   BARTOLI, COSIMO.   Discorsi Historica Universali.   Ven., 1569.
     (First Edition.)
     D.

F.   BARTOLI, COSIMO.   Di modo di mensurare le distantia etc.
     Italicé, 1564.
     L.   The author, a Florentine geometer, wrote also on archi-
               tecture, and general philosophy. He bases his work on
               Apian, Phrysius, Rojas, Orontius, and translates the latter.
               He lived 1503–72.

C.   BEDA.   Historia Ecclesiastica gentis Anglorum.   fo. Antwerp,
     1550.
     D.S.

F.   BEDA.   De Ratione Temporum.   Colon, 1537.
     D.   The Venerable Bede is credited also with treatises on the
               Sphere and the Astrolabe. (fl. 673–735.)   See English
               Catalogue.

BELLEFOREST, FRANÇOIS DE.   Cosmographie.   2 vols.   Paris,
     1575.
     D.   The author was a poet, and his cosmography was an
               abridgement of Sebastian Munster made as a means of
               livelihood. He lived 1530–83. His views are discussed
               by Dee in the *Great and Rich Discoveries,* 1577.

E.   BENJAMIN TUDELENSIS.   Itinerarium.   Trs. by B. Arias
     Montanus.   8°.   Plantin.   1573.
     D.P.   Benjamin of Tudela, a Spanish rabbi, travelled in the
               East about 1160–73. His Travels were first printed in
               Arabic at Constantinople, 1543. B. Arias Montanus, the
               translator, was the author of the Polyglot Bible, and a
               close friend of Ortelius and his circle.

E.   BENZONI, GIROLAMO.   Historia del mondo novo.   Italicé.   8°
     Venice, 1572. (Second Edition.) (First Edition, Venice,
     1565.)
     D.

E. BENZONI, HIEROSIUS.   Histoire du Nouveau Monde.   Geneva, 1579.

D.P.   This is an edition of Benzoni by Urbain Chauveton (Urban Calveton). The Milanese author travelled in America 1541–65. To the Latin edition of his Historia, he added a Latin version of N. de Shalleux's account of Ribault's Last Voyage, which formed part of his *Descriptio Expeditionis Gallorum in Floridam.* This is included in the Latin edition of Chauveton, i.e. *Novae Novi Orbis Historiae. Lib. tres.*

Hakluyt quotes Benzoni as ' Peter Benzo ' in his *History of Western Planting.*

F. BESSON, JACQUES.   Le Cosmolabe.   4° Oporin.   Basle, 1561.

D.   Born in Grenoble, Besson was Professor of Mathematics at Orléans in 1569, and also held the position of Master of the King's Engines to Charles IX. Eden made his acquaintance in France 1563–72, and possessed his books ; Humphrey Cole put one of his devices into practice as reported by W. Bourne. He died in England, a refugee from the Massacre of S. Bartholomew.

F. BESSONUS, JACOBUS.   Instrumenta et Machina.   Large fol. N.D.

D. △   The Latin version of the *Théatre des Instruments.*

E. BEST, GEORGE.   A True Discourse etc.   London, 1578.

D.P.   See English Catalogue.

G. BIRINGUCCIO, VANUCCI.   Pyrotechnia.   Italicé.   4° Venice, 1540 (First Edition).

D.

G. BIRINGUCCIO, VANUCCI.   Le Pyrotechnie en françois.   4°. 1556.

The Italian author, a mathematician, wrote specially on mining and metals, cannon-founding, gunpowder and fireworks. In his *Book of Metals,* partly translated by Eden, he quotes Pliny, Albertus Magnus, Georgius Agricola. He supervised mines in the Eastern Alps for the Venetian Government and travelled to Germany to study mining and mineralogy there.

G. BOCCATIUS, JOHANNES.   De montibus, sylvis, fontibus, lacibus, flumenibus, stagnis, paludibus, maribus liber.   N.D.

L.   First Edition, 1481.

G. BOEMUS, JOHANNES. Omnium gentium mores. 1536.
L.P. See also Catalogue of English books, Prat and Watreman.

C. BOETIUS, HECTOR. Historia Scotica. Paris, 1574.
D. *Under title* Scotorum Historia.
L.P. The 1574 edition had J. Ferrer's addenda. See also the Catalogue of English books. The Scottish historian was strongly criticized by Humfrey Lhuyd in his *Fragmentum*. He wrote also a *Liber de Navigationibus*.

D. BORDONE, BENEDETTO. Isolario. Italicé, 1547 (Fifth Edition).
D.P. This Paduan Maritime Painter, like N. de Nicolai, turned his brush to the making of maps, harbour plans and views. His *Isolario, nel qual si regiona di tutte l'Isole del Mondo, con li loro nomi antichi e moderni*, was first published in Venice, 1528, and again in 1533, 1534, 1537, and 1547. He wrote also a *Descrittione de l'Italia*. He died *c.* 1529.

BORRHAUS, MARTINUS. Cosmographia. 8° Oporin. N.D.
D. This must be the work : *In Cosmographiae Elementa Commentatio Astronomica, Geographica.* Basel. Jo. Oporin. 1555. The R.G.S. copy of the first edition has the autograph of the mathematician P. Gassarius, dated September 1555, i.e. probably a presentation copy on publication. The work appears to be a commentary on the *Sphera* of Apian. Borrhaus was the pupil of Stöfler, the friend of Philip Melancthon.

F. BOURNE, WM. The Arte of Shooting in Great Ordnance. 4° London, 1578.
D. Based on Tartaglia. Dee's friendship with Bourne accounts for the inclusion of a book written in English in his library : he had very few. See also Catalogue of English Books.

F. BOURNE, WM. Treasure for Travellers. 4° London, 1578.
D. As above. See Catalogue of English Books.

E. BREYDENBACH, BERNHARDUS DE. Peregrinatio Jerosolymitana, seu sanctarum perigrinationem opusculum. Spirae, 1502.
D.
L.P. *Under title*, Peregrinationes ad Hierusalem.
The German author travelled to Jerusalem in 1482 and died 1502. The *Opusculum* has maps, plans, and figures; the first edition appeared in 1486, the second in 1490, also at Speier.

BROCARDUS, MONACHUS. Novus Orbis.

D.L.P.   Presumably from the MS. of 1332, *Directorium ad passagium faciendum . . . in terram sanctam.* This mediæval author is not to be confused with Bonaventura Brochard, a Frenchman who travelled to Jerusalem in 1533, and who published a map, *Delineatio et descriptio Jerusalem . . . excusa Parisiis,* 1544. He is mentioned by the Vidame of Chartres as exercising the art of Paracelsus.

D. BRUIN, GEORGIUS ; Novellanum, Sim. ; Hogenburgium Franc. ; editae per, Civitates Orbis Terrarum.
Antwerp, 1573.
L.P.

D. BURCHARDUS. Descriptio terrae sanctae. 8° Venice, 1519.
D.   The original MS. by Burchardus de Monte Sion was dated 1283.

F. CABOTA, SEBASTIANO. Nav. nelli Parti Settentrionali, 1556-7.
Ramusio, Viaggi, 1559.
D.P.

F. CA DA MOSTO, ALOISE DE. Navigatione, 1455. Ramusio, Viaggi, 1550.
D.P.

F. CADAMOSTO, ALOYSIUS. Navigatio ad terras ignotas, Arcangelo Madrignano interprete. Novus Orbis.
D.L.P.

D. CAMDEN, WILLIAM. His Remains of a Greater Work.
L.P.

D. CAMDENUS, GULLELMUS, ANGLUS. Britannia.
L.P.

C. CAMPENSE, ALBERTO. Lettera intorno le cose di Moscovia.
Ramusio, Viaggi, 1559.
D.P.

E. ÇARATOGO, AUGUSTIN (i.e. Zarate). Historia del Peru, en español. 8°. Antwerp, 1555.
D.P.   See also Catalogue of English Books.

G. CARDANUS, HIERONYMUS. De Subtilitate. Lib. XXI. fo. Norimb., 1550, and fo. Basel, 1554.
D.(2).
S.P.

G. CARDANUS, HIERONYMUS. De Varietate rerum. fo. Basel, 1557.

> D.
>
> S.　　　The Pavian mathematician and philosopher, greatly admired by Eden, was an associate of Tartaglia in early life. He visited Scotland to prescribe for Cardinal Beaton in 1552, and on his way through London stayed with Sir J. Cheke and prescribed for Edward VI, on whom he afterwards wrote an epitaph. His two works, cited above, deal with problems of Physics, Natural History, and Cosmography, as well as Metaphysics. Dee discusses Scaliger's edition of the *De subtilitate* in the *Volume of Great and Rich Discoveries*.

E. CARTHIER, JACQUES. Prima Relatione della Terra Nuova . . . 1534. Ramusio, Viaggi, 1556.

> D.P.

E CARTHIER, JACQUES. Seconda Relatione delle Navigatione per lui fatta . . . 1535.
　　Ramusio, Viaggi, 1556.

> D.P.

E. CARTIER, JACQUES. His Navigations. London, 1580.

> D.P.　See Catalogue of English Books.

C. DE LAS CASAS, BARTELEMY. Tyrannie des espagnols perpetuées ès Indies Occidentales. en françois. 8° Antwerp, 1579.

> D.P.　　　On Dee's list of Books important for Navigation. From the Spanish. An English version appeared in 1583.

F. CATANEO, GIROLAMO. Del Misurare. Lib 2. Brescia, 1572.

> D.　　　The author was a contemporary Italian engineer ; his work is mentioned by C. Lucar.

E. CHANCELLOR, RICHARD. Voyage into Moscovia, with the description of the names of the people there. MS. anglicé.

> L.　　　This MS. was probably written for the Earl of Arundel, one of the promoters of the first Muscovy Voyage, and placed in his Library.

C. CHRONICON ANGLIAE. Anglicé MS.

> D.

C. CHRYTAEUS, DAVID. Chronologia Herodoti et Thucydidis. Argent., 1563.

> D.P.　　　Dee has many other works of this voluminous author,

whose real name was Nathan Kochlaff. He visited London and Oxford in 1565, and at the University saw the map of Seb. Cabot, from which he transcribed the inscriptions, publishing them in his *Variorum in Europa itinerum Deliciae.* Herborn, 1594. This appears to have been the map ' cut by Clement Adams ' of 1549. (See Harrisse.) Chrytraeus was a correspondent of Wm. Camden.

C. CIEÇA, PEDRO DE, DE LEON. Chronica del Peru en español. 8° Antwerp, 1554. And in 3 vols. Venice, 1560.

D.(2).P. First edition, Seville, 1553. Third edition, Rome, 1555. On Dee's list of Books important for Navigation. The Seville historian was with Pizarro in Peru for 17 years.

B. CLEOMEDES. De Mundo. Basel, 1561.

D. Greek Astronomer of first century B.C.

G. CLUSIUS, CAROLUS. De simplicibus med. ex occidentali India : Historia aromatum India Orientalis. Plantin. 1574.

D.P.

G. CLUSIUS, CAROLUS. Historia aromatum Indiae. 8°. 1567.

D.

G. CLUSIUS, CAROLUS. De simplicibus medicamentis ex India occidentali delapsi. Anvers. 1574.

D. This work is translated from the Spanish of Nicholas Monardus (later Englished by Frampton) and is on the special list of books endorsed by Dee as useful for Navigation. The translator, Charles de Lecluse, was a famous French botanist (1524–1609) who studied at Louvain, visited England, and travelled much over Europe. His works on the herbs and plants of the E. and W. Indies were studied by the elder Hakluyt. In addition to botanical works he was the author of maps, *Tabula Chorographica Galliae,* Narbonensis, 1565. *Hispaniae Nova Descriptio.* 1570. Ortelius' Theatrum.

F. COIGNET, MICHEL. De l'Art de Naviguer. Antwerp, 1581.

D. A French translation of Pedro de Medina. For Frampton's English Translation, see Catalogue of English Books. Coignet was a friend of Ortelius.

E. COLOMBO, CHRISTOFERO. Navigatio ex jussu Hispani Regis, ad multas insulas hactenus incognitas. Madrignano interprete. Novus Orbis.

D.L.P.

D. COLUMBUS, CHRISTOPHERUS. De insulis in mare indico. N.D.

   L.   Evidently an edition of the *Epistola de insulis noviter repertis*, of which there were many, e.g. Strassburg, 30th September, 1497.

C. COLOMBO, FERNANDO. Historia del mondo nuovo. 8° Venice, 1572.

   D.

E. CONTARINI, AMBROSIO. Viaggio nella Persia. Ramusio, Viaggi, 1559.

      From Viaggi Fatta da Vinetia, etc. Venice, 1545.

   D.P.   The original version, Venice, 1487, and Venice 1524, had the title, *Itinerario del Magnifico et Clarissimo messer Antonio Contarini* . . . *mandado nel anno 1471 ad Usuncassan Re de Persia* . . . and contained descriptions of Allmagna, Pollonia, Lituania, Rossia bassa, Rossia biancha, Tartaria Deuropa, Mengrelia, Zorzania, Armenia, Persia, Media, Tartaria de Asia, Mar de Bachan, cive Caspio, Mar Major. It was an important work of reference for the Near East.

E. CONTI, NICOLO DE. Viaggio nelle Indie Orientali. Ramusio, Viaggi, 1550.

   D.P.

COOPER, THOMAS. Chronicles. London, 1565.

   D.   This was the second of Cooper's editions of the *Epitome of Chronicles* of Languet, continued after 1559 by Rob, Crowley. Cooper refers to Seb. Cabot in relation to the 1553 voyage, but leaves out the statement that he was a Genoese' son (see Harrisse).

A. COPERNICUS, NICHOLAUS. Revolutiones. fo. Norimb., 1543. (First Edition.)

   D△(2).   *Also* Libris Revolutionum, 8° Basel, N.D.

   L.(2).   De Revolutionibus Orbium Coelestium. Lib. 6.

   S.P.   Copernicus (1473–1543) studied first at the University of Cracow, later at Padua, Bologna and Rome. His theory, completed 1530, was first published in the year of his death.

E. CORSALI, ANDREA. Della Navigatione . . . a Cochin. 1517. Ramusio, Viaggi, 1550.

   D.P.

E. CORSALI, ANDREA. Lettere scritta in Cochin, 1515. Ramusio, Viaggi, 1550.

D.P.

E. CORTESIUS, FERDINANDUS. De insulis noviter inventis, narratio, ad Carolem Quintem imperatorem. Novus Orbis.

D.L.P.   The great adventurer's letters to Charles V first appeared in Seville 1522, and were widely translated.

E. CORTESE, FERNANDO. Relationi seconda, terza e quarta, delle sue grandi imprese, con l'acquisto della gran Città del Temistitan Messico, dove hora è detto la Nuova Spagna. 1519–24.
   Ramusio, Viaggi, 1556.

D.P.

E. CORTESIUS, FERNANDUS. Narratio . . . ad Carolum Quintum, translata per Petrum Saguorguam (?) fo. 1524.

D.   On Dee's list of Books important for Navigation.

F. CORTES, MARTIN. The Art of Navigation. trans. by R. Eden.

S.   See English Catalogue.

B. CORVINUS, LAURENTIUS. Geographia, ostendens omnes regiones terrae habitilis, diversa hominum genera. Basel, 1557.

L.P.   The author (1495–1527) was a German, who became Professor at Breslau and Cracow.

B. COSMOGRAPHIAE RUDIMENTA. Auctor Incertus.

L.

C. CUREUS, JOACHIM. Annales Silesiae. Wittenberg, 1571. First Edition.

D.   The author (1532–73), a Silesian physician and historian, studied under Melancthon.

E. CURTIUS, QUINTUS. De rebus gestis Alexandrii Magni. Basel, 1575.

D.   On Dee's list of Books important for Navigation.

A.F. CUSANUS, NICOLAUS, CARDINAL. Opera. Paris, 1514. 2 vols.

D.   Nicholas à Cusa, Cardinal and Bishop of Brescia (1401–64) was the teacher of Georg von Peurbach, who in turn taught Regiomontanus. The Cardinal was a Cartographer, wrote on mathematics, and edited the Alfonsine Tables. The first Paris edition of the *Opera* was published 1511.

E. DAMIANUS À GOES. Commentarius rerum gestarum in India citra Gangem, a Lusitanis 1538. Louvain, 1539.

L.P.

B. DANAEUS, LAMBERTUS. Geographica Poetica. 8° Gen., 1580.

D.L.   The author, Lambert Daneau, an eminent Swiss protestant theologian, was the friend of Anthony Bacon, son of Sir Nicholas Bacon.

F. DASYPODIUS, CONRADUS, HERON. MECHANICUS. Horologii Astronomici. Argent, 1580.

D.   Dasypodius (1530–1600) was Professor of Mathematics at Strassburg, where the famous Astronomical Clock was built (see also Lansdown, 100). His works included an edition of Euclid, 1564.

F. DEE, JOHN. The Art of Navigation, or the British Monarchy. fo. London, 1577.

D.L.   The full title was : *General and Rare Memorials pertayning to the arte of Navigation, annexed to the Paradoxall Compasse in Plaine.* See also the Catalogue of English Books.

F. DEE, JOHN. Euclides, Anglicé. fol. London, 1574 (*sic*).

D. △   See also Catalogue of English Books.

G. DELPHINUS, FREDERICUS. De fluxu et refluxu maris. fo. Venice, 1559.

D.   The author (1477–1547) was a physician and astronomer, native of Padua.

A. DIGGES, LEONARD. Prognostication, with the augmentation of it by his own son Thomas Digges.

L.

F. DIGGES, LEONARD, and DIGGES, THOMAS. Geometrical Practice. (Pantometria.) London, 1571.

D.   See also Catalogue of English Books.

C. DIODORUS SICULUS. Large folio, Basel, 1548.

D.(2).   One edition in Greek, Basel, 1539.
L.(3).   In Greek and in French, and in version of Poggio Florentinus.

S.P.

C. DIODORO SICULO . . . tradotto per il Ramusio. Ramusio, Viaggi, 1550.

D.P.

C. DIOGENES LAERTIUS. Vitae Philosophorum. Large 8°, 1516.

    D.P.   Written in third century, this is a source book for information on early history of Greek thought and practice, including geography.

B. DIONYSIUS AFER or ALEXANDRINUS. De situ orbis, cum commentariis Eustatiis. Paris, 1556.

    D.

    L.   Do. Do. Priscianus interprete.

    L.(2).   Orbis Habitibilis Descriptio, graecé et latiné.

    S.P.   See also Catalogue of English Books.

E. DISCORSO d'un gran Capitano di Mare Francese . . . di Summatra. Ramusio, Viaggi, 1556.

    D.P.

B. DODONAEUS, RAMBERTUS. Cosmographia in Astronomiam et Geographiam Isagoge. Antwerp, 1548.

    L.

E. DRAKE, SIR FRANCIS, and CAPTAIN FURBISHER. Voiage into the West Indies, anno 1585. Anglicé MS.

    L.

C. DUBRAVIUS, JOHN. Historia Bohemica. fo. Basel, 1575.

    D.   John Dubraw, Polish historian (ob. 1553), was Bishop of Olmütz, and published his history in 33 books in 1550.

G. ECKERN, LAZARUS. Bergwerk, opus de mineralibus, germanicé. fol.

    D.

E. EDEN, RICHARD. Decades of the New World. London, 1555.

    S.P.   It is quoted by Dee, although not named in his library catalogue. See also Catalogue of English Books.

E. EMANUEL, REX PORTUGALLIAE. Epistola ad Leonum decimum de victoriis habitis in India et Molucca, etc. Novus Orbis.

    D.L.P.

E. EMPOLI, GIOVANNI DA. Viaggio fatto nell' India. 1503. Ramusio, Viaggi, 1550.

    D.P.

E. EPISTOLAE Indica de praeclaris et stupendis rebus, quas divino bonitas in India et variis insulis, per societatem nominis Jesu, operari dignus est . . . ex editione Johannis Rut, Bergensis.

L.

E. EPISTOLAE Duae, de evangelii profectu apud Indos. Novus Orbis.

D.L.P.

E. EPISTOLAE Indicae. 8° Louvain, 1566.

D.L.

E. EPISTOLAE Indicae et Japonicae. 8° Louvain, 1570.

D.   This volume contains Ja. Navarchus' *Epistola asiatica*, quoted by Dee.

On Dee's list of Books important for Navigation.

E. EPISTOLAE Aliquot Jesuitorum de rebus Japonicis. 8° Coloniae, 1582.

D.   On Dee's list of Books important for Navigation.

E. EPISTOLAE. Rerum a Societatis Jesu in orientem, gestarum seu epistolarum libri. Dil. 1571, and 8° Paris, 1572.

D.(2).   On Dee's list of Books important for Navigation.

E. EPISTOLAE. Rerum Japonicarum . . . seu epistolarum ad annum 1565 liber. 8° Colon, 1574.

On Dee's list of Books important for Navigation.

E. ERASMUS, ROTERDAMUS. Descriptio perigrinationis Petri et Pauli, cum ratione temporum.

L.

E. ESCALANTA, BERNARDIN OF. Discourse, etc., trans. by John Frampton. London, 1579.

D.P.   See also Catalogue of English Books.

G. FABER, Jo. De Muscovitarum Religione. 1526.

This author, Bishop of Vienna, dedicates his work to Archduke Ferdinand, brother of Charles V. It was written at the same time and on the same occasion (see Embassy of Demetrius) as Paulus Jovius' book on Muscovy. This writer must not be confused with Jacobus Faber Stapulensis, or with the Faber (Jacobus Antonius) who translated Pigafetta for the Queen Regent of France, 1522. Eden confuses the three different persons in the Decades.

B. FERNANDEZ, MARTIN, D'ENCISO. Summa de Geographia dirigada al Emperador Carlos V. fo. Hispalis, 1530.

    D.   First Edition, 1519.
On Dee's list of Books important for Navigation. See also Catalogue of English Books, Barlow and Frampton.

G. FERNELIUS, JOH. De abditis rerum causis. fo. Paris, 1551.

    D.   Fernelius (1497–1558) was a French physician and mathematician whom Dee met in Paris, where he held a Professorship. He is credited with computing more accurately the length of the arc of a meridian, and in the work cited, claims in the dedication to Henri II to ' have put our helping hands to the Arte of Navigation and Geographie . . . for by observations of the houres of the Equinoctials, we have invented how, in whatsoever region or place of the world a man shall be, he may know what longitude is'. He is quoted by Eden.

A.C. FICINUS, MARSILIUS. De vita. lib. tres. 8° Basel, 1529.

    D.P.   This celebrated Florentine astronomer (1433–99) devoted himself especially to the study of Plato and Plotinus. He was very widely read and quoted in England. The first edition of the work cited above, which deals in part with Judicial Astronomy, was published at Florence 1489.

E. FIORAVANTE, CRISTOFERO, E MICHELE, G. DI. Descritto . . . del Viaggio di Quirino. Ramusio, Viaggi, 1559.

    D.P.

G. FIORAVANTI, LEONARDO. D'ello spechio di scientia universale. Venice, 1567.

    D.L.   The author, a Bolognese (1500c.–1588) was a famous physician, alchemist and traveller. He is often quoted by Eden. The first edition of the above, his most famous, work was published in 1564. An English translation of one of his medical works appeared in 1562.

F. FOULLON, ABEL. De l'holometre, en françois. 4° Paris, 1555.

    D.   For Abel Foullon see Chapter VIII.

G. FRACASTORIUS, HIERONYMUS. Opera. 4° Venice, 1555.

    D.P.   To this famous Veronese Physician and Poet (1483–1553) Ramusio owed the idea, and in part the material of the Viaggi.

G. FRACASTORO, HIERONIMO. Riposta sopra il detto crescimento del Nilo. Ramusio, Viaggi, 1550.

    D.P.

C. FRAMPTON, JOHN. Discourse of ye Conquest of ye East Indias by Bernardin of Escalanta. London, 1579.
 D. See the Catalogue of English Books.

D. FRANCE. Les fleurs de Royaume de, gallicé, auctor ignotus.
 L.

B. FRANCUS, SEBASTIANUS, WERDENSIS. Cosmographia, De Moribus et vitibus variarum gentium, etc. fo. 1567.
 D.

E. FROBISHER, MARTIN. Le Navigation du, en françois. 8° Geneva, 1578.
 D. Translated from D. Settle's Narrative, by N. Pithou.

E. FROBISHER, M. Narratio Historica de Navigationes. Translated by Freigius. 8° Norimb., 1580.
 D. From the French edition above.

E. GAETAN, JUAN. Relatione del discoprimento dell' Isole Molucche per la via dell' Indie Occidentali. 1542–5. Ramusio, Viaggi, 1550.
 D.P.

G. GALESIUS, AUGUSTINUS. De terrae motu. 4° Bononiae, 1571.
 D.

C. GALFRIDUS MONUMENTENSIS. De gestis regnum Britanorum, lib. ix. 4° Paris, 1517.
 D.L.(2).

E. GAMA, VASCO DI. Navigatione . . . 1497. Ramusio, Viaggi, 1550.
 D.P.

C. GENEBRARDUS, GILBERTUS. Chronographia, Lib iv. Paris, 1567.
 D.P.

F. GEMMA FRISIUS. Arithmetica. Antwerp, 1547.
 D.

F. GEMMA FRISIUS. De Astrolabio Catholico. 8°. 1556.
 D.L.(12).

F. GEMMA FRISIUS. De Radio Astronomico. 8° Paris, 1557, and 4° Antwerp, 1545.
 D.(2).
 S.

A.C. GEMMA FRISIUS. De Principiis Astronomiciis. Antwerp, 1533.

D.

L.(2)   *Under title* : De Principiis astronomiae et cosmographiæ ; de usu globi ; de orbis divisione, et insulis, rebusque nuper inventis. (First Edition, 1530.)
See also Apian.

D.   GERBELIUS, NICOLAS. Descriptio Graecia. Lib. VI.

L.

E.   GILBERT, SIR HUMFREY. Discourse, etc. London, 1576.

D.   See Catalogue of English Books.

C.   GIORGIO, INTERIANO, GENOVESE. della Vita di Zychi, altrimenti Circassi. Ramusio, Viaggi, 1559.

D.P.

B.   GIRAVA, HIERONYMUS. Cosmographia, en español. 4° Mediolani, 1556. (First Edition.)

D.P.   The author was of Tarragona, Spain ; the book is based on Ptolemy and the classics, besides Apian, Phrysius, Glareanus, Munster, Volaterrano, etc. Map is that of Gaspar Vopel of 1547. Second Edition. Venice, 1570.

B.   GLAREANUS, HENRICUS. De Geographia. lib. I. 4° Basel, 1528.

D.L.   Henricus Loritus Glareanus (1488–1563) was Professor at Basel, 1515–21, at Collège de France 1521–24, and later at Friburg and again at Basel. His Geography (First Edition, 1527) is on strictly classical lines, with the addition of two chapters on ' regions outside Ptolemy '. He wrote also a *Helvitiæ Descriptio* (in verse) and *De ponderibus et mensuris*. Dee has also a work of his, *De Asse*.

E.   GODOI, DIEGO. Lettera à F. Cortese. Ramusio, Viaggi, 1556.

D.P.

D.   GODRECCIUS, WENCESLAUS. Epistola in tabulas poloniae a se descriptas. Oporin, 1558.

D.

D.   GOLTZIUS, HUGH. Graeca Magna. fo. 1576.

D.   First Edition. Bruges.

G.   GOROPIUS, JOHANNES, BECANUS. Origines. Antwerp, 1569.

D.P.   The full title runs : *Origines Antwerpianae, sive Cimmeriorum Becceselana novem libris complexa : Atvatica,*

Gigantomachia, Niloscropium, Cronia, Indo-Scythica, Sax-sonica, Ethro-Danica, Amazonica, Venetica et Hyperborea.
Goropius or van Gorp (1518–72) was of Brabant. He studied at Louvain, and travelled in France, Italy, and Spain, settling finally at Antwerp, where he took up the study of Antiquity. He was a friend of Dee's and of Ortelius. In 1546 Henry VIII sought his services to further Sir H. Knyvett's journey into Asia—a project that fell through.

E. GRYNAEUS, SIMON. Praefatio ad Collimitium. Novus Orbis. Basel, 1555.

D.L.   Simon Grynaeus edited the collection of travels gathered by John Huttich, first published at Basel in 1532 and in Paris the same year, of which the full title runs : *Novus Orbis regionum et insularum veteribus incognitarum : una cum tabula cosmographica et aliquot aliis consimilis argumenti libellis.* The world map was by Munster. The separate works making up the collection are listed under their author's names singly. The dedication is to Georgius Tanstetter Collimitius, himself a geographer and cartographer.

D. GUAGNINO, ALESSANDRO. Descrittione della Sarmatia Europea. Ramusio, Viaggi, 1559.

D.P.

D. GUEROULT, GUILLAUME. Epitome de la Chorographie d'Europe. fo. Lugdunum, 1553.

D.   The author was a well-travelled physician and botanist of Caen.

D. GUICCARDINI, LUDOVICO. Descrittione di tutti i paesi.

L.

D. GUICCARDIN, LOUIS. Description de tout le pays-bas. fo. Antwerp, 1568.

E. GUIDE DES CHEMINS. 16° Rouen, 1579.

D.

E. GUIDE DES CHEMINS DE FRANCE, reneu et augmenté. N.D.

L.   The earliest of these French road books dates from the middle of the century. Cf. Carto-bibliographies of Sir George Fordham.

C. GUSMAN, NUNNO DI. Relatione dell' imprese fatte in acquistare molte Provincia e Città nella Maggior Spagna. 1530. Ramusio, Viaggi, 1556.

D.P.

D. GYLLIUS, PETRUS. De Bosporo Thracio. lib. iii. 4° Lugd., 1562.

D.P.

D. GYLLIUS, PETRUS. De Topographia Constantinopoleos. 4° Lugd., 1562.

D.P.   Pierre Gilles (1490–1555) was a French naturalist who first travelled in the Mediterranean to study fish. From this arose his travels in the Near East to study classical lands under semi-barbarous government. He is one of the travellers noted by N. de Nicolai.

F. GYRALDUS, LILIUS GREGORIUS. De Re Nautica. 8° Basel, 1540. (First Edition.)

D.L.P.   Gyraldus (1472–1552) lectured at Ferraria, and wrote for Hercules d'Este. He was a poet and archæologist, and dealt with the navigation of the ancients.

D. GYRALDUS CAMBRENSIS. Cambriae Descriptio. MS.

L.

E. GYRALDUS CAMBRENSIS. Odoporion, seu itinerarium Cambriae. Noviter MS.

L.

D. GYRALDUS CAMBRENSIS. Topographia Hiberniae.

L.(2).

E. HACLUIT, RICHARDE. Book of the Navigations and Travels of Englishmen, anglicé. 3 vols. (i.e. 1599–1600 Edition.)

L.P.

E. HANNONE, CAPITANO DI CARTHAGINESI. Navigatione nelle parti dell' Africa, tradotto dal Ramusio. Ramusio, Viaggi, 1550.

D.P.

E. HARTWELL, ABRAHAM. A Report of the Kingdom of Congo . . . written by P. Pigafetta, and translated by A. H.

L.P.

C. HAYTON, ARMENO. Dell' origine e successione de Gran Cani . . . 1253–1303. Ramusio, Viaggi, 1559.

D.P.

E. HAYTHON. Passagium terrae sanctae. Hagen, 1529.

D.L.

C. HAITHONUS, ARMENUS. ord. praemonstr. De Tartaris Liber. Novus Orbis.

> Quoted by Eden.

D.L.P.

C. HAITHONUS, ARMENUS. De Societate Christianorum et Tartariarum.

L.

C. HAYTONE. Chronicles of the Tartaries in English.

L.

C. HELMOLDUS. Chronice Slavorum. Frankfort, 1581.

> D. The author, a German historian (1138–77), wrote the History of the Slavs from Charlemagne to his own day.

D. HERBERSTEIN, SIGISMUNDUS. Historia Moscovita, fo. Oporin, 1571.

> D.L. i.e. the *Rerum Moscoviticarum Commentarii*. The first edition of the Commentaries was Oporin, Basle, 1549, with woodcut map. The first Italian edition was Venice, 1550, with Gastaldi's map. The second Latin edition, Oporin, Basle, 1551, had the original woodcut map, and included Paulus Jovius, *De Legatione Moscovitarum*. The third Basel edition, 1556, contained additional matter on Herbestein's travels in Poland and Russia, supplied from the family archives by his kinsman Felicianus von Herbestein, Dee's friend. The Antwerp edition (J. Steel's), 1557, had a map copied from the original woodcut, and included two pieces as follows : *Pauli Jovii . . . de legatione Basilii Magni ad Clementum VII ; De admirandis Hungariae Aquis*, by G. Wernher. This edition was reprinted at Frankfort, Heirs of A. Wechel, 1600.

D. HERBERSTAIN, SIGISMONDO, BARONE IN. Commentari della Moscovia . . . 1559. Ramusio, Viaggi, 1559.

> D.P. Eden's translation (1555) must have been from the first or second Basel edition.

C.D.E. HERODOTUS. Large fo. Colonia, 1537.

D.S.P.

C.D.E. HERODOTUS, graecé fo. Heidelberg, 1541.

D.S.

G. HIPPOCRATE. Parte del Trattato . . . de gli Scithi. Ramusio, Viaggi, 1559.

D.P.

G. HITCHCOCK, ROBERT. New Yeeres Gift for England, fo. 1580.
D.   See Catalogue of English Books.

G. HOLLAND, PHILEMON. Pliny in English.
L.

B. HONTERUS, JOH. Cosmographia, lib iv. cum tabulis geo-
      graphiciis.
L.   Published 1541, 1542, 1546, 1561, and widely used in
          England—in Latin Hexameters. With 13 maps. A prose
          work, *Rudimentorum Cosmographiae* libri duo, was pub-
          lished in 1530, and had a reduced copy of Waldseemüller's
          map of 1507. The author lived 1498–1549, and was for
          some time Professor of Geography in Cracow. He was born
          in Transylvania.

C.D. HOLINSHED, RALPH. His Chronicle. 2 vols. London, 1577.
D.

F. HOOD, THOMAS, MATHEMATICUS. Rotula continens sphaeram
      coelestem, expressam in plano duabus hemispheriis, edita per
      T. H. ac dedicata domino Lumley.
L.

F. HOOD, THOMAS. Use of Jacob's Staff, anglicé.
L.

B. L'IMAGE du Monde, Chronique de, auctor incertus, gallicé.
      In meeter.
L.   This is probably the original of William Caxton's Mirror
          of the World.

B. IMAGO mundi, cujus initio est : Operatio divina. MS.
D.

E. INDUS, JOSEPHUS. Navigationes. Novus Orbis.
D.L.P.

D. IRELAND. Ye Image of, with the pictures. 4° London, 1581.
D.

B. ISIDORUS HISPALENSIS. Etymologiarum Opus. Paris, 1509.
D.P.

D. JODOCUS, WOLFGANGUS. Descriptio Marcis Brandenbergensis
      . . . Frankfurt, 1572.
D.

C. JOVIUS, PAULUS. De Legationes Moscovitarum. 4° Frob. 1527.

D.L.S.

D.L.P.   Also in Novus Orbis, and in Eden's Decades.

C. JOVIO, PAULO. Delle cose della Moscovia. Ramusio, Viaggi, 1559.

D.P.   The Bishop of Nocera wrote also *De Legatione Basilii Magni ad Clementum VII* with a *Moscovia Tabula*, 1525. A collection of works, including Moscovia, was published Basel, 1571.

D. JOVIUS, PAULUS. Descriptio Britanniae, Scotiae, Hiberniae, et Orchadum, cum nomenibus antiquis et novis locorum in Anglia et Scotia. Venice, 1548.

L.   The addenda including a *Chronicon* and lives of famous Englishmen are by George Lily. See the Catalogue of English Books under this date.

G. KENTMANNUS, JOH. De Fossilibus; epiphanius de pectorali Aaroni; Gesnerii et alii de gemmis. Tiguri, 1565.

D.

D. KRANTZIUS, ALBERTUS. Saxonia. 8° Coloniae, 1574. Wandali, fol. Frankforti, 1575.

D.(2).L.   First editions.

C. KRANZIUS, ALBERTUS. Daniae, Sueciae, Norwegiae, Chronicon.

L.S.   Includes Ziegler's *Schondia*.

C. KRANZIUS, ALBERTUS. Chronica Regnorum Aquilonarum. fo. 1561.

D.△   The Chronicon as above. The author (1450c.–1517) was of Hamburg and Rostock.

F. LANTERIUS. De Fortificatione. 4° Venice, 1563.

D.

G. LAZIUS, WOLFGANGUS. De gentium aliquot migrationibus. fo. Oporin.

D.L.(2).S. The Viennese author (1514–65) was an historian and
P.   map-maker: he made maps of Austria (1544 and 1545) and of Hungary.

D. LEO, JO. AFRICANUS. De totius Africae Descriptio. Lib ix.

L.   This was the Latin Translation of Ramusio's version by J. Florianus, published in Antwerp, 1556.

D.   LEO, JO.   Description de l'Afrique, tierce partie du monde.
S.   This was Jean Temporal's translation, Antwerp and
     Lyon, 1556.

LEONE AFRICANO, GIOVAN.   Della Descrittione dell' Africa,
     1526.   Ramusio, Viaggi, 1550.
D.P.

C.   LERY, JEAN DE.   Histoire de l'Amerique.   8° Brucellae, 1578.
D.P.   The Burgundian author (1534–1611) studied at Geneva,
     and joined Villegagnon in Brazil in 1556, returning to
     Europe 1558.   His *Histoire d'un Voyage fait en la terre
     de Brésil, autrement dite Amérique*, Rouen, 1578, must be
     the original of the work cited above.

D.   LESSABAEUS,   JACOBUS.   Hannoniae   Descriptio.   Antwerp,
     1534.

C.   LILIUS,   GEORGIUS.   Anglorum   regnum   breve   chronicon.
     Frankfurt, 1565.
L.   This is printed in certain editions of Paulus Jovius, and
     also of Polidore Vergil, q.v.

F.   LINDESAY, ALEXANDER.   His Rutter of the Sea, with havens,
     roades, soundes, etc., from Humber northward, round about
     Scotland, anglicé MS.
L.   See Catalogue of English Books.

LHUYD, HUMFREY (or FLOODE).   Breviarie of Britane, Eng-
     lished by Thomas Twine.   1573.
L.   See Catalogue of English Books.

D.   LHUYD, HUMFREDUS.   Fragmentum Britannicae descriptionis.
     8°   Cologne, 1572.
D.(2).L.(7).

C.   LHUYD, HUMFREDUS.   Historia Brytanicorum, anglicé MS.
D.

G.   LOBELIUS.   Plantorum Historia.   fo.   1576.
D.P.   Is this the *Stirpium* of Lobel and Pena ?   Latter used
     by the elder Hakluyt.

C.   LOPEZ, FERNANDO, DE CASTAGNEDA.   Historia dell' India
     orientali.   2 vols.   Venice, 1577.
D.P.   On Dee's list of Books important for Navigation.

Historia de la India. Antwerp, 1554.

D.   This Portuguese historian (ob. 1559) went to Goa in 1528, and gave his time to historical research there. The first edition of his History appeared in Portuguese in 1551, and a French translation was made in 1553. For the English translation, see Catalogue of English Books.

C. LOPEZ, FRANCISCO, DE GOMARA. Istoria de las Indias. 1552. Hispanicé, 2 vols.

L.P.

C. LOPEZ, FREDERIGO (*sic*) DI GOMARA, e PIETRO DI CIEÇA. Cronica del Peru, 3 vols. Venice, 1560.

D.

E. LOPEZ, THOMÉ. Navigatione verso l'Indie Orientali, 1502. Ramusio, Viaggi, 1550.

D.P.

G. LUCANUS, OCELLUS. De universi orbis natura, graecé, Lovan, 1554.

D.   First edition of this Greek author (fifth century B.C.). Paris, 1539.

C. LUMNIUS, JOH. FREDERIC. De extremo judicio et Indorum vocatione. Antwerp, 1567.

D.   First Edition.
This work was endorsed by Dee as of importance for the Navigations.

B. MACROBIUS. In somnium Scipionis. Lugdunum gryphi, 1542.

D.L.S.P.

C. MAFFEIUS, JO. PETRUS, soc. JESU. Historiarum Indicarum orientalem, lib. xvi.

L.P.

E. MAFFEIUS, JO. PETRUS. Selectarum ex India Epistolarum, lib. iv.

L.P.   The author (1535–1603) was Secretary to the Republic of Genoa, and became a Jesuit father in 1565. He translated Acosta's History of the East Indies into Latin 1570, and wrote the above History at the request of Cardinal Henry of Portugal. His ' Four Volumes of Indishe matters written in Italian ' were translated into English by Willes as *De rebus Japonicis*. See Catalogue of English Books.

G. MAGNUS, ALBERTUS. De Natura locorum totius orbis. 4°
   Argent, 1515.

   D.(2).   The views of this thirteenth-century scholar on the
   habitability of the torrid zone were often quoted.

G. MAGNUS, ALBERTUS. Opera. fo. Venice, 1494.
   D.

MAGNUS, JOHANNES. Historia Gothorum, sueonium, etc. fo.
Rome, 1554. (First Edition.)

D. △.L.S.
   P.   The Archbishop of Upsala (1488–1544) was exiled with
   his brother Olaus by Gustav Vasa of Sweden. Damian à
   Goes sent him his works on the Lapps in October 1540,
   and in his reply of April 1541 Magnus writes: ' *Ceterum
   de meis historiciis Gothicis, ut cito impressae promulgentur
   nihil adhuc polliceri possum, tum quia incertis sedibus erro,
   tum quia me tenuissimae fortunae meae ab illis et plerisque
   aliis gravioribus, piisque studiis plurimum impediunt.* . . .
   *Spero tamen brevi nonnullam consolationem me assequnturum,
   ac noster Olaus me librum suum De mirabilibus rebus et
   moribus Aquilonarium regionum imprimi faciat, fere eisdem
   impedimentis quibus ego laboro, retardatur. Is enim in
   charta Gothica imprimenda aes alienum ad trecentos ducatos
   contraxit.* . . .'

C. MAGNUS, OLAUS. Historia de rebus septentrionalibus. fo.
   Rome, 1555. (First Edition.)

   D.△S.   i.e. the *Historia de gentibus septentrionalibus.* He also
   published a *Tabula terrarum septentrionalium et rerum
   mirabilium in eis ac in Oceano vicino.* Venice. His
   historia is illustrated by woodcuts and maps.

E. MAGNUS, R. P. EPISCOPUS AD THEMISTITAN IN MEXICAM.
   Epistola. Novus Orbis.
   D.L.

C. MALMESBURIENSIS, GULIELMUS, MONACHUS. De gestis
   regum Anglorum. MS.
   L.

E. MANDEVILLE, JOHN. Travail and voiage into the eastern parts
   and into India. Anglicé MS. vetust.
   L.(2).P.

MANDEVILLA, JOANNO DE. Viaggio, Italicé.
   L.   See also Catalogue of English Books.

C. **Marineo, Lucio, Siculo.** Chronica de españa, en español. fo. en Alcala de Henarés. 1539.

> D.   The Sicilian author (1460–1533) left Palermo for Spain 1486, and enjoyed the patronage of King Ferdinand and the Emperor Charles V. Dee endorses his book as of special value for Navigations.

D. **Marlianus, Jo. Bartholomaeus.** Topographia veteris Romae. epitome.

> L.S.   The author, an Italian antiquary (ob. 1560), published his *Urbis Romae Topographia*, lib. v., of which the above is an epitome, in 1534 (Lyon), and again at Berne, 1539.

G. **Marshall, John.** The Times of full seas, low water, springs and neepes for all the times of ye yeare, of the havens about the coasts of France, Flanders, Britane, Wales, Ireland, Spain. MS. dedicated to the Earl of Arundel, with Maps.

> L.   See also Catalogue of English Books.

F. **Marshall, John.** Rutter for the Sea about Scotland, the Islandes of Orkeney and Schetland. MS. Anglicé.

> L.   Dedicated to the Earl of Arundel.

E. **Martyr, Petrus, ab Angleria.** Decades de orbe novo.

> L.(2).P.

E. **Martyr, Peter.** Decades of the New World. (Eden's Translation.)

> S.(D).P.

E. **Martyr, Peter.** De rebus oceanicis, et novo orbe, decades tres.

> L.

E. **Martire, Pietro.** Sommario cavato della sua Historia del Nuovo Mondo scoperte da Christofero Colombo, 1492–1515. Ramusio, Viaggi, 1556.

> D.P.

E. **Martyr, Petrus.** De Insulis nuper repertis.

> L.(2).

E. **Martyr, Pierre.** Les Isles nouvellement trouvées, decades trois, with Trois narrations en françois, 4° Paris, 1532.

> D.   On Dee's list of Books important for Navigation.

C. MATTHAEUS, WESTMONASTERIENSIS. Flores Historiarum. fo. London, 1570.

D. △.L.(2).

P.   Lumley has the note, ' *Ex duabus diversis impressionibus, viz.* 1567 *and* 1570 '. He has also a MS. version.

G. MATTHESIUS, JOH. Bergpostilla de mineralibus Germanicis. Norib., 1578.

D. △.   First Edition. Includes summary Chronicle of Joachim-stal.

B. MAUROLYCUS, FRANCISCUS. Cosmographica (in tres dialogos distincta). 4° Venice, 1543.

D.L.   The Sicilian author (1494–1575) made many translations from the Greek, and wrote also on the lodestone.

F. MEDINA, PIERRE DE. De l'art de naviguer, traduit en François et augmenté par Nicolas de Nicolai, gallicé. Lyon, 1554.

L.   An Italian translation was published in the same year.

E. MEGGEN, JOCODUS À. Peregrinatio Hierosolymitana. 8° Dilinguae, 1580.

        First Edition.

B. MELA, POMPONIUS. De Situ Orbis. Paris, 1540.

D.L.(5).P.

C. MENDOSA, JO. CONDISALVI. De regno China historia, lib. iii, a Marco Hemingio latinitate donati.

L.P.   Juan Gonzales Mendoza of Castille (1550–1620) was a famous missionary to China, and wrote the above history in Spanish in 1585.

E. MENDOZZA, ANTONIO DI. Lettera del discoprimento della Terra Ferma della Nuova Spagna verso Tramontana, 1539. Ramusio, Viaggi, 1556.

D.P.   Quoted by Dee and others.

D. MERCATOR, GERARDUS. Tabulis Ptolomaicus, fo. 1578.

D. △.P.

A. MESSAHALA, ARABUS. De elementis et orbibus celestibus. Norib., 1549.

D.   The author was a famous Jewish astrologer (fl. 800 A.D.) whose work on the Astrolabe was used by Chaucer and in Margarita Philosophica.

G. MEURERUS, NOE. Wasser-recht : hoc est, de jure aquarum, et praesertim Rheni fluminis et aliorum flumenum : de insulis etc. germanicé. Frankfurt, 1570.
D.

D. MICHOU, MATTHIAS À. De Sarmatia, Asiana et Europea. lib. ii. Novus Orbis.
D.L.P. First Edition, 1518. Quoted by Eden, 1554.

D. MICHEOVO, MATTHEO DI. Descrittione delle due Sarmatia. Ramusio, Viaggi, 1559.
D.P. The Polish author (ob. 1533) was a student at Cracow University and later at the German and Italian Universities. His work was widely quoted.

B. MIRROR of the World, anglicé, compiled by Wm. Caxton. 1480.
L. See English Catalogue.

B. MIZALDUS, ANTONIUS. Cosmographia. 4° Paris, 1549.
D.P. The French author (1520c.–1578) enjoyed court patronage and was a friend of Dee's, since he was an expert astrologer. The full title of his above work is *De Mundi Sphera sive Cosmographia lib. tres. :* written in verse, it was dedicated to Marguerite of Valois.

D. MOKERUS, ANTONIUS. Descriptio Hyldegiae Saxoniae. 8° Frankfurt, 1573.
D. First Edition.

D. MOLLER, BERNARDUS. Descriptio Rheni, carmini. Colon, 1570.
D.

B. MUNSTER, SEBASTIAN. Cosmographia. Large fo. Basel, 1572. First Edition, 1536. Dedicated to Charles V.
D. △.L.(2).S.
P.

B. MUNSTER, SEBASTIAN. Cosmographia universale recolta primo da diversi autori per lui, et dapoi corretta per gli censori ecclesiastica. Italicé.
L. His Ptolemy appeared in 1540.

F. MUNSTERUS, SEBASTIANUS. Horologographia. 4° Basel, 1533. First Edition, 1531.
D.L.S. Lumley cites the title : De Compositione Horologium.

B. MUNSTER, SEBASTIAN. Introductio in tabulam cosmographiae. Novus Orbis.

D.L.P. The world map and a section describing it in Simon Grynaeus' compilation.

E. NAVARCHUS, JACOBUS. Epistola Asiatica.

D. i.e. Vol. II of *Epistolae Indicae et Japonicae*, Louvain, 1570. 'A pretty compendium of M. Paulus Venetus, Guilelmus Tripolitanus, Joãs de Plano Carpini, Haytonus Armenius, Joã de Barros, and some such writers of late time, somewhat intermingled with conference of Ptolemy his description of Asiatical parts,' says Dee. The author was the correspondent of Ortelius, to whom he says that he is planning a complete work on this subject.

E. NAVIGATIONE d'un Portoghese compagno d'Odoardo Barbosa, che fu sopra la Nave Vittoria, attorno il Mondo, 1519. Ramusio, Viaggi, 1550.

D.

E. NAVIGATIONE da Lisbona all' Isole di San Thomé . . . scritta per un Pilotto Portoghese . . . Ramusio, Viaggi, 1550.

D.

F. NEANDER, MICHAEL. De Sphaera. Oporin. 1561.

D. The author (1529–81) was born at Joachimstal, and became Professor of Greek at the University of Jena. A great student of astrology, he left many horoscopes, and published also a work, *Synopsis mensurarum et ponderum*. Basle, 1555.

E. NEARCHO. Navigatione di, tradotto dal Ramusio, Viaggi, 1550.

D.

C. NICLAI, HERBON, F. D. Epitome de Indis ad fidem Christi convertandis. Novus Orbis.

D.L.

F. NICOLAI, NICOLAS DE. Pierre de Medina, de l'art de naviguer. Paris, 1554 and 1576.

L. Nicolas made this translation from the first Spanish edition, Valladolid, 1545. 'Traduict de Castillian en François avec augmentation et illustration.' The privilège du Roi is dated Sept. 1550, and the translation had been made ' some time since '. Vincenzo Paletina de Corzula, Michel Coignet and John Frampton (q.v.) also made translations of Medina.

E. NICOLAI, NICOLAS DE. Peregrinationes et Navigationes. N.D. and Les Navigations et Peregrinations. fo. Antwerp, 1577.

D.(2).P. The original work, *Peregrinations et voyages faicts en la Turquie*, was published at Lyons in 1568, the dedication to Charles IX being dated May 1, 1567. The volume was illustrated by pictures from the artist-author's pencil of people of the East. An edition with 60 engraved plates was published at Antwerp in 1576 by John Dee's friend the printer Guilielmus Silvius. This is probably one of those in Dee's library. The work was translated into many languages, including an English version in 1585.

D. NIGER, FRANCISCUS. De situ et moribus Rhetorum.

L.

B. NIGER, DOMINICUS MARIUS. Geographia, fo. Basel, 1557 (written in 1490).

D.L.P. Lumley has the title *Geographiae Commentarii*. The famous Italian author (1454–1504) taught at Ferrara, Bologna, and Rome, and numbered Copernicus among his pupils. An astronomer, and also a great astrologer, D. M. Niger was widely read and quoted throughout the sixteenth century. His works included a Commentary on Ptolemy quoted by Dee.

E. NIZZA, MARCO DA. Relatione del Viaggio fatto per terra à Cevola Regno delle sette Città, 1540. Ramusio, Viaggi, 1556.

D.P.

F. NONNIUS, PETRUS. De Crepusculis. 4° 1543.

D.L. This work contains the description of the ' nonnius '.

F. NONNIUS, PETRUS. De Erratis Orontii. fo. Coimbra, 1548.

D.△. Written against certain views of Orontius Finaeus.

F. NONNIUS, PETRUS. De Navigatione. fo. Basel.

D.△. i.e. De arte atque ratione navigandi, libri duo. Basel, 1566.
First edition, 1546. See Chapter V.

D. NOTITIA utraque cum orientis tum occidentis, ultra Arcadii, Honariique Caesarum tempora, monumentum illustre antiquitatis.

L.S.

D. NOTITIA Provincarum. fo. Froben, 1555.

D.

E. Novus Orbis. fo. Basel, 1555.
> D. △.L.P. The contents are listed separately. First edition 1532. Compiled by John Huttich, with a Preface by Simon Grynaeus, whose name the collection usually bears.

E. Nunez, Alvaro, ditto Capo di Vacca. Relatione delle Indie, e della Nuova Galatia. 1527–36. Ramusio, Viaggi, 1556.
> D.P.

C. Obedienza data a Papa Clementi VII in nome del Prete Jani. Ramusio, Viaggi, 1550.
> D.P.

E. Odorico da Udine, Beato. Due Viaggi, 1318. Ramusio, Viaggi, 1559.
> D.P.

E. Odoricus, ord. frat. min. Itinerarium de mirabilibus orientis et orientalium tartorum. MS.
> L.

B. Orontius Finaeus. Cosmographia. fo. Paris, 1542.
> *Second title*, De Cosmographia lib. iv. 4° Paris, 1553.
> D.(2).L.

F. Orontius Finaeus. De Rebus Mathematicis. Paris, 1556.
> D.

B.F. Orontius Finaeus. Protomathesis viz : De arithmetica practica, De Geometria, De Cosmographia, De solariis horologis, et quadrantibus.
> L.D. First Edition. Paris, 1530.

F. Orontius Finaeus. Quadrans Astrolabicus. fo. Paris, 1534.
> D.

F. Orontius Finaeus. In eos, quos de mundi sphaera conscropsit, libros.
> L.

C. Orosius, Paulus. Historia adversa Paganos. lib vii. 8° 1574.
> D.L.(2). First Edition. Vienna, 1471.
> P. On Dee's list of Books important for Navigation. The translation, with addenda, by Alfred the Great, was familiar to English scholars, e.g. Record, Bale.

B. ORTELIUS, ABRAHAM. Theatrum orbis terrarum.

D.L.(3).P. Dee's copy is 'cum duobus additiomentis', fo. 3 vols.
Lumley has the 1570 and 1575 Antwerp editions with
coloured maps, and the 1592 edition ' ex ultima editione
longé auctori prioribus, cum chartis coloribus depictis'.

Copies were received in England immediately on publication, e.g. by Daniel Rogers, and were kept up to date by
means of supplements, vide Ortelius' correspondance
(Hessels).

C. OSORIUS, HIERONYMUS. Historia de rebus gestis Emmanuelis
regis Lusitaniae. 8° Colon, 1574, and 8° Colon, 1580.

D.(2).L.

P.   First Edition 1571. A history of Portuguese discoveries
1495–1521.

C. OVIEDO, GONZALO FERNANDO D'. Historia dell' Indie occidentali (lib. 3) cavata da libri scritti di pietro Martyri. 4° Ven.,
1534.

D.P.   On Dee's list of Books important for Navigation.

Oviedo was surveyor of the gold mines and smelting
works in the Indies from 1513. He advocated to
Charles V. the use of the trans-Panama route to the
Emperor's Spiceries, rather than the Magellan Strait route
sought by the expeditions of 1525 and 1526. This work
is the *Summario* usually ascribed to the editorship of
Ramusio.

C. OVIEDO, GONZALO FERNANDO D'. Historia Generale, etc., in
lib. xx. Ramusio, Viaggi, 1556.

D.P.

C.D. OVIEDO, GONZALEZ FERNANDO D'. Summario . . . della
sua Historia Naturale e Generale dell' Indie Occidentali.
Ramusio, Viaggi, 1556.

D.P.   From '*Indiae Historiae Generalis Summaria*', Latin
original of *Summario* written in 1525 during a visit to
Spain.

B. P(OWELL), D(AVID). Certain Brief Rules of Geography,
London, 1573.

L.

A. PARACELSUS. Astronomia Magna, germanicé. Frankfort,
1571.

D.   Dee has a large number of books and MSS. of this great
alchemist.

C. PARIS, MATTHAEUS. Historia de rebus angliciis. fo. London.
D. △.L.(2). Lumley has the title, *Historia Major.*
P.

E. PAULUS JAPONUS. De Japonicis rebus libri epistolarum
quattuor.
L.P.

E. PAULUS, MARCUS, VENETUS. De Regionibus Orientalibus
Lib. 3. Novus Orbis.
D.L.P.   Lumley has also a MS. version, *De conditionibus et
consuetudinibus orientalium regionum, lib.* 3 ; while Dee
quotes various readings, and appears to have had copies
not catalogued.

E. POLO, MARCO. Delle cose de Tartarie e dell' Indie Orientali.
1250. Ramusio, Viaggi, 1559.
D.P.

C. PEDRO, DON, DE PORTUGAL. Libro del Infante, en espagñol,
4° Caragoça, 1538.
D.   On Dee's list of Books important for Navigation.

E. PEREGRINAGGIO di tre Giovanni figliuoli del Re di Serendippo,
etc. 8° Venice, 1557.
On Dee's list of Books important for Navigation.

G. PEREGRINUS, PETRUS. De magnete, seu rota perpetui motus.
Augusta Vindelic. 1558.
D.   Petrus Peregrinus or de Mahariicuria was the contemporary and friend of Roger Bacon, i.e. fl. circ. 1265.
The Augsburg edition of his work above cited was edited
by Achilles P. Gasserus, and dedicated to the Emperor
Ferdinand. Dee's personal copy bears the date 1562, and
he has added the names of Maurolycus and Nolanus to the
editor's list of authorities on the magnet. He has also a
marginal note, ' *De terrae motu Copernici Hypothesis* '.

F. PEUCER, GASPAR. De Sphaera etc. primo. 8° Wittenberg,
1551. First Edition.
D.P.   Full title, Elementa doctrinae de circulis coelestibus et
primo motu.
The German author (1525–1602) was a student at
Wittenberg under the Rectorship of Melancthon, whom he
succeeded in 1560. His mathematical teachers were
Rhaeticus and the famous Erasmus Reinhold. He was a
friend of Hugh Languet, Ortelius and Camden.

F. PEUCER, GASPAR. De dimensionae terrae. Wittenberg, 1554. First Edition.

D.

A. PEURBACHIUS, GEORGIUS. Tabulae Eclipsium. fo. Vienna, 1514.

D.P.   Peurbach (1423–61) was the pupil of Nicholas à Cusa, and the teacher of Regiomontanus. After lecturing at Ferrara, Bologna and Padua, he became Professor of Mathematics at Vienna. His works included a Table of Sines, and a *Theoricae novae planetarum*, Venice, 1495, often printed with other works. De Rojas ascribes to him the first mapping of a country by geometrical methods.

G. PICCOLOMINI, ALESSANDRO. Della grandezza della terra, è dell' acqua. 4° Venice, 1558.

    The author, a Tuscan mathematician, published also *De la Spera del Mondo* and *De la Stelle Fisse*, 1540.

PIGAFETTA, ANTONIO. Viaggia atorno il Mondo, 1519–22. Ramusio, Viaggi, 1550.

D.P.   From the French translation by Faber of the MS. given by the author to the Queen Regent of France, 1522, which was printed.

E. PIGAFETTA, PHILIP. A Report of the Kingdom of Congo, translated by A. Hartwell.

L.P.   See English Catalogue.

E. PINZONUS Navigatio, Madrignano interprete. Novus Orbis.

D.L.P.

E. PLANO CARPINI, JO. DE. De Tartaria et Tartaris. MS.

L.P.

G. PLINIUS (CAIUS, SECUNDUS). fo. Froben, 1554.

D.P.   Dee had also a copy (uncatalogued) of Plinius Secundus lib. 2. with commentaries of Jacob Milichius, 1543. His copy is dated January 1550, Louvain.

G. PLINIE, Anglicé, translated by Philemon Holland, doctor of physic, 1566.

L.

B. POSTELLUS, GUILELMUS. Cosmographia. 4° Oporin, 1561.

D.L.P.   i.e. *Cosmographiae disciplinae compendium, cum synopsis rerum toto orbe gestarum.* Basel, 1561. Lumley has the title : *Cosmographiae disciplinae compendium, ad divinae providentiae arctissimam demonstrationem conductum.*

D. POSTELLUS, GUILELMUS. De Etruria. 4° Florence, 1552.
    First Edition.

> D.   i.e. *De Etruria regionis, quae prima in orbe europaeo
> habitata est, originibus, institutis, religione et moribus.*

G. POSTELLUS, GUILELMUS. De Originibus, seu de varia historia
    totius orientalis, maxime Tartarum, Persarum, Turcorum,
    etc. Oporin, 1553.

> L.D.P.   Guillaume Postel (1505–1581), one of the most learned
> men of his age, the friend of Dee, N. de Nicolai and Ortelius,
> was a Hebrew and Arabic scholar. From Constantinople
> he brought back Arabic books and MSS. including Abulfeda
> Ismael's geography, which he was forced to pawn with
> Otto Duke of Bavaria in 1549. Among his most popular
> works was *De Universitate seu Cosmographia*, Paris, 1563.
> He wrote also *Des Merveilles des Indes et du Nouveau
> Monde, où est demonstré le lieu du Paradis terrestre*, Paris,
> 1553 ; *Description de la Terre Sainte*, Paris, 1553 ; *De la
> république des Turcs*, etc., etc.

C. PRISEUS, JOH. Historia Britannicae Defensis. 4° London,
    1573.

> D.L.

F. PROCLUS, De Sphaera. 8° 1547 ; Argent, 1539 ; and Basel,
    1561.

> D.(3).L.(2). Lumley's copies are : ' Thomo Linacre interprete ', i.e.
> P.   the edition of Thomas Linacre, published first by the
> Aldine Press in 1499.

B. PTOLOMAEUS, CLAUDIUS. (1) Geographia cum tabulis, large
    folio, Argentoratum, 1513.

> D.(4).L.(5).S.(3).
> P.   The Edition, Aeschler-Übelin, with Waldseemüller's
> Tabulae Novae, Ringman's translation. On Dee's list of
> Books important for Navigation.

> D.   (2) Geographia Graecé. 4° Froben, 1533.
> Probably the same as the first complete Greek edition
> (no maps) published by Erasmus at Basel. Both Lumley
> and Sir T. Smith had Greek editions. There was also in
> 1533 a reprint of Werner's edition of 1514 (q.v.), with a new
> introduction and an addendum describing some of the
> instruments invented by Apianus.

> D.   (3) Geographia, large fo. Basel, 1545.
> A reprint of Munster's 1540 edition.

D.△ (4) Geographia. Large fo. Basel, 1551.

D.L. (5) Geographia, lat. per Moletius. 4° Venice, 1562.

> Lumley has ' Olim a Bilibaldo Pirckemeíro translata, et nunc correcta a Josepho Moletio mathematico : ejusdem Josephi commentaria amplissima in septimum librum. Tabulae etiam diversum regionum, 64 antiquae, et 27 novae, tipis aeris excussé '. This was the edition with contradictory world maps and a reprint of the Gastaldi-Zeni map. Dee probably brought it home after a visit to Italy in 1563. Willes also used it, to judge from his references to Moletus.

B. PTOLOMAEUS, CLAUDIUS. De geographia libri octo, è graeco traducti, et nominis graecis appositis. Jo. Novimagi Opera. Coloniae, 1540.

> L.   A new Latin translation by the distinguished mathematician and philosopher Novimagus or Bronckhorst : no maps. The number of books in Ptolemy varied between 7, 8, and 10.

A. PTOLOMAEUS, CLAUDIUS. Almagestum cum commentariis, graecé.

> D.   An abridgement of this work edited by Regiomontanus appeared Ven. 1496.

A.B. PTOLOMAEUS, CLAUDIUS. Omnia Opera.
> L.

B. PTOLOMAEUS, CLAUDIUS. Planisphaerium cum commentariis. fo. Venice, 1558.
> D.

D. PUBLIUS, VICTOR. De Regionibus urbis Romae.
> L.

E. QUIRINO, PIETRO. Viaggio et Naufragio, 1431. Ramusio, Viaggi, 1559.
> D.P.

F. RAMUS, PETRUS. Arithmetica, etc.
> D.

D. RAMUSIO, J. B. Informatione dell' Isola Giapan, novamente scoperta. Ramusio, Viaggi, 1550.
> D.P.

G. RAMUSIO, J. B. Discorso sopra il crescer de Fiume Nile. Ramusio, Viaggi, 1550.

D.P.

RAMUSIO, J. B. Navigationi et viaggi, italicé. fo. Ven. 2 vols. (*sic*).

D. △.P.   Contents listed separately.
                    It is remarkable that Lumley's Library Catalogue contains no mention of this book.   Only the first volume was available when Eden wrote the Decades, and while Richard Chancellor was alive.

E. RAWLEY, SIR WALTER. Discourse of Guiana.

L.P.

F. RECORDE, ROBERT. Castle of Knowledge.

L.P.

F. RECORDE, ROBERT. Pathway of Knowledge.

L.

F. RECORDE, ROBERT. Whetstone of Witte.

L.

F. REGIOMONTANUS, JOH. De Torqueto, astrolabio, armillari, etc. Norib., 1544.
        Lumley has the Italian edition, Instrumenta Astrologica.

D.L.S.

A. REGIOMONTANUS, JOH. Tabula Primi Mobilis.   Vienna, 1514.

D.

A. REGIOMONTANUS, JOH. Epitome ptolemaei Almagestum. Norib., 1550.

A. REGIOMONTANUS, JOH. Tabulae Directionum et Projectionum. Norib., 3 vols., 1552.

L.   This volume contains methods and tables for casting horoscopes. That on instruments, published in 1544, contains additions by Joannes Schoner, and George Peurbach's *Libellus* on the geometrical square, showing *inter alia* its use for finding the distance of inaccessible objects, a foundation operation for mapping. Regiomontanus (1436–76), Peurbach's pupil, lectured at the great Italian Universities before residing at Nürnberg. A wealthy citizen financed the making of his instruments. Martin Behaim boasted himself a pupil of Regiomontanus when in Lisbon, although he could hardly have come under the master's direct teaching. The 1492 Globe, however, is an indication of Nürnberg workmanship and interests at the time.

A. REINHOLDUS, ERASMUS. Ephemerides Tab. 1552.
D.P.   First Edition.

A. REINHOLDUS, ERASMUS. Tabulae Directionarum. Tub., 1554.
D.S.   First Edition.

Reinhold (1511–53) taught mathematics and astronomy at Wittenberg until 1552. His works included a translation of the Almagest and of Peurbach's New Theory of the Planets. He was a noted student of Judicial Astrology, and his tables were very widely used.

G. REISCH, GEORGIUS. Margarita Philosophica. 4° Arg., 1504.
D.L.(2).   The above edition was published ' cum additionibus, qui in aliis non habentur'. One of Lumley's copies, too, had the supplements on Architecture, the Astrolabe, the Torquetum and the Polimetrum of Waldseemüller, a forerunner of the theodolite. The author (1470–1523) was a close associate of the school of St. Dié, and his text-book, containing an outline of all the generally taught academic sciences, was widely read, the editions, authorized, and unauthorized, being very numerous indeed.

C. RELATIONE d'un Secretario di F. Pizarro, della Conquista . . . del Peru . . . 1534. Ramusio, Viaggi, 1556.
D.P.

E. RELATIONE d'un gentilhuomo del F. Cortese. Ramusio, Viaggi, 1556.
D.P.

E. RELATIONE d'un Capitan Spagnuolo del discoprimento e conquista del Peru fatta da F. de H. Pizarro, 1531. Ramusio, Viaggi, 1556.
D.P.

B. RINGELBERGIUS, JOACHIM FORTIUS. Lucubrationes.
L.   Numerous works including a Cosmographia. The author (1499–1536) was of Antwerp, and a student at Louvain. He taught philosophy and mathematics in France and Germany.

D. RITIUS, MICHAEL. De Regibus Francorum, Hispaniorum, Hierosolymitae, Neapolae et Siciliae : Hungariae. Froben. 1534.
D.

F. ROBERTUS, LINCOLNIENSIS (GROSSE TESTE). Tractatus de
   Sphaera. MS.
   D.

F. ROJAS, JUAN DE. Commentarii in Astrolabium. Paris, 1550.
   L.   The author was a disciple of Gemma Phrysius, with whom
          he appears to have studied at Louvain in 1545, afterwards
          proceeding to Paris. Thus he may have been known to
          Dee. His book contains all the current examples of
          geometrical and instrumental mensuration, including
          Phrysius' account of triangulation.

B. ROMAN, HIERONYMO. Respublicas del mundo, divididas en
   xxvi libros, duobus tomis en español. En Medina del Campo.
   1575.
   D.

E. RUBRUCK, GUIL. DE. ORD. FRAT. MIN. Itinerarium ad partes
   orientales, et de gestas tartarorum orientalium. MS.
   L.P.   One of the MS. used by Hakluyt from Lumley's Library.
          Dee knows it through Roger Bacon.

F. RUSCELLI, GIROLAMO. Precetti della militia moderna. Ven.,
   1572.
   D.   The Italian author edited an Italian edition of Ptolemy,
          Venice, 1561. He was working on a World Geography at
          his death, in 1566.

F. SACROBOSCO, JOH. Sphaera. 4° Paris, 1516. Antwerp, 1547.
   D.(2).L. Lumley has the title, *Sphaera Mundi, cum tribus com-*
   P.   *mentis*. Dee has also a MS. version. See also English
             Catalogue, and cf. Pedro Nunez, who was not the first
             Portuguese editor. A Spanish edition (in Latin) appeared
             at Alcala in 1526 with comments of Petrus Cirvellus.

SAXOGRAMMATICUS. Historia Danica. fo. 1576.
   D.L.S. Sir T. Smith's copy was sent to him from Denmark by
           Sir J. Borthwick. The writer was of the early thirteenth
           century.

G. SCALIGER, JULIUS CAESAR. De Subtilitate adversus Cardanum.
   4°. 1557.
          A criticism of Cardanus' work of that name, which is
          freely quoted. Contains the passage as to the Great
          Arctic Gulf discussed in detail by Dee in his *Volume of
          Great and Rich Discoveries*.

F. SCHONER, JOH. Opera Mathematica. fo. Norimb., 1551.

> D. △.   The famous globe-maker (1477–1547), teacher in the Gymnasium of Nürnberg, wrote on astronomy, astrology, arithmetic and geology. His globe and tract prepared to illustrate Magellan's voyage are quoted by Gemma Phrysius. The Opera cited above was posthumously published by his son Andreas.

F. SCHONER, JOH. Gnomonica, de horolog. Norib.

> D.

D. SEMPRONIUS, C. De divisione et chorographia Italiae, cum Jo. Annii commentariis.

> L.

SHUTE, JOHN. A faithefull friend and remembrance to a general of an army in divers respects. MS.

> L.   The writer was also author of a *Treatise on Architecture,* based on Vitruvius.

B. SIDEROCRATIS, SAMUEL. Geographia. 4° Tubingen, 1562.

> D.

D. SIMLERUS, JOSIAS. De Republica Helvetiorum et Descriptio Vallesiae. 8°. 1576.

> D.

D. SIMLERUS, JOSIAS. De Alpibus. Tiguri, 1574.

> D.

D. SIMLERUS, JOSIAS. Epitome Bibliotheca Gesneri. fo. 1555.

> D. △.(2).   The author (1530–76), a friend of Dee, succeeded Conrad Gesner in the chair of Mathematics at Zurich.

B. SOLINUS, JULIUS. Polyhistor. Lugdunum gryph. 1537.

> D.L.(4).S.
> P.   See also English Catalogue.

E. STEFANO, HIERONIMO DE SAN. Viaggio nelle Indie. 1499. Ramusio, Viaggi, 1550.

> D.P.

F. STÖFLER, JOH. De Astrolabio. fo. Tubingen, 1535.

> D.   i.e. *Elucidatio Fabriciae ususque astrolabii, a Joanne Stoflerino Justingensi viro Germano.* Oppenheym, 1513. Containing details of construction of astrolabe, and the stock geometrical measurements of towers, etc.

A. STÖFLER, JOH. Ephemerides, ab anno Christi, 1495–1544. 4° Tubing., 1544.

D.S.

F. STÖFLER, JOH. In Procli Sphaerum. fo. Tubing., 1534. First Edition.

D. The Suabian Mathematician (1452–1531) was Professor of Mathematics at the University of Tübingen.

STOW, JOHN. Chronicles. 1567 and 1573.

D.(2).

B. STRABO. Geographia graecé. Large fol. Basel, 1544.

D.L.(3).S. Lumley has two Epitomes and one complete copy in
P. seventeen books.

B. SYLVESTER, BERNARD. Cosmographia. MS.

D. Bale calls him *Vir humanis scientiis eruditus*, and Savile has a copy of the MS. See also English Catalogue.

D. SYLVIUS, AENEAS (PIUS II). Descriptio Asiae et Europae. 8°. Colon. 1531.

D.I.P. Lumley's copy has the title : *Pius Papa, Cosmographia Asiae et Europiae elegens descriptio*, i.e. Paris edition of 1509. The first edition was Cologne 1477, and the book begins : *Pii II Pontifici Maximi Historia Rerum ubique gestarum, cum locorum descriptions non finita Asia Minor incipit.* Hence the short title, *Historia Rerum*, by which it was known to Columbus and his contemporaries.

D. SYLVIUS, AENEAS, postea PAPA PIUS SECUNDUS. Omnia Opera.

L.

D. TABULAE sive Chartae novi orbis, ad maritimos navigationes usus accomodatae. MS.

L.

F. TAISNER, JOH. De natura magnetis, etc. Colon. 1562. First Edition.

D.L. For etc. read : *et ejus effectibus : item de moto continuo.* The French author (1509–62) was tutor to the pages of Charles V, and went with the Emperor to Tunis in 1535, later settling at Cologne. This was the work Eden brought home for translation.

F. TAISNER, JOH. De Annulo Sphaerico. 4° Antwerp, 1560.

D. First Edition, De Usus Annuli Sphaerici Palermo. 1550.

F. TAISNER, JOHN. Of ye Lodestone. 4° London.

D.

F. TARTALEA, NICHOLAS. Rerum Arithmeticarum et geometricam, partes quattuor posterioris. fo. Ven., 1560.

D.

F. TARTAGLIA, NICOLO. Quaesiti et inventioni diversi. 4° Ven., 1554. First Edition, 1546.

D.L. The Italian Mathematician (1506–57) was born at Brescia and associated with Cardanus. He taught at Venice in 1535, when he published his *Nuova Scienza* 1537 : also at Verona, Vicenza, and Brescia. He deals with the question of instruments for field survey in the *Quaesiti*, and also with problems of gunnery. Both Bourne and Lucar made translations from him, and Dee commends him as a great man writing in the vernacular. His *Generale Trattato di numeri et misure*, Venice, 1556–60, was very popular.

G. THESORO Universale : Libro dell' Abaco, il quale insegna fare ogni regione mercatile con la tariffa. Ven., 1548.

D. This may be an edition of the elementary work on arithmetic, algebra and practical geometry of Francesco Feliciano de Lazesio (Verona 1490–1536c.), first published in Venice 1517–18, which went through many editions. A Venetian arithmetician, Giovanni Mariani, published mercantile tables under the title *Tariffa perpetua* in 1535.

D. THEVET, ANDRÉ. Cosmographie de Levant, en françois. 4° Lugdunum, 1554. First Edition.

D. THEVET, ANDRÉ. Cosmographie, en françois. fo. Paris. 2 vols. 1576.

D.P. Probably the 1575 edition which was in Frobisher's ship's library.

D. THEVET, ANDRÉ. Les singularités de L'Amerique, en françois. 8° Plantin. 1558. Also published in Paris the same year.

D. In Frobisher's ship's library. The author (1502–1590) travelled in the Near East 1549–54 under the patronage of the Cardinal of Lorraine, and went with Villegagnon to Brasil 1555–6. He was subsequently made Historiographer and Cosmographer Royal, and had a reputation in excess of his merits.

C. TOMICH, MOSES, PERE. Historias e conquistas de cathalunia en cathalane. Barcelona, 1534.

    D.   Endorsed by Dee as important for Navigation.

E. TRANSYLVANUS, MAXIMILIANUS. De Moluccis Epistola. First Edition, Cologne, 1523.

    L.(2).(D).

    P.   Lumley quotes the full title as *Epistola de Moluccis Insulis, itemque aliis plurimis mirandis quae novissima Castillanorum navigatio Caroli quinti imper., auspiciis nuper invenit.* Written on 24 October 1522 to the Archbishop of Salzburg.

E. TRANSILVANO, MASSIMILIANO. Epistola della detta Navigatione fatta . . . 1519–22, attorno il Mondo. Ramusio, Viaggi, 1550.

    D.P.

D. TSCHUDI, AEGIDIUS. Descriptio Rhetae Alpinae, germanicé. 4° Basel, 1560.

    D.   The Latin translation : *Descriptio de prisce ac vera Alpina Rhaetia*, Bale, 1538, was made by Sebastian Munster.

            The Swiss author (1505–72) was a pupil of Glareanus, with whom he went to Paris. He was the author of many maps of Switzerland, etc.

E. TURLERUS, HIERONYMUS. De Peregrinatione. 8° August, 1574.

    D.   Turler's Traveller was translated into English in 1575. See English Catalogue.

F. UBALDI, GUIDO. Planisphaeriorum universalium Theorica. Pisa, 1579.

    D.   The noble Italian author (1543–1601) was an amateur mathematician and student of science.

E. ULLOA, CAPIT. FRANCESCO D'. Navigatione per discopire l'Isole delle Specierie fino al mare detto Vermeio 1532–39. Ramusio, Viaggi, 1556.

    D.P.

D. VADIANUS, JOACHIM. Epitome trium terrae partium, Asiae, Africae, et Europae locorum descriptionem continens, praecipue quorum Lucas in Actes Evangelistae meminere. Zurich, 1534, with map.

L.(2).P.   The Swiss humanist, Vadianus or van Watt, published an edition of Dionysius Afer, Vienna, 1515, of Pomponius Mela with commentaries, Basel, 1522, and some Swiss topographical matter. He gave his library (still extant and including an Ulm Ptolemy) to the municipality of St. Gallen, 1549.

C.   VALESIO, H.   Compendio delle Chronice di Polonia.   Ramusio, Viaggi, 1559.

D.P.

E.   VARTHEMA, LUDOVICO.   Itinerario dell' Egitto, etc.   Ramusio, Viaggi, 1550.

D.P.

E.   VARTOMANNUS, LUDOVICUS, ROMANUS PATRITIUS.   Navigationum Aethiopiae, Aegipti, Arabiae, Persidis, Syriae, Indiae intra et extra Gangem, libri septem, Arcangelo Madrignano interprete.   Novus Orbis.

D.L.P.

E.   (VARTHEMA) LUIS, MICER, PATRICIO ROMANO.   Itinerario; videl. de la Ethiopia, Egipto, Arabias, e India, etc., vuelto de Latine en Romance por christoval de Arcos.   Hispalis, 1520.

D.   Endorsed by Dee as important for Navigation.

E.   VASQUEZ DI CORONADO, FRANCESCO.   Relatione del Viaggio alle dette sette Città.   1540.   Ramusio, Viaggi, 1556.

D.P.   This is the story held in the sixteenth century to be so critical for determining the configuration of the West coast of North America.

E.   VASQUEZ DI CORONADO, F.   Sommario di due sue lettere, del Viaggio fatto da Fra Marco da Nizza alle sette Città di Cevola.   1539.   Ramusio, Viaggi, 1556.

D.P.   Quoted by Dee in the *Volume of Great and Rich Discoveries*.

E.   VERRAZZANO, GIOV.   Relatione della terra per lui scoperta al Rè Christianissimo.   1524.   Ramusio, Viaggi, 1556.

D.P.

G.   VERSTIGANE, RICHARD.   Restitution of decaid Intelligences touching the antiquities of England.

L.P.   By Richard Rowlands who edited the *Post of the World*. (See English Catalogue.)

E. VESPUCCI, AMERIGO. Lettere due . . . di due sue Navigationi, 1502-4. Ramusio, Viaggi, 1550.
D.P.

E. VESPUCCI, AMERIGO. Sommario delle dette sue Navigatione,
1501. Ramusio, Viaggi, 1550.
D.P.

E. VESPUSIUS, ALBERICUS. Navigationum Epitome. Novus
Orbis.
D.L.P.

E. VESPUSIUS, ALBERICUS. Navigationes. Novus Orbis.
D.L.P.

E. VESPUCE, EMERIC DE, FLORENTIN. Le Nouveau Monde et
Navigationes faict par. 4° Paris, N.D. en françois.
D. First published *circ.* 1515.
On Dee's list of Books important for Discovery.

E. VIAGGI Due, in Tartaria par alcuni Frate, 1247. Ramusio,
Viaggi, 1559.
D.P.

E. VIAGGO d'un Mercante, che fu nella Persia, 1507-20. Ramusio,
Viaggi, 1559.
D.P.

E. VIAGGIO scritto per un Comito Venetiano del Mar Rosso . . .
nella India 1537-8. Ramusio, Viaggi, 1550.
D.P.

E. VILLEGAGNON, CHEVALIER DU. Voiage en America, descritte
par un de ses gens, gallicé. [1557 ?]
L.

G. VITAE virorum illustrium, etc. Basel, 1563.
D.

F. VITELLIONIS, Perspectiva. Norib., 1538.
D.

F. VITRUVIUS, MARCUS. Architectura cum commentariis Danielis
Barbari. fo. Venice, 1567. Also De Architectum. Arg.,
1543.
D.(2).L. The First Edition of this famous architectural treatise
was Rome, 1486, and there were at least twenty-five editions
before 1575. Book ix deals with sundials.

G. **Vivius Sequestor.** De fluminibus, fortibus, etc.

    L.

C. **Walsingham, Thomas.** Historia Brevis.

    D.

G. **Watreman, William.** Of the Fardle of Fasshions, dedicated to Henrie Earle of Arundel.

    L.   See Catalogue of English Books.

B. **Wernerus, Joh.** In Ptolemaei geographiam, etc. Norimb., **1514.** First Edition.

    D.L.   A Paraphrasis, says Lumley. Contained Werner's new single-heart projection. The author (1468–1528) was the teacher of Reisch, author of *Margarita Philosophica* : he was a very notable mathematician, and belonged to Nürnberg.

E. **Wintzenbergerus, Daniel.** Itinerum Germaniae libellus. Dresden, 1578.

    D.   Presumably a road-book.

D. **Wissenburgius, Wolfgang.** Declaratio tabulae quae descriptionem terrae sanctae continet. Argentorati, 1538.

    L.

F. **Witekindus, Herman.** De Sphaera. Heidel. 1573.

    D.

C. **Xeres, Francesco de.** Relatione della Conquista fatta da F. Pizarro del Perù e Provincia del Cushco, chiamata la Nuova Castiglia. 1523–33. Ramusio, Viaggi, 1556.

    D.P.

C. **Xeres, Francesco de.** Relacion de Peru al Emperador Carlos V°. Hispalis, 1534.

    D.   On Dee's list of Books important for Navigations.

C. **Xeres, Francesco de.** De la Conquista del Peru y del Cuzco. Italicé. 4° Venice, 1535.

    D.   On Dee's list of Books important for Navigations.

F. **Zacutus, Abraham.** Almanach Perpetuum.

    D.   The basis of the tables used by the early Portuguese navigators. (*Regimento do Spera*.)

E. **Zeno, Nicolò e Antonio.** Dello scoprimento dell' Isola Frislanda, etc. Ramusio, Viaggi, 1559.

    D.P.

E.   ZENO, FR. CATERINO.   Viaggio en Persia, italicé.   fol. Venice, 1558.

D.P.

E.   ZENO, CATERINO.   Viaggio en Persia, 1450.   Ramusio, Viaggi, 1559.

D.P.

F   ZIEGLERUS, JACOBUS.   De Sphaera, etc.   4° Basel, 1536.

D.

G.   ZIEGLERUS, JACOBUS.   In Plinii naturalis historia, librum secundum.   fo. Basel, 1531.

D.   Dee has another edition (see under Pliny) of this book, which is critical for geography.

D.   ZIEGLERUS, JACOBUS, LAUDANUS.   Syria, Palestina, Arabia, Petraea, Aegiptus, Schondia.   Regionum superiorum singulare tabulae geographicae (i.e. set of maps).   Argent, 1532.

L.   Ziegler's *Historia Schondiae* was one of his best known works, but is not in either library catalogue. It was included in editions of Krantzius' *Chronicon*, q.v., and excerpts were made by Eden in the Decades.

APPENDIX III

ILLUSTRATIVE AND EVIDENTIAL DOCUMENTS

DOCUMENT 1

EXTRACT FROM: INFORMACŌN FOR PYLGRYMES UNTO THE HOLY LONDE, 1498: MEDITERRANEAN CLIMATE

'In this city the said pilgrims tarried a month. And there was great heat. For from May to Halowmesse there groweth no grass, it is so burnt with the heat of the sun.

And then about Allhallowmesse beginneth grass, herbs and flowers to spring. And it is there then as in summer in England, so in winter it is temperate, nor cold but little. There is never snow, nor frost with ice. And if there come any frost with a little ice, they will show it each to other for a marvel. And from May till the latter end of October there is no rain nor clouds but right selde. But ever the sun shineth right clear and hot. And about saint Martin's time the sun is as hot there as it is in August in England. And so it is in Rhodes and Cyprus, and all that country eastward.'

DOCUMENT 2

INTERLUDE OF THE FOUR ELEMENTS: ARGUMENT

'Here follow divers matters which be in this interlude contained.

Of the situation of the four elements, that is to say, the earth, the water, the air and fire, and of their qualities and properties, and of the generation and corruption of things made of the commixtion of them.

Of certain conclusions proving that the earth must needs be round, and that it hangeth in the midst of the firmament, and that it is in circumference above 21,000 miles.

Of certain conclusions proving that the sea lieth round upon the earth.

Of certain points of cosmography, as how and where the sea covereth the earth, and of divers strange regions and lands, and the manner of the people.

Of the generation and cause of well-springs and rivers, and of the cause of hot fumes that come out of the earth, and of the cause of the baths of water in the earth that be perpetually hot.

Of the cause of the ebb and flow of the sea.

Of the cause of rain, snow and hail.

Of the cause of the winds and thunder.

Of the cause of the lightning, of blazing stars, and flames flying in the air.'

DOCUMENT 3

RICHARD WILLES ON GEOGRAPHERS

(From the Dedication of ' The History of Travayle,' 1577)

' Who but Geographers doe teach us what partes of the earth be colde, warme or temperate ? Of whom doe we learne how to divyde the world into partes, the partes into provinces, the provinces into shires ? of Geographers. Unto whom have wee to make recourse for Mappes, Globes, Tables and Cardes, wherein the dyvers countreys of the Worlde are set down ? unto Geographers. Set Geographie asyde, you shall neither be able to get intelligences of the situation and strength of any citie, nor of the limites and boundes of any country, nor of the rule and government of any kingdome, nor be able wel to travayle out of your owne doores. Wil you see what wise and experte travaylers, skilful in geometry and astronomye, (for that is to be a Geographer in deede) be able to doe ? Looke you on the King of Portingales title : the two partes, of the three therein, were achieved by Vasques Gama, and other travaylers adventures. Consider the fruites, the drugges, the pearle, the treasure, the millions of golde and silver, the Spanyardes have brought out of the West Indies since the first viage of Columbus. The great commodities our nation reapeth by the travayle of our countrymen into Barbary, Guiny and Moscovia, wil be sufficient testimony unto all us Englishmen, what it is to be a skilful travayler, what to bee a paineful Geographer, and learned.'

DOCUMENT 4

EXTRACTS FROM BARLOW'S GEOGRAPHIA

(a) *Cape bon esperance.* This lond on the coste is mountaynes and rockys very asperous, the people be verie light on fote and strong in ther armes to throwe. From manicongo to this thei be all idolaters and useth little shells called carocolitas for their money . . .

Sophala stands in 19 degrees ½ this is a land of moche golde and here the king of Portugale caused an other castel to be made for to restatte or bie golde as he hath in gynee and thys was called the myna nova and the people of the country brought thider much golde for things of little valour and for lacke of good gouvernance thet a captene ded there the people of the countrey overthrew the castle and kylled all that were in it . . .

(b) (Continued from the extract in text, p. 57.)

Now by this your grace may well apperceive what parte of the universall is discovered, and what ther resteth for to discover. It is clerely seen by the Cosmographia that of iiij partes of the world the iij partes be discovered, for out of Spayne thei saile all the indies and sees occidentales and from portingale thei sayle all the indies and sees orientalles, so that between the waie of the orient and the waie of the occident thei have compassed all the world, the tone departeing from Spayne toward occydent and the other out of portyngale toward orient thei have mette together. And also by the waie of the meridian there is a grete parte discovered by the Spaniards, so ther resteth this waie of the north onelie for to discover which resteth onto your graces charge, for that the situation of this realme toward that partie is more apte for it then eny other and also for that your grace hath taken farre enter-pryse to discover this part of the world alredy and such an enterprise ought not to be lefte of, although the folowyng thereof hathe not succeded as you gracis wil and desire was, for in the people, shippes, derotas and provicions such ordre maye be taken that without dout and if it please god it shal folowe unto your gracys purpose. And for suche an enterprise no men shuld thinke upon the cost in comparison to the grete profyght that maye thereby secede, nor thinke ther labour grete where so moche profyt honor and glory maye follow unto this our naturall realme and king. And as for jopardies and perills, thys waie of navigation well considered and pondered shall seme moche less perill then all the other navigations as it maie be proved by verie evident resons. And for to speke somewhat of the commoditie and utilitie of this navigation and discovering it is very evident that the sees whereas every man will saie that ther is difficultie and daunger and that thei take for impossible to saill, those seas thei maie saile with light and day alwais, without darkness or eny night. Wherefore there is diffrence betwene thes perelles and navigation, whereas contynuallie thei mai se round about them and on the contrary where in every 24 houres thei shal saile the moste parte in darknes and nyght and at that tyme thei must saile at Aventure for thei shall see no thinge about them. I thinke ther is none so ignorant but this doth perceive. And specyallie what avauntage is this for those that discovereth new countreis, for to saile always by light and day. As for the costes and sees alredie dyscovered wheras the waie is knowen it seemeth lesse peryll to saile by nyght but in those parties for to dyscover it is very difficill to saile by nyght, and yet thei have not lefte with darknes to procure to discover londs and sees unknowen. How moche more shuld thei count us for ferefull and of litil stomak to leve of suche an enterprise which maie be done with contynnuall light. Moche more passing this little space of navigation which is counted dangerous, maie be 3 ¢ leges before thei come to the pole and other as moche after thei hav passed the pole, it is clere that from thens foreward the sees and lond is temperat as it is here in England and then it shall be in the will of them that discover to chose the cold countries, temperat, or hote, in the degre that thei will. ffor ones passe the pole thei maie chose at their plesure to declyne to what part thei lyste, for and if thei will take toward orient thei shall enjoye of the regions of the tartarians which hath ther vertente toward the southe, and from thens folowing the cost thei shal go to the londs of the china, and from thens forward to the cataio orientall which is of the mayne lande the moste orientall countying from our habitation, and if from thens thei wyl contynue ther navigation following the cost which turneth toward occydent, thei shal come to melaca, and from thens to all the indies that we call orientales, and so contynuying that coste thei maye come home by the cap bon espera and so to have gone allmost round aboute the worlde.

And if thei will sayle in passing the pole toward occident, thei shal go to the backside of all the new found land that is dyscovered by your graces subjectes, till they come unto the southe see on the backside of the indies occidentales, and so contynuying ther navigation thei maie turne by the stret of magalianas unto this realme, and so to compasse the worlde about by that parte.

And if in passing the pole artike thei will saile streite toward the pole antartike thei shall enclyne to the londs and islonds that have ther situacion betwene the tropicons and under the equinoctiall which without dout be the most richest londs and islonds in the worlde for all the golde, spices, aromatikes, and pretiose stones, with all other thynges thet we have in estimation, from thens thei come.

And beside all this yet the commoditie of this navigation by this waie is of so grete advantage over the other navigations in shortning of half the waie, for the other must saile by grete circuits and compasses, and thes shall saile by streit wais and lines.

(c) [*The Parana*].

Cape S. Maria standeth in 35 degres and all the coste to the islonde of S. Catalina to this cape is shoald by the londe and the londe is very low. On the northeast parte of the Cape is a good river and porte for shyps and on the other side entereth the River Solis which is a verie grete river, for at the beginning it is 25 or 30 leges broad betwene Cape S. Maria and Cape Blanco. And within the ryver 20 leges is an islond called the Isle of Lobos marinus about the which islond be many seals in so grete abondance thet ther maie be shyppes laden with them in short tyme. This ryver goeth in to the lond 75 leges at west and by northe wher is another ryver called S. Salvador which is a gode rode for shyps. This ryver of Solis is dangerous for grete shyppes for in it be manie bankes and shoalds that hath not passing 2 or 3 fadom of water, and betwene the cape S. Marie and the ryver S. Salvador be dyvers islands wher be founde topasias and other pretious stones. And by this ryver of S. Salvador is another grete ryver called Ornay [Uruguay] which turneth northe and northe easte, and by it is another grete ryver of lengthe and brede. We went up it above 300 leges, with a galeon a bricandyn and a carvel and all thys ryver is of fresh water. It dothe nother ebbe nor flowe but alwaies the streme goeth one waie into the see and there cometh so grete abondance of freshe water out of this ryver that 5 or 6 leges into the see ye shall take freshe water, and certen tymes of the yere in June, July and August the water of the ryver dothe increase verie high.

And ye shal understonde that all the coste from Cape Frio unto the India occidentale is called Nova Hispania. Thei have 2 wynters and 2 sommers. And from cape Frio to the strete of magelianos thei have but one wynter and one somer as wee have here that dwell withoute the tropics estival toward the pole arctike. But thei have alwaye at midday the sonne northe of them in suche wyse as when it is mid-sommer with us it is chrystmasse with them and when it is chrystmasse with us it is midsommer with them and so it is with all them that inhabit on the southe syde of the equinoctiale towarde the pole antartike. . . . Along the ryver Parana is a goodlie playne countrey of goodlie woodes of divers kinds of trees that be alwaies grene winter and sommer. Ther be manie wild beestes and a straunge facion of shepe [guanacos], ostryches [rheas] and redde deere which the Indies do hunt by diverse waies but not with dogges, for ther be none in the contrie but certyn mastiffs that we brought with us out of Spayne. . . .

This ryver of Parana is a merveillous goodlie ryver and a grete for of 3 hundred leges and above thet we went up in it the narrowest place from one shore to another was above 2 or 3 leges bredth. This ryver is fulle of goodlie islonds and pleasaunt for thei be fulle of trees of dyvers sortes and the leves of them alwaies grene and the boughs hange doune into the water and manie straunge birdes brede in them. . . .

(d) [*Magellan's Voyage*].

From Cape Sant Marie to Cape Blanco which standeth on the other side of the River Solis is 31 leges, and from cape Blanco to the fret of Mageleanas is 330 leges. The Fret of Mageleanas standeth in 52 degres toward the pole antartyk and Englonde standeth in the same degre toward the pole arctick and by this frete out of the ocean sea thei passe into the southe sea, which was founde and dyscovered in the yere 1520 by a portingale called magalianas which departed out of Seville with his armie in the yere 1519 for to dyscover the islonds of the Moluccas that waie. And of 5 shyppes that he had with hym one was lost before thei came to the said frete and another returned back ageyn and he with two more [i.e. 3 vessels] passed the fret and went by manie riche islonds and or he came to the Moluccas he was slayne in an islond called Mata by his owne folie and so were many of his people. And those that rested in the three shyppes seeyng ther captayne and many of the company slaine and had not company to furnish ther 3 shyppes thei toke out of one of them which was moste feeblest all the ordnaunce and such thynges as they myght save and after set the shyppe on fyre becaus there enemyes shoulde heve no profyt of her and with these 2 shyppes that rested thei went into the islonds of Moluccas, where thei were lade with cloves and cynamon and other spyces and one of these shyppes came home to Seville laden with spyces by the waie of cap bona spera in the yere of oure lorde 1523 and the other shyppe was taken there by the portingales as afterward it was knowen, so that this shyppe which came home to Seville whiche was called the Victoria had gone east and west almost rounde about the worlde, for hee had departed from

Seville and passed the Strait of the Magalianos by the west and came home to Seville againe by the cape of bon spera which is at easte.

(e) *Martın Fernandes de Enciso. Suma de Geographia*, 1519

Transcript of section on fourth quarter of earth, elaborated by Barlow into the appeal for a discovery by the north.

' Pues que es dicho dela parte que esta desde la isla del fierro hazia el poniente y al austro, digamos de una parte de tierra que esta en esta segunda parte hazia al setentrion, la qual tierra se dize la tierra del labrador.   Esta tierra del labrador esta en 57 grados, esta al norweste de Galizia y leste veste con Escocia.   Esta tierra del labrador tiene al oesta ala tierra de los baccalaos que es tierra de grandos pesquerias y larga.   Estan los baccallaos al oeste de galizia é parte dellos al Oeste quarta al norweste : y tienen muchos puertos y buenos y mucha tierra poblada y muchas islas delanta todas pobladas.   dizen qu ay enella muchas pieles para enforros muy finas.   La tierra del labrador esta al norte delos açores.   Ay desde los açores fasta ala tierra del labrador trezientas leguas, y desde Galizia ala tierra del labrador trezientas y cincuenta.   Ay desde galizia ala tierra de cavallaos [*sic* for bacallaos] quinientas y treynta leguas, esta la tierra de los cavallos [bacallaos] en 49 y en 50 grados.'   [End of Text.]

Author's note as follows :

' Haze fin la suma de geographia con la espera en romance y el regimiento del sol y del norte por donde los mareantes se pueden regir y governar enel marear.   Assi mesmo va puesta la cosmographia por derrotas y alturas : por donde los pilotos sabran de oy en adelante muy mejor que fasta aqui yr a descobrir las tierras que ovieren de descobrir. Fue sacade est a suma de muchos y autentichos autores.   Lonviene a saber dela historia batriana, los dos tholomes, Eratosthanes, Plinio, Strabon, Josepho, Anselmo, La biblia, la general historia y otros muchos.'

[Contracted forms have here been written out in full, but varied spellings of the same word and/or misprints are as in the original.]

Document 5

(i) Nicholas de Nicolai to the Cardinal of Lorraine, 1556 ?

Dedication of his version of the Scots' Rutter

' Entre aultres fortunes moy estant à la cour du Roy Henry huitième d'Angleterre avec son Admiral (qui depuis est mort) Duc de Northumberland, tumba entre mes mains un nombre de cahyers contenans la Navigation de Alexandre Lyndesay faicte par le commandement du Roy d'Ecosse Jaques cinquiesme alentour de son Isle (qui est son Royaume) avec toutes les particularitez notables qu'il estoit possible de remarquer en une telle navigation pour

instruire puis apres tous les autres mariniers ausquels il en conviendroit faire une semblable. Considerant avec combien de grans
travaux ce peu de Papier avoit este escrit, je ne m'n evoulus dessaisir que je n'en eusse retenu pardevers moy une coppie, laquelle
j'a longuement delaissee entre mes aultres memoires, et certes
Monseigneur, je l'avois du tout oubliée, si U.R.S. par le gracieux
accuiel que lanne passée receut de vous *ma Charte nouvelle de Bou-
lonnois* ne m'eut eveillé le couraige pour m'employer en aultres
semblables desseings, par lesquels je peusse pour le moins monstrer
que je ne veux point demeurer ingrat à vous rendre les services
ausquels vous m'obligeastes à jamais à vous et à votre Maison au
dernier camp d'Amyens tout ainsi que de jour enjour vous vous
obligez par vos bienfaicts tous ceux qui ont quelque bonne reputation
d'homme de lettres et entendus es sciences dont ils font profession.
Ainsi donc Monseigneur, je me sus travaille à faire ceste Charte et
ce Livre de la Navigation d'Escosse sur les memoires que j'en avois
de longue main, et pense y avoir bien peu oubliée à l'augmenter et
enricher de ce qu'on pourroit demander de mon industrie. Mais si
m'estimeray-je aucunement ce mien travail si vous Monseigneur,
et Messeigneurs les Princes de vostre tres illustre Maison (lequelle
s'est tousjours monstrée la plus ferme coulonne qui aye point
soustenu le Royaulme et l'estat d'Ecosse jusques à ce jour) ne
monstrez par vostre humain et gracieux accuiel que ce tres humble
don par lequel je remets encore un aultre Royaume d'Escosse et les
Mers d'alentour, en vostre puissance, vous soit venu à gré et à
plaisir.'

(ii) NICHOLAS DE NICOLAI TO THE DUC DE JOYEUSE, ADMIRAL
OF FRANCE

(1583 *edition of the Pilote Escossais*)

. . . ' En l'an 1546 que Milord Dudley Admiral d'Angleterre, et
depuis Duc de Northumberland, vint de la part de Henry 8 son Roy,
jurer la paix au le grand Roy François, ayant esté adverty que j'avois
faictes peu d'années au paravant, et d'une carte et description
Geographique de l'Isle et Royaume d'Angleterre en laquelle j'avois
observé plusieurs choses notables et non vulgaires : ne cessa qu'il
ne me l'eust tirée des mains, non touteffois sans tres-honnorable re-
compense, comme il estait magnanime et liberal : et tant me per-
suada que voyant la paix bien establie, j'obtemperay aysement (pour
le desir que j'avois de veoir et de me rendre tousjours plus capable
au service de ceste Couronne) de m'en aller avec luy, où je demeuray
environ un an, fort bien traicté, voire jusques à me descouvrir

plusieurs importans affaires de sa charge d'Admiral, entre lesquelles pour mieux m'attirer à ses desseins, me communiqua un petit livret escrit à le main en language Escossois, contenant la navigation du Roy d'Escosse Jaques cinquième du nom faicte - autour de son royaume . . . avec toutes les particularitez notables, dignes d'estre remarquees en une telle navigation : ensemble la carte marine assez grossement faicte, pour instruire apres tous les mariniers, auxquels il en conviendroit faire une semblable. Et considerant avec combien de grands travaux ce peu de papier avoit esté escrit, je ne m'en voulus dessaisir sans en retenir une coppie : et estant de retour en France, à l'advenement du bon Roy Henry II . . . je feiz parler ledict livret François, par l'ayde de feu Maistre Jehen Ferrier, tres-docte Escossois, et l'ayant mis au nect a avec sa carte, le presentay à sa Majesté, qui l'envoya incontinent au Sieur Leon Strozzi, Prieur de Capua, Cappitaine generale de ses galleres et moy aussi, el allasmes avec seize galleres et autres forces, assieger le Chasteau St. André. . . .

Et certes, Mon Seigneur, le dict oeuvre a longuement demeuré parmy mes autres memoires, où je l'avois au tout oblié. . . .'

DOCUMENT 6

JEAN ROTZ : TRAICTE DES DIFFERENCES DU COMPAS AYMENTE
(Dedication. MS.)

' Au noble Roy dangleterre :

Nous lisons es histoires anciennes trespussant et tresnoble prince, que les gentz despryt de plusieurs nations et en especyal les grecz et latins si sont quelques foys transports en estranges contries pour visiter les hommes Renomez en Icelles. Cest donc a bien von droict que les plus excelentz personnages du monde, ou se sont ja presentez devant vostre face Royalle, ou sont enflammez dung merveilleux desir de mous voyr et vous saluir : estimantz grande louenge et gloire Immortelle avoyr este trouvez dignes de vostre tant gratieuse et debonnaire Raccueil. Du nombre desquelz combien que je ne merite estre compte, et non obstant vostre admirable humanite et douleur de Roy plus que populaire, ma donne hardiesse de me presenter devant votre personne, non pas ayant les mains voydes. . . . Il nappartient devant ung de ceuls desquelz il est escript aux pseaulmes ' Jay dict vous estes dieues,' mais sy non du tout voydes, a tout le moyns playns de pou de chose. Cest a scavoyr dung livre que je supply estre dedie et consacre a vostre sacree maieste, compose a lutilite et recreation de tous ceules quy ont affection de gouster les fruictz savoureux de lastrologie et science marine :. avec linvention et artifice dung Instrument lequel aussy Je desire sil vous plaise, sire, estre daussy bon coeur receu quil vous est present. Car veu vostre divin esprit tres grand scavoyr tres haulte puissance, veu aussy le nombre presque infiny tant des vaillants mariniers de vostre Riche Royaulme, Comme des plus beaulx mieuls esquippez navires quil est possible de voyr, avec les grosses bourses et trafficques des marchantz de vostre pays, je may sceu penser que aultre prince mondict livre peust estre plus eureusement addresse que a vostre serenissime personne, ni communique a peuple quy en fut plus digne que le vostre. Or il est bien vray quil nest en langue entendu de vostre commune poppulaire : aussy ne lay je pas voullu, combien je le peusse faire. Car jay use ugne partie de mon age en ce florissant royaulme et ay appris au moins mal que jay peu la langue diceluy. Et la cause, sire, ce a este pource que de tous temps vous aves ayme la langue françoise. Et a celle fin que auttant quil vous plairoit vous en peussiez joyr tout seul et a part vous, et qua lexemple dalexandre le grand, feussiez non seullement par puissance plus excelent que voz subjetz, mays aussy par science. Touttefoys sil vous semble bon quil feuse translatte au commum langage de ce pays, pour l'instruction et enseignment de voz mariniers, il nya homme en vostre Royaulme voyue, quasy au monde, quy ne sestimast bien heureux de commencer ugne oeuvre plaisante et agreable a ung sy grand et redoubte prince. Laquelle seroit cause comme jestime qu'on trouveroyt en pou de temps, autant ou plus de bons et perfaictz pillottes et astrologues de marine en angleterre, quey aultre lieu du monde. Sur cest endroit je feroys la fin de moy espitre, tres cher sire, nestoit quil me semble que je me doivy escuser de ne vous avoyr offert quelque carte marine. Ce que jeusse faict et feroys nestoit que je ne fays doubte qu'on vous en a aucy devant presente grand nombre de bonnes et belles. Parquoy je supply tres humblement a vostre sacree maieste, quelle se veuille contenter pour le present de ce livre, auquel vous pourrez voyr comment toutes cartes sont moyns certaines que n'estime la pluspart des hommes. Ce plus oultre, sire, je vous plaira n'avoyr esgard a la matiere et estoffe de l'instrument mays seulement a ce que cest le premier et seul encore pour le jourdhuy faict de ceste invention. Laquelle comme jespere vostre sacree maieste tiendra estre de grande utilite et recreation tant pour la mer que pour la terre.'

DOCUMENT 7

REFERENCES TO PERSONS

(*a*) CHANCELLOR.

(i) *Thomas Digges, Alae sive Scalae,* 1573. Cap 9. Sig. K 2. ' Tamen ne in minimis mihi quiquam aliorum tribuam, liberè fateor, illam partiendi radium in plurimas sensibiles partes rationem, a me inventum non fuisse, sed diu hic in Anglia a plurimis peritissimis Mathematicis usurpatam. Primus tamen qui ea divisionum ratione usus est, qui inadmodum ex auditu accepi, quidem fuit nomini RICHARDUS CHANSLERUS, peritissimus et ingeniosissimus Artifex Mathematicus, cuis nomen eo libentius publicare decrevi, quod jam e vita discesserit, neque monumentum suarum virtutum ullum publicum reliquit, praeter Instrumenta quaedam summa arte fabricata, et dulcissimam suae singularis peritae (in nonnullorum Mathematicorum adhuc superstitium amisis) memoriam.'

(ii) *Clement Adams. Navigationes ad Moscoviam* 1554. ' Omnium consensu vicit RICHARDUS CHANCELLERUS, vir ob multa ingenii documenta spectabilis, in quo uno summa conficiendi negotii spes erat. Hunc aluerat Henricus Sydneus.'

(iii) *Richard Eden, Decades of the New World.* 1555. ' RICHARD CHANCELLOR told me that he heard Sebastian Cabot report that (as far as I remember) either about the coast of Brazil or Rio de Plata, his ship or pinnace was suddenly lifted from the sea and cast upon land.'

(iv) *Bale, Catalogue of English Writers.* 1559. ' RICHARDUS CHAUNCELLOR, post prima bonarum literarum studia, omnem curam in siderum contemplatione collocans, in astrologia pleraque scipsisse dicitur, sed librorum suorum titulos non vidi. cl. 1556.'

(v) *Thos. Churchyard : a prayse and Reporte of Master Martyne Frobisher's Voyage to Meta Incognita.* May 10, 1578. ' There were many of his [Sir H. Willoughby] company that found out Moscovia at that present time, which men ought not to be forgotten. I knew myself two of them, the one called CHANCELER, the other Borrowes [i.e. Steven], which CHANCELER especially was the odde man of his time, for matters touching the sea.'

(vi) *Extract from Dee's Catalogue of his MSS.* 1583. ' No. 58. Inventa quaedam geometrica, papyro fo. My oune hand, of Richard CHANCELLOR and Thomas Topely.'

(vii) *Extract from Dee's List of his own Works,* 1592. ' The Astronomicall and Logisticall rules and canons, to calculate the Ephemerides by, and other necessary accounts of heavenly motions :

written at the request and for the use of that excellent Mechanician Master RICHARD CHANCELLOR, at his last [sic] voyage into Moschovia, Anno 1553.'

(*b*) DEE.

(i) *Thomas Digges ; Preface to his 'Alae'.* 1573. 'De plura de hujus stellae historia scribere non decrevi ; quia eximius vir. JOANNUS DEE (quem in reliqua Philosophia admirandus, tum harum Scientiarum peritissimus, quem tanquam mihi parentum alterum Mathematicum veneror, quippe qui tenerrima mea aetate harum suavissimarum semine menti meae inseruerit, alia à Patre meo prius sata amicissime fidelissimeque nutriverit atque auxerit,) hanc sibi tractandam assumperit materiam, quam ita absoluturum esse, ut in Dei optimi Maximi gloriam, et Mathematicarum Artium studiosorum detectationem, utilitatem et admirationem summam brevi prodeat, nihil dubito.'

(ii) *Gascoyne's Preface to Gilbert's Discourse.* 1576. 'So now let me say that a great learned man (even Mr. DEE) doth seem very well to like of this Discovery, and doth much commend the writer, the which he declareth in his Mathematical Preface to the 'English Euclide'. I refer thee (Reader) to peruse the same, and think it not strange though I be encouraged by so learned a foreleader, to set forth a thing he hath so well liked of.'

(iii) *Edward Worsop : Sundry Errors. September*, 1581. 'Great pains were taken at the time of the impression by M. Doctor Whitehead, a profound learned man, and M. JOHN DEE who is accounted of the learned Mathematicians throughout Europe ye Prince of Mathematicians of this age. . . . His mathematical preface unto these elements is a work of such singularity and necessity to all students of the Mathematicalls that I wish them to make it a manual.'

(iv) *William Bourne : Treatise on Optical Glasses.* Lansdown, 121 (*circ.* 1578). 'For that there ys dyvers in this Lande that can say and doth knowe muche more, in these causes, then I ; and specially M. DEE and allso Mr. Thomas Digges, for that by theyre learninge, they have reade and seene many moo auctors in those causes. And allso, theyre ability ys such, that they may the better mayntayne the charges.'

(*c*) DYER.

(i) *Humfrey Cole to Burghley, London, Dec.* 1578. *Lansdown* 26 (*No.* 22). 'Right honourable, whereas Mr. EDWARD DYER presented to your honour a peece of green ore which he had of me.'

(ii) *John Dee, To my loving frende Mr. John Stowe. Harleian*, 374. ' Mr. Stowe, you shall understand that my friend Mr. DYER did deliver your books, and the two only : who took them very thankfully, but as he noted, there was no reward recommended at them. What shall hereafter, God knoweth. . . . I hast this 5 of Dec.' [no year].

(iii) *John Frampton. Dedication of Marco Polo to Edward Dyer*, 26 *Jan.* 1579. ' I found no man . . . to whom so many Scholars, so many travelers, and so many men of valor, suppressed or hindered with poverty, or distressed by lack of friends in Court, are so much bound as to you. . . . I have found myself . . . more bound to you than to any man in England.'

(iv) *Richard Hakluyt : Preface to 1st Edition of the Principal Navigations*, 1589. ' In respect of generall incouragement in this laborious travaile, it were grosse ingratitude in mee to forget, and wilfull maliciousness not to confesse that man, whose onely name doth carie with it sufficient estimation and love, and that is MASTER EDWARD DYER, of whom I will speake thus much in few wordes, that both my selfe and my intentions herein by his friendly means have been made known to those, who in sundry particulars have much steaded me.'

(*d*) LUMLEY'S LIBRARY.

(i) *Richard Hakluyt : Preface to the 2nd Edition of The Principal Navigations*. 1599. ' Here thou hast his [Chancellor's] voiage penned by himselfe (which I hold to be very authentical, and for the which I do acknowledge myselfe holding unto the excellent Librarie of the right honourable my Lord LUMLEY).'

(ii) ' I had free access unto the right honourable my L. LUMLEY his stately library, and was permitted to copy out of ancient manuscripts, these two journals and some others also.'

(*e*) P. NUÑEZ.

(i) *John Dee to Mercator, July 20, 1558 (Propaideumata).* ' Viro illus legavi eruditissimo, gravissimoque, qui Artium Mathematicarum unicum nobis est relictum et decus et Columen : nimirium D. D. PETRO NONIO SALACIENSI.'

[See also Select Letters, Document 9, ii.]

(ii) *Isaac Casaubon's Transcript of Dee's List of MSS.* ' 33. De Triangulorum rectilineorum Areis lib 3. demonstrati ad excellentissimum Mathematicum PETRUM NONIUM conscripti. A° 1560.'

DOCUMENT 8

EXTRACTS FROM THE COMPENDIOUS REHEARSAL OF JOHN DEE. NOVEMBER 9, 1592

(i) 'I went beyond the sea (Anno 1547 in May) to speak and confer with some learned men, and chiefly Mathematicians, as Gemma Phrysius, Gerardus Mercator, Gaspar à Mirica, Antonius Gogava, etc. And after some months so spent about the Low Countries, I returned home and brought with me the first Astronomers staff in brass, that was made of Gemma Frisius devising, the two great Globes of Gerardus Mercator's making, and the Astronomer's ring of brass, as Gemma Frisius had newly framed it : and they were afterwards by me left to the use of the Fellows and Scholars of Trinity College.'

(ii) 'To my library were also appertaining, certain rare and exquisitely made instruments Mathematical. Among which was one excellent, strong, and fair quadrant (first made by that famous Richard Chancellour) of five foot semi-diameter : wherewith *he and I* made sundry observations meridian of the sun's height, as partly may appear by *our* writings in my Ephemerides A° 1554, A° 1555.

There was also an excellent Radius Astronomicus of ten foot long, and having the staff and cross very curiously divided into parts equal, after Richard Chancellor's Quadrant manner. This great instrument was in such a frame placed and laid, that it might most easily be wielded of any man to any position for practice in heavenly observations or *mensurations on earth*.

[Also] Two Globes of Gerardus Mercator's best making on which were my divers reformations, both Geographical and Celestial. . . .

There were also divers other instruments, . . . of Gerardus Mercator his own making for me purposely.

There were sea-compasses of divers sorts and for variation.

A water-clock made by one Dibbley . . . by which time might . . . be measured in the seconds of an hour.'

DOCUMENT 9

SELECT LETTERS

(i) *Odet de Selve to the King of France.*   *May 23, 1547*

' Sire je vous envoye quelques cartes et ung livre de la navigation d'Ecosse que j'ay eues d'ung painctre françoys dont j'ay aultresfoys escript à monsieur le connestable [i.e. from Nicholas de Nicolai]. Bien est vray, Sire, que ledict livre qui estoyt en langaige escossoys

ne se trouvera paz comme je crains des mieuz traduitz, car celluy
quy s'en est meslé est ung Escossays que n'entend paz trop bien la
langue françois, et ne m'a esté possible d'en recouvrer d'aultre
fidelle icy, ne de garder l'original du dict livre en escossoys lequel
je vous eusse envoyé quand et quand, mais ledict painctre l'a retiré
et porté en France, comme je croy.'

(ii) *Dee to Mercator. July* 20, 1558. *Propaideumata*

' Ad Gerardum Mercatorem Rupelmundanum, Mathematicum et
Philosophum Insignem. . . . Cum autem in literis tuis ad me, ferè
omnibus, quid ipse prae manibus habeam, à me scire, soles contendere : et in illis certè, quas ante nominavi, penultimis mecum
egisti maximè, ut magnum illud opus meum Apodicticum, de Arte
nova (ut te voces) quam primum vel in lucem darem, vel ejus te ut
participem facerem : me scias praeter periculosissimum, quo toto
jam proxime elapso anno laboravi, morbum, alia etiam multa (ab
illis, qui etc. [*sic*]) esse perpessum incommoda, quae mea studia
plurimum retardavere : Viresque etiam meas, nondum posse
tantum sustinere studii laborisque onus, quantum illud, Herculem
penè (ut perficiatur) requiret opus. Unde si mea haud queat opera,
vel absolvi, vel emitti, dum ipse sim superstes : Viro illud legavi
eruditissimo, gravissimoque ; qui artium Mathematicarum unicum
nobis est relictum et decus et Columen : nimirium D.D. Petro Nonio
Salaciensi : Illumque, obnixè nuper oravi, ut, si quando post-
humum, ad illum deferetur hoc meum opus, benigne humaniter-
que sibi adoptet, modisque omnibus, tanquam suo, utatur : absol-
vere denique, limare, ac ad publicam Philosophantium utilitatem
perpolire, ita dignetur, ac si suum esset maximè. Et non dubito,
quin ipse (si per vitam valetudinemque illi erit integrum) voti me
faciet compotem : cum et me tam amet fideliter : et in artes,
Christianae Reipublicae summa necessarias, graviter incumbere, sit
illi à natura insitum : voluntate, industria, usuque confirmatum.
Tuis igitur votis, de laborum meorum evulgandis monumentis,
nondum me posse satisfacere, licet jam clare satis docui. Si tuae
tamen petitioni de scriptorum meorum habendo catalogo, non
responderem, merito me maximae damnares ingratitudinis. En
tibi ergo eorum Titulos, quae per medias meas, maximasque dificul-
tates, ita a me mihi composita, scriptaque extant, ut eadem (cum
viribus valeam corporis, dulcique fruer ocio) in publicum producere
(non mihi tantum esse cognita) exoptem maxime.'

[Follow the names of eleven works of which those relevant to
Geography are in the Catalogue of English Books.]

' Aliorum adhuc tacebo nomina, qui tamen ante istorum quosdem (annuente Deo) publica frui luce possint. Hoc autem opusculum (numero duodecimum) levi munitum armatura, tanquam explora-torem, in varias emitto regiones : ut vera mihi doctorum pro-borumque hominum referat judicia votaque, haec a me tanta tractari, lucique promitti argumenta. . . .

Jam restat ut te maxime oram, egregia tua Inventa, tam in excellentissima illa Philosophiae parte, quae physica vocatur, quam in geometricis, et geographicis rebus, publicis (quam primum queas) ut committas hominum studiis : sic enim Rempublicam literarium (de qua annos ante multos, multi magnisque tuis laboribus, es optime meritus) istis utilissimis tuis, novisque Inventis, eximio profecto amplificabis. Valeas.

(iii) *Thomas Champneys to Cecil.*   3 *Nov.,* 1566.   (State Papers, Domestic, Elizabeth, under date cited)

' Right honourable, my humble duty remembered, it may pleas you to be advertised that at my departing forth of England there was one Jenkinson who had taken in hand to travell to the Cathaia, but being upon his voyage was forced to return, by what lott I know not. Considering how long we have desired the discovery of the said country and all the great benefit her majesty might enjoy thereby, I have according to my bounden duty written unto her highness, not only of the commodities there to be had, but also the ready way for the short discovery of the same, as by her majesties letters most plainly doth appear, most humbly desiring your honour to expedite the same with answer, that thereby I may resolve the. party who attendeth here her majesty's pleasure. Thus praying to the dear living God long to continue your health with daily increase of honour. From Naples the 3 of November 1566.

Your honours most humble during life,

THOMAS CHAMPNEYS.'

(iv) *Thos. Bannister and Geoffrey Ducket (agents of the Muscovy Company) to Cecil. Aug.* 12, 1568.   State Papers. Col-onial Series. No. 2415.

' [The Muscovy Trade] will furnish the Queen's navy with cables, cordage, masts, sails, pitch and tar, whereby her Grace is delivered out of the bondage of the King of Denmark and the town of Dantsike. It makes the passage into Persia [imperfect] have better hope than ever of bringing the trade of spices this way. This matter of Persia touches the Italians and strangers very neer ; for the Italians have had the whole trade of silk and much spices brought by the Venetians, and the Flemings in like case have the staple of all spices placed at Antwerp by the Portugals. [The Company] mind to appoint Bassington [i.e. Bassendine] with two mariners and interpreters to pass from Pechoray in a Russian boat with the first open water in spring along the coast eastwards for a trial of the north-east passage, which will be done at a small cost, and as their masters say to more purpose than if two barks should be set out.' [Calendar précis of original.]

(v) *Richard Hakluyt of the Middle Temple to Ortelius.*
circ. 1566

' Neque ullo modo omittendum est Fretum Trium Fratrum suo in loco ab oculos proponere, quoniam adhuc spes est tandem aliquando id inveniri posse, sic autem in charta collocari ad confringendum eorum cosmographorum errorem qui hujus modi fretum nequaquam expremiunt : asservendo Fretum Trium Fratrum nomen sortitum fuisse a tribus fratris, qui ut recitat Gemma Frisius ex Europa navigantes ea loca praeterierunt. Pleniumque introducendo lib. 2, cap. 67 ex Cornelio Nepote (qui ante Christum natum 57 annos scripsit) commemoratem quosdem Indos ad littora Germaniae tempestate appulsos, et a Sueviae rege Quinto Metello Celeri in Gallia tum proconsuli allatos : et Dominicum Marium Nigrum pagina 590 de Mari Indico verba facientem inferendo. Historiam insuper a Francisco Lopete de Gomera prolatam de Indis quibusdem in littore Germanico, tempore Frederici Barbarossae imperatoris projectis adhibendo. Othonem denique in Gothica historia de quibusdem Indis in eandem terram vi tempestatum projectis adjiciendo : qui varias ob causes nulla alia via agi potuerunt. Quibus aliisque ejusmodi nostri aevi si qua sit, superveniret experientia. Ut certo sciant homines fretum esse, Pervulgatum est enim (sed praeter auditum habetur nihil) nostra aetate Hispanos quosdem ab ulteriore parti Floridae hoc fretum praeteriisse, orisque Germaniae appulisse. . . .

. . . Per Danielem Rogerium, magistri Ortelii consanguinem, in Flandriam transmittende.'

(vi) *John Dee to Burghley, 3rd Oct.,* 1574. Lansdown, 100

' For the last 20 yrs past and longer it may be very truly avouched, that I have had a marvellous zeal, taken very great care, endured great travail and toil, both of mind and body : and spent very many hundred pounds, only for the attayning some good and certain knowledge in the best and rarest matters Mathematicall and Philosophicall. How little or how much therein, the eternal God

hath imparted to me (for my talent) he only best knoweth.   But
certainly by due conference with all I ever mete withe in Europe,
the poor English Briton (il favorito di vostra Excellentia) hath
carried the Bell away.

. . . whom your Lordship knoweth (or may know) that
Emperors, Kings, Princes, Dukes, Marchises, Earls, Barons, and
other many men, of great power and magnificent courage, have
sued unto (in my time) to enjoy my simple talent in their service
or company.'

(vii) *John Dee to A. Ortelius. Jan.* 16, 1577

' Et quod tu olim in Asiaticae tuae Tabulae aliquot locis, et alibi,
a nostris Brytanis expectare, immo et contendere videris : Idem
et ego ut aggrederentur, et ante aliquot annos commonui, et nunc
ut perficiant vel maxime hortor, insto, urgeo.   Veterumque aliquot,
illud iter, aliqua ratione commemorantium, conquiro monumenta, ac
perlustro : indeque nonnulla in Methodum aliquam Nauticam
digero : Quo tam praeclarum tandem perficiatur opus.   Nimirum
ut suis veris terminis illam primum habemus circumscriptam Orbis
Terrarum partem, quae cum omnium maxima, tum humanae Originis
et Redemptionis, Campus est unicus et celeberrimus et omnium
praeterea Artium optimarum Parens . . . Sed ut ad Geographica
nostra redeam negocia.   Orandus nunc mihi intimè venis (optimi
Orteli) ut literis quam primum possis me reddes certiorem, ex quo
Authore quave ratione informatus, in Atlantidis septentrionali ora
ascripseris Cap. de Paramantia : et Los Jardinòs : et illa alia quae
primus ipse et solus in ea parte depinxeris : Hos si feceris, literario
cum foenore fiet, tibi acceptissimo. . . .

Hiis hoc tempore (Humanissime mi Orteli) te salutare volui.
Gratiasque tibi habere ingentes ob Candorem illum tuum, et
humanitatis officia, quibus me exceperis, Bibliothecam tuam dum.
ante aliquot annos inviserem : mihique Nostratis Humpfredi
Lhoydi Brytanicos commonstrares Commentariolos.   Literas autem
ad me vestras, vel per Birkmannorum famulos apud vos, vel per
eruditissimi viri et amici mei D. Danielis Rogerii industriam,
expeditissime et tutissime deferri posse, haud te latere arbitror.
Festinacione profecto aliqua opus est.   Nostri enim homines ad
Boreales Atlantidis partes maritimas, iterum iter maturant.   Elapso
namque anno fretum Groenlandicum salutarunt tantum.   Sed ita
tamen, ut magnam (probabilibus rationibus) conceperint spem,
universam illam Oram circumnavigandi : et ad ipsum usque
Eorum Mare illac penetrandi. . . .'

(viii) *Sir P. Sidney to Hugh Languet.* *Oct.* 1, 1577

' I wrote you a year ago about a certain Frobisher who, in rivalry
of Magellan, has explored that sea which he supposes to wash the
north part of America. It is a marvellous history. After having
made slow progress in the past year, so as only to pass in the autumn
the Faroe Isle and an island which he supposes to be Frisland, discovered by the Venetian Zeni, he touched at a certain island for the
purpose of recruiting himself and his crew.' [Follows story of a
young man picking up a piece of glittering earth, who ' showed it
to Frobisher : who . . . not believing that the precious metals
were produced in a region so far to the north, considered it of no
value '. Follows account of second voyage.] ' It is therefore at this
time under debate [cf. Lok documents] by what means these our
labours can be still carried on in safety against the attacks of other
nations, among whom the Spaniards and Danes seem especially to
be considered : the former as claiming all the western parts by right
from the Pope ; the latter as being more northerly and therefore
nearer : and relying on their possession of Iceland they are better
provided with the means of undertaking this voyage. They are also
said to be sufficiently skilled in navigation.'

(ix) *Hugh Languet to Augustus, Elector of Saxony.*
Nov. 27, 1577

' Forbisserus natione Anglus, homo rei nautici peritissimus, jam
per aliquot annos procul ad Septentrionem navigavit, sperans se
posse reperire fretum, per quod navigare possit in mare quod
Hispani nominant del Sur, et inde ad Moluccas insulas, in quibus
proveniunt aromata, et in Indiam Orientalem : nam existimiunt
novum orbem repertum ab Hispaniis esse Insulam, quae ab
orientem et meridiem separetur a continente freto Magellicano, et
ad occidentem et septentrionem eo freto quod ipse investigat. Cum
autem amnem obambularet in quadem insula plane inculta ad quam
aquandi gratia appulerat, quidam ex ejus comitibus conspicatus
glebam rutilentem, collegit eam ac ipsi ostendit : a quo cum
contemui viderit, retenuit tamen eam apud se et secum in Angliam
vexit, uti cum eum aurifabro ostendisset, is eam conflavit, ac
reperit esse aurum fere purum. . . .
    . . . Omnes volant eo navigari.'

(x) *Mercator to Ortelius.* 12 *Dec.,* 1580. (Hessels. No. 99)
' Magno me affecerunt gaudio literae tuae, imprimis quod diu
desideratam Chinam nectus sis, tum novae illius Anglicanae naviga-

tionis communicatione, cujus initia per Rumoldum alias misisti. Quod tanto studio, navigationis hujus cursum occultent varieque de itinere et regionibus visis loquuntur, non aliam esse causam persuasum habeo quam quod opulentissimas ditiones hactenus ab Europeis (quin et ab Indis ipsis Oceanum navigant) nondum accessas repererint. Hujus argumento mihi sunt ingens ille argenti et lapidum preciosum thesauru, quam ex preda se nactos fingere omnino suspicior, tum id quod hic scribam : Hoc anno mense Aprili ad me scriptum fuit ex Anglia eos mercatores qui cum Muscovitis commertia habent, atque apud eos stationem habent, in sinu Amalchii maris sive septentrionalis, peritissimum quemdam navarchum Maio jam elapso claviculum mittere statuisse, nomine Arthurum Pitte, eique in mandatis dedisse ut una navi veloce in biennium commeatu necessario instructa, omnia littora Asiae septentrionalia perlustraret etiam ultra Tabin promontorium, quem ea causa potessimum emissum suspicor ut classem quae per fretum Magellanicum processerat in Peru, Moluccas, et Javam, inde redeuntem quereret, eique occurreret. Itaque hanc classem non alia via quam per occidentem et borealia Asiae reversam omnino arbitror, fretum enim illud quod septentrionalia Americae ambit ad paucos tantum gradus maximi circuli a Groenlandia in occasum per Frobisherum lustratum est, idque multis scopulis impeditum, ut hanc viam Draeckiam tentasse non sit verisimile, praecipue si ex Asia tanto onustus thesauro rediit. Multi enim brevior erat illi in occidentem reditus, et quidem jam antea dimidia circiter parte notus, nimirum a Vaigatz insula et Nova Zemla deinceps in Angliam usque. Hujus Arthuri navigatio quia sub silentio mihi communicata fuit, dissimulato et tu ejus aliquid te nosse, interim tamen per amicos undecumque rei actae veritatem expiscaveris, qui si multos conveniant atque interrogent, non poterunt illi tam " splendide mentiri " ut non se prodat veritas. . . .'

(xi) *Frobisher and Hall to Dee.* 1576

' To the worshipful and our approved good friend M. Dee, give these with speed. This 26 day of June 1576 I arrived in Shotland in the Bay of Saint Tronions in the latitude of 59 degrees 46 minutes. I and M. Hall make our dutifull Commendations to you, with as many thanks as we can wish, till we be better furnished with farder matters to satisfy our duties for your frendly Instructions : which when we use we do remember you, and hold ourselves bound to you as your poor disciples, not able to be Scholars but in good will for want of lerning, and that we will furnish with good will and diligence to the uttermost of our powers. The cause of our stay here was to stop a leake I had in the Michael . . . [news of voyage] . . . Your loving frend to use and command, Martin Frobisher. Yours to command, Christopher Hall.'

(xii) *Dee to Sir Francis Walsingham ('my singular good friend and patron'). May 14, 1586. From Leipsic*

' If you send me Master Thomas Digges, in her Majesty's behalf, his faithfulness to her Majesty, and my well-liking of the man, shall bring forth some piece of good service. But her Majesty had better to have spent or given in Alms a million of Gold than to have lost some opportunities past. No human reason can limit or determine God his marvellous means of proceeding with us. He hath made of Saul (E.K.) a Paul.'

(E.K. was Edward Kelly ; the reference is to Kelly's supposed secret of transmutation.)

DOCUMENT 10

PASSAGES RELATING TO THE PARADOXALL COMPASS

(i) From Dee's manuscript list of his own writings, Vitellius, C. VII

Inventum mechanicum Paradoxum, de novâ ratione, delineandi circumferentiam circularem, Unde (valdè rara) alia dependent Inventa. Lib. i. a° 1556.

(ii) *General and Rare Memorials pertayning to the Perfecte Arte of Navigation. London, 1577*

' I must note unto you, even here, that one of those injuries was above the rest so notorious : and withall so well [1] known to be an injury, that the last year [i.e. 1576] a certain Mechanicien (being busied about matter of Navigation) calling to remembrance the same injury : being a fowle and impudent brag, that an English Mariner (now above 20 yeres sins, had made to divers honest men, of the new Sea Instrument, newly also called the Paradoxall Compass, as to have been of his own invention) was so inflamed with indignation against this arrogant Mariner, his abominable impudency . . . that he made earnest request to this gentleman [i.e. Dee] (the true Inventor of this Instrument Paradoxall) . . . speedily to detect such shameless braggers.'

(iii) *Preface to the English Euclid, 1570*

' The Arte of Navigation demonstrateth how, by the shortest

[1] M. Steven and M. William Borough, two of the chief Muscovy Pilots (after the incomparable M. Richard Chancellor his death), can be sufficient witnesses thereto.

good way, by the aptest direction, and in the shortest time, a sufficient ship . . . be conducted.

What nede the master Pilote hath of other Artes, here before recited it is easie to know: as of Hydrographie, Astronomie, Astrologie, and Horometrie. Presupposing the common base and foundacion of all, namely Arithmetike and Geometrie, so that he be hable to understand and judge his own necessary instruments: whether they be perfectly made or no: and also can (if nede be) make them himselfe. As Quadrants, the Astronomer's Staff, the Astronomer's Ryng, the Astrolabe Universall, an Hydrographicall Globe, Charts hydrographicall, true (not with parallel meridians). The Common Sea Compas: the Compass of Variacion: the Proportionall and *Paradoxall Compasses* (of me invented [margin 1559] for our two Muscovy Pilotes, at the request of the Company). Clockes with spryng: houre, half houre, and three houre Sandglasses: and sundry other Instruments. And also, be hable, on Globe or Playne, to describe the Paradoxall Compasse: and duly to use the same to all manner of purposes whereto it was invented.'

(iv) *Extract from Dee's List of his own MS. writings*, 1592

' The Britishe Complement of the Perfect Arte of Navigation. A great volume: in which are contained our Queen Elizabeth her Arithmeticall Tables Gubernatick: for Navigation by *the Paradoxall Compasse* (by me invented anno 1557) and Navigation by Great Circles: and for longitude and latitudes: and the variation of the Compasse, finding most easily and speedily: yea, (if need be) in one minute of time, without sight of Sun, Moon or Star: with many other new and needful inventions Gubernatick.'

(v) *John Davis: Seaman's Secreates*, 1594

' Horizontall Navigation manifesteth all the varieties of the ships motion within the horizontal plaine or superficies, where every line drawn is supposed parallel.

Paradoxall or Cosmographicall Navigation demonstrateth the true motion of the ship upon any course assigned in longitude, latitude and distance, either particular or general, and is the skilful gathering together of many horizontall motions into one infallible and true motion Paradoxall.

The third is Great Circle Navigation, which teacheth how upon a great circle drawne betweene any two places assigned (being the only shortest way from place to place) the ship may be conducted, and is performed by the skilful application of horizontall and Paradoxall Navigation. . . .

The Instruments necessary for a skilfull Seaman are the Sea Compasse, a Cross Staffe, a Quadrant, an Astrolabie, a Chart, an instrument magneticall for the finding of the Variacion of the Compass, an Horizontall plaine sphere, a Globe and a *Paradoxall Compass* . . . but the Sea Compass, chart and Cross Staffe are instruments sufficient for a seaman's use : the Astrolabie and Quadrant being instruments very uncertain for sea observations.'

Document ii
Proposals for the North-West and North-East Passages

(i) Undated Document (probably 1566-7) in Latin and English. The Latin title and English version (which lacks a title) are transcribed.

The English text is as follows : ' In the country of America toward the north about the sixtie degree, there is an elbowe of land lying verie farre into the sea, which is called the Head of Labrador. And on the south side there is a very broad bay lying towards the west, of such breadth that it seemeth both in the very entry and after, to be a great sea, for it lyeth at about 3 or 4 hundred miles. And hath very many islands, and all the year throughout there are in the same huge heapes of ice, which bay is called Dusmendas.

In the year of our lord 1496 in the reign of King Henry VII, Sebastian Cabotto who afterwards was chief pilot of Spayne was sent out of England by the said king with two ships to find out the passage from the north sea to the south, that the way into the countries that are called Mangi, Sepango and Cataya might be opened. Whereby Sebastian Cabot, going forth on his voyage by the coast of the Ilands, that so he might come into America, about the sixty degree found great mountains of ice and islands covered with snow in the month of July, when he was but under 60° only, toward the north. Which country, finding contrary to his expectations, he went round about, and beholding so great an abundance of ice, was in doubt that he would find any way, and therefore returned into England again. Which hills of ice there grow because divers rivers of sweet waters round [run] down from the other side of the promontory. Which is not of the salt sea water. For it is to be noted that the sea itself never freezeth. This daily experience we have by the ships which yearly go out of England into Muscovia, leaving in early summer season, and return from there into England in five months space. At which time of the year our countrymen find no huge ice or snow there, although they pass under the 72 or 73 degrees, which is 12 or 13 degrees nearer the pole than Cabot was.

Moreover in the year of our lord 1500 one Gaspar Cortereal also, a pilot of portingale, from the north part of America was in those islands with two ships and brought with him from thence threescore captives and slaves.

But to find out the passage out of the north sea into the south, we must sail to the 60 degree, that is from 66 unto 68. And this passage is called the narrow sea or strait of the three brethren. In which passage at no time in the year is ice wont to be found. The cause is the swift running throw of sea into sea. In the north side of this passage John Scolus, a pilot of Denmark, was in 1476.

The south side also of this passage was found of a Spaniard in a° 1541, who travelling out of new Spayne with a certain band of soldiers, was sent by the vice-roy into this coast. Who when he was come to this coast found certain ships in a certain haven, which came hither out of Cataya laden with merchandize, having on their flagge hanging out of the foreshippes certain birds painted, called Alcatrizae. The mariners also declared by signs that they came out of Cataya into the port in 30 days.'

Latin Title : ' Declaratio quo cursu sit navigandum ex Boreali mari in Australe ut sic perveniatur in Regiones quae Sepengo et Mangi vocantur, et inde in Catayam et Molouchos, ubi Aromata petuntur.'

(ii) *A suggestion for a search by Iceland for the North-West Passage. Fragment in Otho E VIII. fol. 216, circ. 1567–8*

. . . [the] passage or straight of [the three brethren lieth in 67] degrees, and is not so dangerous as [the way to Mu]scovia is, which is in 72 degrees, and the [way very da]ngerous for coulde and ise, and notwithstanding [this] passage to Muscovia is traded V monthes in the [year].

And this passage by the northwest at 67 degrees [is easy] to be searched, and the same may be sayled in xxx^{tle} [Days from] Englande to the saide passage of 67 degrees.

The which passage being knowne wolde make a grete trade [to] those weste partes where be manye rich merchandizes, and the passage lyeth farre from any Prynce that might hinder.

And I think verley that with the value of CCCli of money this passage might be known and truly certified by means of some of the shippes that trade yerely to Iseland for fishe.

For this passage is to be sayled from Iseland in 8 or 10 daies, and they having CCCli allowed them towards their charges wolde willingly searche the saide passage, and ii or iii to be sent from hence in the said shippes to bring true knowledge of the same.

And be yt remembered this passage at 67 degrees to Catayo is but 6000 leagues, and to pass by the straighte of Magilanus to the said Cataya is 15000 leagues. As also the [said] passage of 67 degrees in the moneth of June ther is no darke nighte, but is bryghte day all the 24 houres.

(iii) *Anthony Jenkinson's Arguments for a North-East Passage*
(From his Address, May 30, 1565, S.P. Domestic Elizabeth)

. . . We should not fear at all but rather be encouraged to travayle and serche for this passage, being for so long time continual light of the sonne (if the seeson be duly observed). And lyke as there is variety of opynyons touching this passage out of this our occian into the east occian, some affirming the same by the north-west, taking their aucthorytie of certeyne authors who wrote by conjicture, which opynyon as I doe not wholly dissent from, So am I fully persuaded that to the north-east there is no doubt of a passage to be found, for that lyke as I at my being in Scythia and Bactria, I divers times talked and conferred with divers Cathayans who were there at that present in trade of merchandize, touching the commodities of their countrey and how the seas aborded unto them, I learned from them that the sayd seas had their course to certayne northerly regions with whom they had traffique by seas. So also having conference with the inhabitants of Zugary and other people of Samoyedes and Colmackes, whose countreyes lye very far northerly (and nere whereunto I gesse the said passage to be, which people sayle alongst the said coastes fishing after the greet fishe called the Morse for the bennefyte of his teethe), of whom I had gathered that beyonde them the said land and coastes trende and tende to the East and to the southwarde, and that the Cur-rauntes and Tydes run eastsoutheast and westnorthwest very vehemently, which manifestly argueth a passage. Further this last yere at my being in themperor of Moscovia his Courte yt chenced thet there came thether certen of thinhabitants of the foresaid Countreye to present unto the said Prynce a certain strange Hedd with a horne therein which they had fownde in the Iland of Vagattes which is not farre from the river of Obbe and the meyne land of Zugory. And for thet themperour neyther anny of his people knew what it was for the straungeness thereof, He commanded thet such strangers as were thought to have any judgement therein shoulde see the sayme to be asked theyre opynion what they thought it to be. Amonge whom yt was my chaunce to be. And so was it founde by the reporte of them that before had seen the like to be the hedd and horne of an unicorne which is in no small prayse and estimation of the said prynce. Then I, imagininge with myself from whence the said hedd shoulde come, and knowing that Unicorne are bredd in the land of Cathaye, Chynaye and other the Orientall Regions, fell into considering that the said hedd was brought thither by the course of the sea, for how else could thet hedd have come to thet Iland of Vagettes. Other reesons are to be alleged for the proffe of the said passage whiche for feare to be tedious I omit. . . .

(iv) *The Muscovy Company's answer to Mr. Gilbert's Articles Jan. 24 1566/7.* S.P. Dom. Eliz. XLII. No. 5

'The company have from the beginning of the first attempt minded the discovery of Cathay, and have made divers attempts thereof and are determined so to do again, *either by the northeast or by the northwest.* They desire to bear the rule and ordering of all discoveries toward the said partes, agreeing to their privileges, etc., wherein they will not refuse, but desire, the good advice, helpe, and conference of Mr. Gilbert, if it please him, with reasonable conditions, to enterprise it or to assist them therein.'

(v) *Extracts from the Ledgers of the Plantyn Press, quoted by Denucé: Oud. Nederlandsche Kaartmakers*

(a) 8 *Aug.* 1558. Nicholas England of London buys a parcel of maps, including:
Mappa [Mundi] by Gerard Mercator.

(b) 13 Nov. 1566. Jan Desserans, bookseller, of London, buys a parcel of maps, including:
2 copies Mappa Angliae of Mercator.
2 copies Mappa Europae of Mercator.
3 copies Mappa Mundi of Vopellius.
3 copies Mappa Mundi of Ortelius.

(c) 19th Oct. 1566. Humfrey Toy and Nicholas England, of London, buy a parcel of maps including:
3 copies Mappa Angliae of Mercator.
4 copies Mappa Mundi of Ortelius.

(d) 24 Dec. 1566. Jann Desserans buys:
4 copies Mappa Mundi of Vopellius.
5 copies Mappa Mundi of Ortelius.
3 copies Mappa Angliae of Mercator.

(e) 20 Feb. 1567. Jan Desserans buys:
6 copies Mappa Mundi of Vopellius.
5 copies Mappa Mundi of Ortelius.
2 copies Mappa Europae of Mercator.
2 copies Mappa Angliae of Mercator.

(*f*) 15 April 1568. Jan Desserans buys :
    1 copy Mappa Mundi of Vopellius.
    1 copy Mappa Septentrionalis of Jode.
    1 pair of Gemma Phrysius's Globes.

(*g*) 3rd Juy 1568. Jan Desserans buys :
    1 copy Mappa Mundi of Vopellius.
    1 copy Mappa Mundi of Ortelius.

(*h*) 23 July 1568. George Bishop, bookseller, of London, buys :
    2 copies Mappa Angliae of Mercator.
    4 copies Mappa Mundi of Vopellius.

(vi) *Lettre de Plantin à Jehan Desseran, du 21 mars, 1568*
(Quoted from Denucé as above)

' Jai une paire de globes de Gemma Frigius que j'ay faict faire avec les meridiens ou cercles de cuivre et ne le puis donner moins de seize florins et douze patars. Si les voules avoir mandes les, on les vous envoyera. Les ordinaires du dict Gemma, qui ont les Cercles meridionaux de bois puis-je bien vous envoyer a onze florins la paire. Ceux de Mercator (dont j'espere recevoir incontinent apres Pasques) ne puis-je donner moins de 24 florins la paire.'

' 15e April 1568. Envoyé a Desseran a Londres en une mandelette appart :

2 Globes de Gemma, 1 celeste et ung terrestre, avec le cercle de cuivre .. .. fl. 24.'

DOCUMENT 12

GEOGRAPHICAL IDEAS RELATING TO FROBISHER'S VOYAGE. 1576

(i) *Michael Lok's Account of the Preparation. Written* 1577.
(Otho E. VIII).

' [The] learned man Mr. John Dee hearing the common [report] of this new enterprise, and understanding of the prepa[ration] for furniture of the Ships, being thereby persua[ded] that it would now proceed, and having not been acquainted with our purpose in any part before, about the 20th. day of May, A° 1576 of his own good nature favouring the enterprise in respect of the service and commodity of his natural country, came unto me desiring to know of me the reasons of my foundation and purpose in this enterprise, and offering his furtherance therof, with such instructions and advice as by his learning he could give thereon. Whereupon I conceived a great good opinion of him, and therefore appointed a time of meeting at my house, whereat were present Martin Frobysher,

Steven Burrough, Christopher Hall, with other. Where freely and plainly I laid open to him at large my whole purpose in the traffic of merchandise by that new part of the world, for the benefit of the Realm by many means, as well in the countries of East India, if this way the sea be open, as also otherwise, though that this New land should chance to bar us from the sea of India. And also declared such conjectures and probabilities as I had conceived of a passage by sea unto the same sea of East India by that way of the north-west from England. And for the proof of these two matters, I laid before him my books, authors, my cards and instruments, and my notes thereof made in writing as I had made them of many years study before. Upon which matters when he had thus heard and seen, he answered that he was right glad to know of me this much of this matter, and that he was greatly satisfied in his desire above his expectation, and that I was so well grounded in this [here the MS. is burnt, and conjectural words are added in brackets] . . . [Like]wise he shewed me all his [books, authors, and certain writings of] his own : and also showed me his [carde ? instruments ?] which I did very well like. And afterw[ards so long as] the ship remained here, he took pains [to demonstrate] the Rules of Geometry and Cosmography for [the better instruct]ion of the Masters and Mariners in the use of Instruments for Navigation in their voyage, and for [Cas]ualities happening at sea, which did them service, whereby he deserves much commendation.'

(ii) *Michael Lok on Sir H. Gilbert's Services.* (Otho E. VIII, *vide supra*).

' Also Humphrey Gilbert, Knight, hath been of many years (as I am informed) a great good wisher to this like enterprise. And since I became acquainted with him (which was about Easter last 1575 [sic for 1576] I have heard him make divers good discourses in the favour thereof. . . . Although to say truth without giving any offence : neither that book [i.e. the Discourse] coming out so late, not yet his former discourses being none other than were well known to us long before, were any manner of causes or instructions to the chief enterprisers of this new voyage of discovery, to attempt the same or to direct us therein. And William Burrough, although he was not so well persuaded of this enterprise that he would venture his money therein, yet in respect of the service of his country, he did take pains to produce a master and many mariners for the ships, and agreed to the route to be followed by the captains . . . and besides those named above M. Lok does not know any one who had helped the enterprise.'

(iii) *Michael Lok on Frobisher's First Voyage*, 29th Oct. 1577. (Otho E. VIII).

' Neither nede I [say any]thing touching the naturall Riches and infinite T[reas]or, and the great Traffic of rich Merchandise that is in those countries of Cathay, China India and o[ther] countries thereabouts, for that every boke of history and cosmography of those parts of the world, which are to be had of every Prynters shop, does declare the same at large. . . . But of the matters that chiefly moved me to enterprise my money therein so largely, I will say briefly that three things chiefly moved me thereto. First the great hope to fynd our English seas open unto the Seas of the East India, by that way, which I conceved by the great likelyhood thereof which I found by reading the histories of many men's travailes toward that parte of the Worlde. Whereby we might take passage by sea to those rich Cuntries for traffik of merchandize, which was the thynge I chiefly desired.

' Secondly I was assured by manifold good proofs of divers Travailers and histories, that the countries of Baccaliaw (sic) Canda, and the new found Landes thereto adjoining, were full of people : and full of such commodities and Merchandize as are in the countries of Lappia, Russia, Moscovia, Permia, Pechora, Samoietza, and the Cuntries thereto adjoining : Which are furres, hydes, wax, tallow, oyle and other. Whereby if it should happen those new Landes to stretch to the North Pole, so that we could not have passage by Sea that way which we sought to the Northwestward, to pass into East India, yet in those same new lands to the northwestward might be established the like Trade of Merchandize as is now, in the other said countries of the [MS. burnt].'

(iv) *Michael Lok's Notes on the Frobisher Voyage.* 26th Jan. 1578/9. (Dom. Eliz. 129.)

' I devised a writing wherein was joined with him in Commission Christopher Hall and Owen Griffin, Master of the Ships, and Nicholas Chancellor, Merchant, and purser of the voyage, who were known for trusty men, without whose consent he should not command nor carry the ships.

' Now when Martyn Frobisher was returned home again in October 1576 with his strange men of Cataye, and his great rumour of the passage to Cataye, he was called to the Court and greatly embraced and liked of the best. And upon his great information of many great matters of his new world, it pleased her Majesty's honourable Privy Council to direct their letters and Commissions unto Sir William Winter, Mr. Thomas Randall, myself and others to call unto us

Martyn Frobisher and Christopher Hall, and to take account of them of their doings.'

(v) *Do. do. Lansdown, 230.*

' He arrived on the north coast of the land of Labrador amongst certain great Islands, which he took to be the Straits of the Sea betwene the main lands of America and Asia to pass to Cathay . . . and now he being thens returned home again of that first voyage he was examined of his doings therein by Sir Wm. Winter, Mr. Thomas Randolph, Anthony Jenkinson, Michael Lok and others ; thereunto appointed by Commission of her Majesty's Privy Council, concerning the passage to Cathay, at which time he vouched to them absolutely with vehement words, speeches and oaths, that he had found and discovered the Straits, and open passage by Sea into the South Sea called Mar del Sur which goeth to Cathay, and by the way had found divers good ports and harbours for passage of all the navy of her Majesty's ships, and affirmed the same by divers arguments of the depth and colour of the water, the sight of the head lands on both sides of the Straits at the west end thereof opening into the broad sea, called Mar de Sur, and the setting of the tides with a flood from the west out of the said South Sea. And by divers other arguments, by demonstration in the charts and maps, which things the commissioners believed to be true upon his vehement speeches and oaths of affirmation.

' All the which matter by him affirmed, is found to be false by his two later voyages made thither since that time, wherein those affirmed lands of America and Asia are found to be but small islands, and the tydes setting from the west is like to be nothing by the setting of the stream from one headland to an other, of those islands which are there in number infinite. And now the passage to Cathay is by him left unto us as uncertain as at the beginning, though thereupon hath followed great charges to the Company.'

(vi) *Ortelius' visit to England after Frobisher's first voyage.*

(a) Hakluyt's Reference in the *Discourse of Western Planting* 1584. p. 102.

' Abraham Ortelius, the great geographer, told me, at his last being in England, 1577, that if the wars of Flanders had not been, they of the Low Countries had meant to have discovered those parts of America, and the north-west Strait before this time. And it seemed that the chief cause of his coming into England was to no other end, but to pry and look into the secrets of Frobisher's voyage : for it was even then, when Frobisher was preparing for his first return into the north-west.'

(*b*) Dee's Reference to this visit : *Volume of Great and Rich Discoveries*. Vitell. C. VII. fol. 264.

' . . . that learned geographer Abraham Ortelius whose company also (since my first letters sent over) I have had of late in my poor house at Mortlake.'   Margin : ' June 1577.'

(vii) *Preface to Bourne's Regiment of the Sea, 2nd edition,* 1580.

' It is also very necessary for them that would attempt any voyages of discovery to find out the passage to come to Catay and China, and the Islands of the Moluccas, into the northwards, or into the east by Nova Zemla, or to the west by that way that Captain Frobisher hath begun to the northwards of Baccalaos and Labrador, for it is to be supposed that amongst the broken lands and islands, that there may be found passage upon the north part of America, but the great quantity of ice may somewhat hinder the prosperity of that discovery.   And yet notwithstanding, my opinion is, that it is not frozen there so much to have such huge quantities of ice, but that it may be frozen more farther unto the north parts, and so by some current or stream brought thither, and so is stayed upon the coast of Labrador and Baccalaos, by the means of this great current that cometh out of the bay of Mexico, alongst the north side of Florida, unto Baccalaos, or new found land.'   [i.e. the ice is brought south by the Labrador Current and stayed by the Gulf Stream.]

(viii) *Wm. Camden.   Annales.   Under date,* 1576.

' Erudita etiam ingenia accensa honesto studio disjunctissimas orbis terrarum regiones, et Oceani secreta explorandi, excitarunt bene nummatos habendi cupiditate non minus inflammatos ad detegendum si quod esset fretum in Septentrionali Americae parte, quo ad opulentam Cathaiam navigaretur et Orientes Occidentesque opes mutuo commercio conjungerentur.   Eruditi illi probabiliter differuerunt, ex ea parte fretum patere, pro concesso assumentes.   Quo proprius ad littus acceditur, eo minorem esse aquarum altitudinem, sed ab occiduo Islandiae littore navigantibus experientia teste, mare altius occurrere, ut continuum Mari illi quod *del Sur* nautae vocant, ex altera Americae parte videatur.   Deinde quod cum Oceanus diurno primi Mobilis motu feratur, Americae objectu repercussus, Septentriones petat ad *Cabo Fredo,* id est, *Promontorium Frigidum,* ubi loci per fretum aliquod in Mare del Sur exoneretur, sin minus, eadem violentia in Lappiam et Finnarchiam reverberaretur, qua in Australi mundi plaga à Freto Magellanico insuloso et tantae motis aquarum incapaci ob insulosas freti angustias, per Orientalia

Americae littora ad *Cabo Fredo* repercutitur. Testes adhibent
Antonium Jenkinsonum Anglium, quo non alter Septen-
trionalem mundi plagam plenius novit, qui docuit molem aquarum
ex Mari Cronio in *Mare del Sur* necessario effundi, Bernardum item
le Torr Hispanum, qui affirmavit se à Moluccis in Americam re-
vertentem, supra Aequatorem Septentriones versus vi aquarum ab
Aquilone in navem irruente in Moluccas fuisse rejectum, aliaque
producunt ut hoc comprobarent. Quibus illi nummati persuasi,
Martinum Forbisherum ut hoc fretum detegeret cum tribus aphractis
mittunt, qui Harwico solvens xviii Junii, ad ix Augusti vel sinum
vel fretum intravit sub latitudine lxiii.'

DOCUMENT 13
THE SINUS MAGNUS AND STRAITS OF ANIAN

(i) *Marco Polo, Ramusio's Edition of* 1559. Lib. III, Cap 5.
fol. 51.

' Partendosi del porto di Zaituna si naviga per Ponente alquanto
verso Garbin, mille, et cinquecento miglia, passando un colfo
nominato Cheinan, ilquel colfo dura di longhezza per il spatio di due
mesi, navigando verso la parte di Tramontana, il qual per totto
confina verso Scirocco con la provincia di Mangi, et dall' altra parte
con Ania, et Toloman, et molte altre provincie con quelle di sopra
nominate.'

[' Starting from the port of Zaitun, and steering by the west and
somewhat south, for 1500 miles, you pass a gulf called Cheinam,
which gulf extends in length for a distance of two months' sail
towards the north, and is bounded towards the south-east by the
province of Mangi, and on the other side by Ania, Toloman, and
many other provinces already mentioned.' Free Translation.]

(ii) *Gemma Phrysius, Cosmographia Principae*, 1530. Printed in
Apian's Cosmography, 1533. Chap. XXX.

' Qui deinde sequuntur regiones terra Florida et Bacalearum regio,
non adeo sunt lustratae *nisi secundum littus*. Sunt hic regiones
feracissimae auri omniumque animantium, campi amoenissimi,
montes excelsi, et fluvii placidissimi, civitates et turres et domus
adfabre constructae, adeo ut nostra Europa non multo inferior
habeatur haec pars. Populi sunt affabiles, et contractus non
fugientes, plures eorum ichthiophagi sunt, alii ophiophagi. . . .
Hanc partem terrae multi Asiae adnectunt, dicuntque continentem
esse, sed horum retro nulla est, igitur necque temere assentiendum
puto. Ego cum ex navigationibus Hispanorum et aliorum possem
multa adducere quibus hujus descriptionis incommoditatem osten-

derem, adducam tantum unum argumentum, ne videar omnino frustra huic opinioni reclamare : Marcus Venetus, qui omnia regiones Indiae orientalis lustravit, ibique ad annos plures habitavit, scribit lib. 3 se per regionem Mangi ad oceanum iusque, pervenisse, ibique navem conscendisse ; et per Garbinem (qui est inter meridiem et zephyrum) ad Cyambam navigasse miliaribus italicis 1500. A Ciamba delatus est deinde miliaribus totidem ad Javam majorem insulam versus austrum fere. Quonam pacto possit quispiam ex terrae novae latere orientali, cum per eam transitus non sit, versus meridiem ad Java majorem navigio profiscisci ? cum haec insula nunc observata sit apud Indiam. At ego rem incertam experientae et lectorum juditio committo.'

(iii) *Gemma Phrysius. Globe of* 1537. Inscriptions.

(i) Fretum articum sive trium fratrum, per quod Lusitani ad Orientem et ad Indos et adndos et Moluccas navigare conati sunt.

(ii) Quii populi ad quos Joannes Scolvus Danus pervenit, circa annum 1476.

(iii) Quia Lusitani nunquam navigarunt ultra Cârbâ [for Ciambam] metropolim Sinarum in qua urbe etsi lequios et naves eorum viderint, tamen nec ipsi Lusitani nec Sinarum populi unquam ad ipsos navigarunt propter periculosissimam navigationem. Verum tamen Gaspar Corteralis qui dum detectis ex Lusitania terris septentrionalibus ex Sinarum regione deinceps ultimum orientem lustraret, lequios se circumvectum et Cataianos Tartarosque sibi conspectos fuisse asseruit, tamen se aut suos nusquam terrae exponere ausus fuit. Ideoque de illis regionibus nihil veri et comperti haberi potest nisi quantum ex narratione Marci Veneti et ipsius Gasparis Corterealis collegi potest ; quos potius hoc in loco duximus imitandos quam ultimum orientem veluti omnino incognitum preterire.

(iv) *John Dee, Volume of Great and Rich Discoveries.* Vitellius, C. VII. (Imperfect through fire.)

(a) ' 1577 May 15. Great doubt of the Periplus of Asia northeast quarter, and of Atlantis north-west corner.' [Chapter heading.]

Fol. 170 v. ' I advise you to make a Chorographicall Plat of M. Paulus orientall travails according to the printed phrases of M. Paulus and you shall find such contradictions and repugnances that you shall not be able to put the description down in all respects as the said printed text informeth.'

Fol. 171 v. ' And one other occasion of erring hath been Ptolemy his wrong turning and describing of Sinus Magnus in that place and in that respect where indeed no Sinus is or was : nor any Sinus in respect of arching or encompassing the Asian sea coasts can be perceived or probably admitted, as Ptolemy did greatly mistake it, and not only by his numbers, but by his own expressed text is to be controlled therein to his no small disgrace. I am sorry for it. . . .'

174 r. 'Seeing the former words of M. Paulus Venetus most expressly do warn us of a marvellous great bay or gulf to be even thereabout where the very pinch of our Bout-Saylings of both Asia and Atlantis do consist. . . . I will just a little examine the text of M. Paulus, which in this case is so doubtful.'

Fol. 175 b. '. . . this Cheenam gulf is not that large Gulf of two months sailing.'

Fol. 177 r. ' For he [Marco Polo] considereth the two sides of his Grand Gulf, and on the one he saith ' per tutto confino verso scirocco' that is coming southerly from the head of this great bay being northerly, ' con la provincia di Mangi ' coming from thence south-east. For before you had of Sir Giovan di Barros that the coast of Mangi did chiefly (to the northward) run verso maestro : that is north-west : therefore contrariwise coming from the northerly parts it lieth verso sirocco. What a damp may here fall on some men's minds when they may perceive M. Paulus to make mention of Ania Province and Toloman Province as in firm land of the sea coast continued with that north-west corner of Asia ! Seeing even against the same place and under the same latitude (in manner) in Atlantis north-west corner are mentioned the province of Ania (or Anian) and Tolm kingdom and mountains. . . .'

(b) Fol. 179 v. 'But by the way you may first note, that the Pycnemian or Pygnean (the Infidell) which this last year was brought from the north-west discovery, being axed (while he was yet with our countrymen in those quarters), if they in their country had any Gold or Sylver or Cloth, or sundry other things : he woulde make evident signe that no such things were to be had in that kingdom of Pycknemay or Pycknea (which some of our men said he termed Pygmenai and other Pyckenay and other Pycknea) but all that was demanded by sign (of the like thing showed) to be at Mania : and pointed westerly towards it, and would have guided our men toward it (if they would) and added that it was but one moon sayling thither. Whereby it would appear that the city or province of Mania is rich, famous and great : as having some part not far [here a portion is destroyed] and very likely to be the same [burnt] which we term Ania Province.

Fol. 180 r. 'And so hath Ortelius set it in his book of Theatrum

Orbis Terrarum in the chart of Tartaria (being the 27 chart in that edition) where it standeth to the north of Mangi : and is so also in his Great Chart of Asia, (which is the more likely by reason that M. Paulus might be thought to account Ania as in Asia) and likewise that the Infidel Pycnean (appertayning to Atlantis) might reasonably so make account of it as to be on their mayn, knowing no other. And seeing Gerardus Mercator in his last Universal Chart and Ortelius in two of his small charts (one of the Type of the whole Earth and the other of Atlantis only) do in Atlantis most northerly corner note Regnum Anian and Anian. And then more southerly and next in order to it the mountain of Tolm and Tolm Regnum (which seems to me a word contracted from Toloman).

Returning then to these Provinces of Anian and Toloman, thus I find it recorded in M. Paulus Lib 2. cap. 48. Tholoman é una Provincia verso Levante, le cui genti adoraro gli Idoli etc. from [sic] Amu Province to this are otto giornate.

And both the one and the other are (in the best charts of Asia yet published) set in the harte almost of India extra Gangem, otherwise named Inde the Less. . . .

Rhamusius in his India placed upon his second volume hath thus : Toloman, Provincia di' Tartaria, and so of Ania, Ania Provincia di Tartaria.

. . . How aptly I have here placed this record of Magellan his strait finding, as well to answer our Mexico passenger withall, as to be an advice to all discoverers upon such a purpose to be very circumspect, patient, and constant, till the uttermost search be made : and that perfectly and not imperfectly. And when our Mexico Travailer hath taken such order of search at his ferry place towards Cathay, and hath withall given so good witnes and so exquisite a search and trial, then I will listen to his report ; and still make most account of the verity, which I nothing doubt of upon my former discourses and evidences *to be such as will be favourable to Ania Straits* : but with small cause called straits, if we heer of no straiter girding in of the sea by the land approaching than by two days sailing over. And thus this pleasant examination of the slender news of the passage to Cathay from Mexico shall end in this place : and when the post shall return with an answer of my letters [Margin : A° 1577. May 13] this day from me sent, with certain of the former interrogatories to the learned Gerardus [Mercator] to require answer to, from his friend that wrote him these News ; then if there be thereof any matter worthy the place and memorial having in this treatise, and I by God his favour in life and health, I will friendly impart the same unto you.'

(v) *G. Postellus to Ortelius. April* 1567.

' Nam extremam Asiam plusquam tribus horis retraxit, contra Marini sententiam, et inde fecit ut Aurea Chersonese, quae certe Atlantidis pars Australis ea est, quem in ortu suo Americam in occasu Peru jam vocamus, et quae mox a regno aureo del dorado ut Hispani dicunt rursus ut olim Ania Chersonesus dicetur, fecit inquam Ptolomeus, ut ab orto fere horis altero Hemisphaeria attraheretur, una cum Magno Sinu suo ad Asiam extremam. Et in haec peccata incidit, ex ea falsa imaginatione qua putabat nostro Hemisphaerio Asiatico omnia contineri. Hinc in aliud extremum collapsus Vopellius eo quod hac adulatione et re omnino tunc dubia aures Caroli V prurire titillarique senserat, tot errata quot vocabula scribens continuam cum Atlantide Asiam fecit, et Indiarum vocabula donavit Atlantidem, ita ut Hispani involarint in Indiarum nomen separatum ab India plusquam quadrante universi. Tanti est auri fames, ut, etc. . . .'

Document 14

Hints at Plans for various Discoveries. 1575-80

(i) *Volume of Famous and Rich Discoveries.* Vitellius, C. VII.

(a) Fol. 60 r. ' The Indians voyage unto the king of Sweden his jurisdiction is a principal point to make reckoning upon, for a Scythian and an orientall wishful voyage, for all Asia the Great of us to be traded withall, *and farder.*'

(b) Fol. 60 v. ' Note this principal point of Dfina mouth, and the mouth of Tanais, accounted now but one meridian : that, for the Scythian Sea easterly navigation ; and this other, *for the inland easterly journeys to Cathay* to be reckoned on.'

(c) Fol. 68 v. ' Judgement [may be] had of our longitudes coming to answerable to other inland places of Asia of like longitude : yea and to them of the Erythraean and Indian Sea coasts also, conformably by their meridians concurrent to the uttermost bounds oriental : till we be sure that we are in due place to turn our course southerly *to the New and Oriental Guinea*: and so not only to have accomplished and made expert the Periplus Scythian and Asiaticall, but to *enter and proceed upon the farder discovery* of that part which is yet least known to Christian men, and lies in the eye of Envy, of other great Conquerors Christian : and most apt for British wisdom, manhood, and travail to be bestowed henceforwards : not refusing, but rather using withall the Merchants trade, in the mean space also, of Cambalu, Quinsay, and all the Oriental parts of Asia, and the Isle of Chryse now supposed to be called by the name of Japan.'

(d) Fol. 79 r. 'But I trust with one or two complete surveys, after *this to be performed by my travail* (if God will), or by my setting on [sundry] other by sundry means in divers places of [the] world ; that all the north-east part of Asia, with the two principal cities thereof, Cambalu and Quinsay, will become to the Brytish natural inhabitants of this Monarchy so well known, as are the coasts of Denmark and Norway and their Periplus.'

(e) Fol. 191 r. 'And that by the one with the other taking effect, may be an undoubted warranty of the possible periplus of Asia : *and of farder matter* to this Brytish kingdom both honourable and profitable : more than is yet credible.'

(f) Fol. 216 r. 'But when upon either *myne own Asiaticall Travailes,* or of other men their account rendered (by my assignment and instructions dealing therewith) there shall have been made an Asiaticall Survey of the north-eastern quarter of Asia : then (through God his goodness) you are to receive the image of the Verity Cosmographical, yet greatly missed, of one of the chief portions of the whole world.'

(g) Fol. 205. 'And as for Pheneth, son to Duodennin, who was the chiefe and one of the first discoverers by sea, though his brother Beach and Ithab and their father Duodennin were noted to dwell in one great Province generally named Caruba, yet that Beeth (or Beach) had his own portion called after his name (as the manner was) it is very likely, and what may be said of *Beach the Province lying near the sea coast, which doth abound with gold* and other things to men's great commodity very serviceable, and yet to this day by the name of Beach known ; and where it lieth I will not here discourse, but leave this warning or advice to other.'

[Margin] 'Note. For this is [the phrase ' This Beach of other is written LO ' is deleted] one of your principall places to trade unto in some respects.'

(h) Fol. 206 r. 'And of all this digression we may gather good testimony to our principal matter very profitable. As of the Periplus of Asia : *if this land of Beach,* by Beach or Beeth (brother to Pheneth the great discoverer by see), and that out of the Scythian Ocean, sailing in manner by shores, *was come unto, possessed, and so named. Which with good advise is to be dealt with* : as neither squeamishly in refusing all, nor too lightly in deposing all to be true. . . .'

(i) Fol. 248 b. '. . . note the records thereof to some evidence of proving the Asian Periplus and *the Navigation* from Cap Comfort or this most comfortable Brytish Kingdom *to the land of Beach etc.*

to be open and commodiously enough possible, if skilful sailors and discrete captains use the opportunity of year and place requisite thereto.'

(ii) *John Dee. Pety Navy Royall.* 1577. p. 62.

(a) 'There remayne also to be declared the reasons why my Instructor [Dee himself] doth wish and advise part of the publik threasory to be bestowed upon some two or three honest men who should be skilfull in Far-Forreyn languages. As, in the Sclavonian or Muscovite, the Arabik vulgar, the Turkish, the Tartarian, the Chiny language, the Canadian, and the Islandish etc. For that (within these next few years following) with men of *all these Cuntries and farder,* Great Affayres are by some of our Country-Men to be handed : if God continue his Gracious Direction and Ayde thereto, as he hath very comfortably begun : and that, *by means not yet published.'*

(b) 'Moreover some Part [of the public treasury] to be bestowed on Four Christian Philosophers, skilfull or to become skilfull, and also excellent, both in Speculation and also practice of *the Ancient and Secret Philosophy :* which is not vulgar, but which may be most comfortable and profitable to some courteous Kalid [1] his disposition, etc. By which titles of matter left unspecified hitherto, it may evidently appear that my Instructor [Dee himself] hast (as it were) but opened the door of his philosophical and political Brytish furniture to be favourably viewed by them whose insight is sharp and profound : whose zeal and care also, for the State Publick of this Monarchy to become most Christianlike happy (in all respects), is ardent and not luke-warm.'

(c) Fol. 63. 'No King nor Kingdom hath by Nature and Human Industry (to be used) any more LAWFUL and more peaceable means (made evident) whereby to become in wealth far passing all other : in strength and force INVINCIBLE : and in honourable estimation triumphantly famous over all and above all other.' [i.e. than Britain.]

(d) Dedication to 'M. Christopher Hatton, Esquyer.'

> Whereof such lore as I (of [2] late)
> Have lernd, and for Security
> By Godly means, to Garde this State,
> To you I send now carefully.

---

[1] Kalid was a mediaeval Jewish writer on the Occult: the reference here is probably to one of the prominent Initiates in Dee's circle.

[2] Margin: A° 1576.

Unto the Gardians, most wise,
And Sacred Senat, or Chief Power
I durst not offer this Advise
(So homely writ) for fear of Lowr.

But at your will, and discreet choyce,
To keep by you, or to imparte,
I leave this zealous Publik voyce :
You will accept so simple parte.

M'Instructors freend did warrent me,
You would do so, as he did his :
That Redy [1] freend can witness be
For Higher States,[2] what written is.

(iii) (a *Ortelius: World Map of* 1564.
' Locach Regio videtur hic poni a M. Paulo Veneto.   Latinum
exemplar habet Boeach sed male ut fere omnia nos Italico usi
sumus.'

(b) *Mercator : World Map of* 1569.
' Beach provincia aurifera quam pauci ex alienis regionibus adeunt
propter gentis inhumanitatem.'

(iv) *Extracts from John Dee's Diary.*   (Halliwell's Transcript.)
' 1581.   June 30.   Mr. John Leonard Haller, of Hallerstein by
Worms in Germany, receyved his instructions manifold for his
Journey to Quinsay, which Journey I moved him unto, and instructed him plentifully for the variation of the Compass, observing
in all places as he passed.'

' 1582.   Sept. 10.   Mr. J. Haller of Hallerstein by Worms in
Germany came agayne to me to declare his readiness to go toward
Quinsay, and how he would go and lye at Venys all this winter,
and from thence to Constantinople.'

' 1583.   Jan. 19.   Mr. John Leonard Haller went to London, and so
to go toward Scotland.'

(v) *Extract from a 'Petition of divers gentlemen of the West part
to the Queen for permission to adventure overseas.'*   (SP. Dom. Eliz.
no. 63, and Lansdown C.)   22 March 1573/4.
' The voyages to Ghynea and the trafficking in the Gulf of Mexico
and the very places of the Spaniard's possession, hath in the precedent of Hawkins voyage been defended by your Majesty and
Council as friendly and lawful, much more so this which is put a
passing in the open sea by them to places that they neither hold or

---

[1] Margin: E. D. Esq. (i.e. Ed. Dyer).
[2] i.e. Queen Elizabeth.

know. Beside that not only traffic, but also possession, planting of people, and habitation, hath been already judged lawful for other nations in such places as the Spaniards and Portugals have not already added to their possession. As is proved by your Majesty's most honourable and lawful grant to Thomas Stuclee and his company for Terra Florida. Also the French men's inhabiting in Florida and Bresil, who albeit they acknowledge the Pope's authority in such things as they graunt to pertain to him, yet in this universal right of traffic and temporal dominion, they have not holden them bound by his power.'

Endorsed by Burghley : ' A discovery of lands beyond the ecquinoctiall [i.e. equator]. 1573.'

DOCUMENT 15
MISCELLANEOUS DOCUMENTS

(i) *A note in Dee's handwriting as to the charts of northern Asia which he gave to Pet and Jackman.* Otho E. VIII. fol 79. Copy in Lansdown 122, No. 5. ' [25] May A° 1580 with which [instructions] a new Chart made by hand [was] given also to eche of the two Masters, expressing theyr Cath[ay] voyage more expertly than any other yet published.'

The instructions referred to (printed by Hakluyt) were at first signed △, but to this has later been added ' May 15. By me John Dee.' Dee's Diary mentions a visit to the Muscovy House for the Cathay Voyage, May 17 1580.

(ii) *Note in John Dee's hand to Nicholas Chancellor's narrative of Pet and Jackman's voyage.* Otho E. VIII.

' Hugh Smith did enform me by mouth and made a little draught with his own hand of this place and hereabouts. A° 1582.'

(iii) *Critical Passage from Claudius Clavus Map,* 1427.

' Gronlandiae insulae chersonesus dependet a terra inaccessibili a parte septentrionis vel ignota propter glaciem. Veniunt tamen Kareles infideles, ut vidi, in Gronlandiam cum copioso exercitu quotidie, et hoc absque dubio ex altera parte poli septentrionalis. Non ergo alluit oceanus limen terrae recte sub polo, ut omnes autores prisci aulumnant : nec dicit mendacium nobilis miles Johannes Mandevil Anglicus, qui dixit se de Seres Indiae mavigasse versus unam insulam Norvagiae.'

(iv) *Richard Madox, Diary. March* 15. 1582. Cotton App. XLVII.

' I being with Mr. Cyprian Lucar he brought me to his neighbour Mr. Ashley who maketh plaine cards, this man is of Shropshire.

He had prepared beeds and other devises to vente with Mr. Humfrey Gilbert who is now about another viage.   He told me he thought to see when a letter dated at London ye first of May should be delyvered at China before midsummer following. . . .   He avouched upon report, as he sayd, of ye indians, yt there was a sailable passage over America between 43 and 46 degree throe which he sayd Sir Francis Drake came home from the Moluccas.'

(v) *Dee's reference to the contemporary popularity of Maps and Charts.   Preface to Euclid*, 1570.

'Some, to beautify their Halls, Parlers, Chambers, Galeries, Studies, or Libraries with ; other some, for things past, as battles fought, earthquakes, heavenly firings, and such occurrences, in histories mentioned : therby lively as it were to view the place, the region adjoining, the distance from us, and such other circumstances : some other, presently to view the large dominion of the Turk : the wide Empire of the Muscovite : and the little morcel of ground where Christendom (by profession) is certainly known, little I say in respect of the rest, etc. [sic] : some other for their own journeys directing into far lands, or to understand other men's travels . . . liketh, loveth, getteth and useth, Maps, Charts, and Geographical Globes.'

INDEX